MY BOOK HOUSE
THE TREASURE CHEST

THE TREASURE CHEST

Here's a heigh and a ho! for the treasure chest,
    And a ho! for the pure, pure gold,
And a ho, heigh-ho! for the precious things,
    And the secret gems untold!

Here's a heigh and a ho! for the purpose strong,
    And the bold stout hearts that roam,
And sail the Seven Seas of Life,
    To bring such treasures home!

THE TREASURE CHEST
of MY BOOKHOUSE

Edited by
Olive Beaupré Miller

CHICAGO
The BOOKHOUSE for CHILDREN
PUBLISHERS

Printed in U. S. A.

LIST OF STORIES AND POEMS

LIST OF STORIES AND POEMS

LIST OF STORIES AND POEMS

LIST OF STORIES AND POEMS

A Song of Drake's Men

ALFRED NOYES

The moon is up: the stars are bright:
　The wind is fresh and free!
We're out to seek for gold tonight
　Across the silver sea!
The world was growing grey and old;
　Break out the sails again!
We're out to seek a Realm of Gold
　Beyond the Spanish Main!

*From *Collected Poems*. Reprinted by permission of Frederick A. Stokes Company.

THE ENCHANTED ISLAND*
Howard Pyle

BUT it is not always the lucky one that carries away the plums; sometimes he only shakes the tree, and the wise man pockets the fruit.

Once upon a long, long time ago, and in a country far, far away, there lived two men in the same town and both were named Selim; one was Selim the Baker, and one was Selim the Fisherman.

Selim the Baker was well off in the world, but Selim the Fisherman was only so-so. Selim the Baker always had plenty to eat and a warm corner in cold weather, but many and many a time Selim the Fisherman's stomach went empty and his teeth went chattering.

Once it happened that for time after time Selim the Fisherman caught nothing but bad luck in his nets, and not so much as a single sprat, and he was very hungry. "Come," said he to himself, "those who have some should surely give to those who have none," and so he went to Selim the Baker. "Let me have a loaf of bread," said he, "and I will pay you for it to-morrow."

"Very well," said Selim the Baker; "I will let you have a loaf if you will give me all that you catch in your nets to-morrow."

"So be it," said Selim the Fisherman, for need drives one to hard bargains sometimes; and therewith he got his loaf of bread.

So the next day Selim the Fisherman fished and fished and fished and fished, and still he caught no more than the day before; until just at sunset he cast his net for the last time for the day, and, lo and behold! there was something heavy in it. So he dragged it ashore, and what should it be but a leaden box, sealed as tight as wax, and covered with all manner of strange letters and figures. "Here," said he, "is something to pay for my bread of yesterday, at any rate;" and as he was an honest man, off he marched with it to Selim the Baker.

*Taken from *Twilight Land*. Used by permission of the publishers, Harper & Brothers.

12

THE TREASURE CHEST

They opened the box in the baker's shop, and within they found two rolls of yellow linen. In each of the rolls of linen was another little leaden box; in one was a finger-ring of gold set with a red stone, in the other was a finger-ring of iron set with nothing at all.

That was all the box held; nevertheless, that was the greatest catch that ever any fisherman made in the world; for, though Selim the one or Selim the other knew no more of the matter than the cat under the stove, the gold ring was the Ring of Luck and the iron ring was the Ring of Wisdom.

Inside the gold ring were carved these letters: "Whosoever wears me, shall have that which all men seek—for so it is with good-luck in this world."

Inside of the iron ring were written these words: "Whosoever wears me, shall have that which few men care for—and that is the way it is with wisdom in our town."

"Well," said Selim the Baker, and he slipped the gold ring of good-luck on his finger, "I have driven a good bargain, and you have paid for your loaf of bread."

"But what will you do with the other ring?" said Selim the Fisherman.

"Oh, you may have that," said Selim the Baker.

Well, that evening, as Selim the Baker sat in front of his shop in the twilight smoking a pipe of tobacco, the ring he wore began to work. Up came a little old man with a white beard, and he was dressed all in gray from top to toe, and he wore a black velvet cap, and he carried a long staff in his hand. He stopped in front of Selim the Baker, and stood looking at him a long, long time. At last—"Is your name Selim?" said he.

"Yes," said Selim the Baker, "it is."

"And do you wear a gold ring with a red stone on your finger?"

"Yes," said Selim, "I do."

"Then come with me," said the little old man, "and I will show you the wonder of the world."

"Well," said Selim the Baker, "that will be worth the seeing, at any rate." So he emptied out his pipe of tobacco, and put on his hat and followed the way the old man led.

Up one street they went, and down another, and here and there through alleys and byways where Selim had never been before. At last they came to where a high wall ran along the narrow street, with a garden behind it, and by-and-by to an iron gate. The old man rapped upon the gate three times with his knuckles, and cried in a loud voice, "Open to Selim, who wears the Ring of Luck!" Then instantly the gate swung open, and Selim the Baker followed the old man into the garden.

Bang! shut the gate behind him, and there he was.

There he was! And such a place he had never seen before. Such fruit! such flowers! such fountains! such summer-houses!

"This is nothing," said the old man; "this is only the beginning of wonder. Come with me."

He led the way down a long pathway between the trees, and Selim followed. By-and-by, far away, they saw the light of torches; and when they came to what they saw, lo and behold! there was the sea-shore, and a boat with four-and-twenty oarsmen, each dressed in cloth of gold and silver more splendidly than a prince. And there were four-and-twenty black slaves, carrying each a torch of spice-wood, so that all the air was filled with sweet smells. The old man led the way, and Selim, following, entered the boat; and there was a seat for him made soft with satin cushions embroidered with gold and precious stones and stuffed with down, and Selim wondered whether he was not dreaming.

The oarsmen pushed off from the shore and away they rowed. On they rowed and on they rowed for all that livelong night.

THE TREASURE CHEST

At last morning broke, and then as the sun rose, Selim saw such a sight as never mortal eyes beheld before or since. It was the wonder of wonders—a great city built on an island. The island was all one mountain; and on it, one above another and another above that again, stood palaces that glistened like snow, and orchards of fruits, and gardens of flowers and green trees.

And as the boat came nearer and nearer to the city, Selim could see that all around on the house-tops and down to the water's edge were crowds and crowds of people. All were looking out towards the sea, and when they saw the boat and Selim in it, a great shout went up like the roaring of rushing waters.

"It is the King! It is the King! It is Selim the King!"

Then the boat landed, and there stood dozens and scores of great princes and nobles to welcome Selim when he came ashore. And there was a white horse waiting for him to ride, and its saddle and bridle were studded with diamonds and rubies and emeralds that sparkled and glistened like the stars in heaven, and Selim thought for sure he must be dreaming with his eyes open.

DONN P. CRANE

But he was not dreaming, for it was all as true as that eggs are eggs. So up the hill he rode, and to the grandest and most splendid of all the splendid palaces, the princes and noblemen with him, and the crowd shouting as though to split their throats.

And what a palace it was!—as white as snow and painted all inside with gold and blue. All around it were gardens blooming with fruit and flowers, and the like of it mortal man never saw in the world before.

There they made a king of Selim, and put a golden crown on his head; and that is what the Ring of Good Luck can do for a baker.

But wait a bit! There was something queer about it all, and that is now to be told.

All that day was feasting and drinking and merry-making, and the twinging and twanging of music, and dancing of beautiful dancing-girls, and such things as Selim had never heard tell of in all his life before. And when night came they lit thousands and thousands of candles of perfumed wax; so that it was a hard matter to say when night began and day ended, only that the one smelled sweeter than the other.

But at last it came midnight, and then suddenly, in an instant, all the lights went out and everything was dark as pitch—not a spark, not a glimmer anywhere. And, just as suddenly, all the sound of music and dancing and merry-making ceased, and everybody began to wail and cry until it was enough to wring one's heart to hear. Then, in the midst of all the wailing and crying, a door was flung open, and in came six tall and terrible black men, dressed all in black from top to toe, carrying each a flaming torch; and by the light of the torches King Selim saw that all—princes, noblemen, dancing-girls—all lay on their faces on the floor.

The six men took King Selim—who shuddered and shook with

THE TREASURE CHEST

fear—by the arms, and marched him through dark, gloomy entries and passageways, until they came at last to the very heart of the palace.

There was a great high-vaulted room all of black marble, and in the middle of it was a pedestal with seven steps, all of black marble; and on the pedestal stood a stone statue of a woman looking as natural as life, only that her eyes were shut. The statue was dressed like a queen; she wore a golden crown on her head; and upon her body hung golden robes, set with diamonds and emeralds and rubies and sapphires and pearls and all sorts of precious stones. As for the face of the statue, white paper and black ink could not tell you how beautiful it was. When Selim looked at it, it made his heart stand still in his breast.

The six men brought Selim up in front of the statue, and then a voice came as though from the vaulted roof: "Selim! Selim! Selim!" it said, "what art thou doing? To-day is feasting and drinking and merry-making, but beware of to-morrow!"

As soon as these words were ended the six black men marched King Selim back whence they had brought him; there they left him and passed out one by one as they had first come in, and the door shut to behind them.

Then in an instant the lights flashed out again, the music began to play and the people began to talk and laugh, and King Selim thought that maybe all that had just passed was only a bit of an ugly dream after all.

So that is the way King Selim the Baker began to reign, and that is the way he continued to reign. All day was feasting and drinking and making merry and music and laughing and talking. But every night at midnight the same thing happened, the lights went out, all the people began wailing and crying, and the six tall, terrible black men came with fantastic torches and marched King Selim away to the beautiful statue. And every night the same voice said—"Selim! Selim! Selim! What art thou doing? To-day is feasting and drinking and merry-making; but beware of to-morrow!"

So things went on for a twelvemonth, and at last came the end of the year. That day and night the merry-making was merrier and wilder and madder than it had ever been before, but the great clock in the tower went on—tick, tock! tick, tock!—and by and by it came midnight. Then, as it always happened before, the lights went out, and all was as black as ink. But this time there was no wailing and crying out, but everything was silent as death; the door opened slowly, and in came, not six black men as before, but nine men as silent as death, dressed all in flaming red, and the torches they carried burned as red as blood. They took King Selim by the arms, just as the six men had done, and marched him through the same entries and passageways, and so came at last to the same vaulted room. There stood the statue, but now it was turned to flesh and blood, and the eyes were open and looking straight at Selim the Baker.

"Art thou Selim?" said she; and she pointed her finger straight at him.

"Yes, I am Selim," said he.

"And dost thou wear the gold ring with the red stone?"

"Yes," said he; "I have it on my finger."

"And dost thou wear the iron ring?"

"No," said he; "I gave that to Selim the Fisherman."

The words had hardly left his lips when the statue gave a great cry and clapped her hands together. In an instant an echoing cry sounded all over the town—a shriek fit to split the ears.

The next moment there came another sound—a sound like thunder—above and below and everywhere. The earth began to shake and to rock, and the houses began to topple and fall, and the people began to scream and to yell and to shout, and the

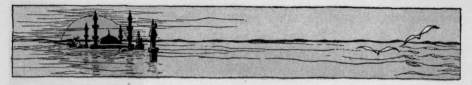

waters of the sea began to lash and to roar, and the wind began to
bellow and howl. Then it was a good thing for King Selim that
he wore Luck's Ring; for, though all the beautiful snow-white
palace about him and above him began to crumble to pieces like
slaked lime, the sticks and the stones and the beams to fall this
side of him and that, he crawled out from under it without a
scratch or a bruise, like a rat out of a cellar.

That is what Luck's Ring did for him.

But his troubles were not over yet; for, just as he came out
from under all the ruin, the island began to sink down into the
water, carrying everything along with it—that is, everything but
him and one thing else. That one other thing was an empty
boat, and King Selim climbed into it, and nothing else saved him
from drowning. It was Luck's Ring that did that for him also.

The boat floated on and on until it came to another island
that was just like the island he had left, only that there was
neither tree nor blade of grass nor hide nor hair nor living thing
of any kind. Nevertheless, it was an island just like the other;
a high mountain and nothing else. There Selim the Baker went
ashore, and there he would have starved to death only for Luck's
Ring; for one day a boat came sailing by, and when poor Selim
shouted, those aboard heard him and came and took him off.
How they all stared to see his golden crown—for he still wore it—
and his robes of silk and satin and the gold and jewels!

Before they would consent to carry him away, they made
him give up all the fine things he had. Then they took him
home again to the town whence he had first come, just as poor as
when he had started. Back he went to his bake-shop and his

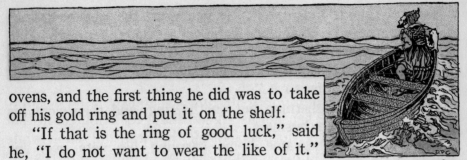

ovens, and the first thing he did was to take off his gold ring and put it on the shelf.

"If that is the ring of good luck," said he, "I do not want to wear the like of it."

That is the way with mortal man; for one has to have the Ring of Wisdom as well, to turn the Ring of Luck to good account.

And now for Selim the Fisherman.

Well, thus it happened to him. For a while he carried the iron ring around in his pocket—just as so many of us do—without thinking to put it on. But one day he slipped it on his finger and that is what we do not all of us do. After that he never took it off again, and the world went smoothly with him. He was not rich, but then he was not poor; he was not merry, neither was he sad. He always had enough and was thankful for it, for I never yet knew wisdom to go begging or crying.

So he went his way and he fished his fish, and twelve months and a week or more passed by. Then one day he went past the baker shop and there sat Selim the Baker smoking his pipe.

"So, friend," said Selim the Fisherman, "you are back again in the old place, I see."

"Yes," said the other Selim, "awhile ago I was a king, and now I am nothing but a baker again. As for that gold ring with the red stone—they may say it is Luck's Ring if they choose, but when next I wear it may I be hanged."

Thereupon he told Selim the Fisherman the story of what had happened to him with all its ins and outs, just as I have told it to you.

"Well!" said Selim the Fisherman, "I should like to have

a sight of that island myself. If you want the ring no longer, just let me have it; for maybe if I wear it something of the kind will happen to me."

"You may have it," said Selim the Baker. "Yonder it is, and you are welcome to it."

So Selim the Fisherman put on the ring, and then went his way about his own business.

That night, as he came home carrying his nets over his shoulder, whom should he meet but the little old man in gray, with the white beard and the black cap on his head and the long staff in his hand.

"Is your name Selim?" said the little man, just as he had done to Selim the Baker.

"Yes," said Selim, "it is."

"And do you wear a gold ring with a red stone?" said the little old man, just as he had said before.

"Yes," said Selim, "I do."

"Then come with me," said the little old man, "and I will show you the wonder of the world."

Selim the Fisherman remembered all that Selim the Baker had told him, and he took no two thoughts as to what to do. Down he tumbled his nets, and away he went after the other as fast as his legs could carry him. Here they went and there they went, up crooked streets and lanes and down by-ways and alley-ways, until at last they came to the same garden to which Selim the Baker had been brought. Then the old man knocked at the gate three times and cried out in a loud voice, "Open! Open! Open to Selim who wears the Ring of Luck!"

Then the gate opened, and in they went. Fine as it all was, Selim the Fisherman cared to look neither to the right nor to the left, but straight after the old man he went, until at last they came to the seaside and the boat and the four-and-twenty oarsmen dressed like princes and the black slaves with the perfumed torches. Here the old man entered the boat and Selim after him, and away they sailed.

To make a long story short, everything happened to Selim the Fisherman just as it had happened to Selim the Baker. At dawn of day they came to the island and the city built on the mountain. And the palaces were just as white and beautiful, and the gardens and orchards just as fresh and blooming as though they had not all tumbled down and sunk under the water a week before, almost carrying poor Selim the Baker with them. There were the people dressed in silks and satins and jewels, just as Selim the Baker had found them, and they shouted and hurrahed for Selim the Fisherman just as they had shouted and hurrahed for the other. There were the princes and the nobles and the white horse, and Selim the Fisherman got on his back and rode up to the dazzling snow-white palace, and they put a crown on his head and made a king of him, just as they had made a king of Selim the Baker.

That night, at midnight, it happened, just as it had happened before. Suddenly, as the hour struck, the lights all went out, and there was a moaning and a crying enough to make the heart curdle. Then the door flew open, and in came the six terrible black men with torches. They led Selim the Fisherman through damp and dismal entries and passage-ways until they came to the vaulted room of black marble, and there stood the beautiful statue on its black pedestal. Then came the voice from above—"Selim! Selim! Selim! what art thou doing? To-day is feasting and drinking and merry-making, but beware of to-morrow!"

But Selim the Fisherman did not stand still and listen, as Selim the Baker had done. He called out, "I hear the words! I am listening! I will beware to-day for the sake of to-morrow!"

I do not know what I should have done had I been king of

that island and had I known that in a twelve-month it would all come tumbling down about my ears and sink into the sea, and maybe carry me along with it. This is what Selim the Fisherman did (but then he wore the iron Ring of Wisdom on his finger, and I never had that upon mine).

First of all, he called the wisest men of the island to him, and found from them just where the other desert island lay upon which the boat with Selim the Baker in it had drifted.

Then, when he had learned where it was to be found, he sent armies and armies of men and built on that island palaces and houses, and planted there orchards and gardens, just like the palaces and the orchards and the gardens about him—only a great deal finer. Then he sent fleets and fleets of ships, and carried everything away from the island where he lived to that other island—all the men and the women and the children, all the flocks and herds and every living thing, all the fowls and the birds and everything that wore feathers, all the gold and the silver and the jewels and the silks and the satins, and whatever was of any good or of any use, and when all these things were done, there were still two days left till the end of the year.

Upon the first of these two days he sent over the beautiful statue and had it set up in the very midst of the splendid new palace he had built.

Upon the second day he went over himself, leaving behind him nothing but the dead mountain and the rocks and the empty houses.

So came the end of the twelve months.

So came midnight.

Out went all the lights in the new palace, and everything was as silent as death and as black as ink. The door opened, and in came the nine men in red, with torches burning as red as blood. They took Selim the Fisherman by the arms and led him

to the beautiful statue, and there she was with her eyes open.

"Are you Selim?" said she.

"Yes, I am Selim," said he.

"And do you wear the iron Ring of Wisdom?" said she.

"Yes, I do," said he, and so he did.

There was no roaring and thundering, there was no shaking and quaking, there was no toppling and tumbling, there was no splashing and dashing, for this island was solid rock, and was not all enchantment and hollow inside and underneath like the other which he had left behind.

The beautiful statue smiled until the place lit up as though the sun shone. Down she came from the pedestal where she stood and kissed Selim the Fisherman on the lips.

Then instantly the lights blazed everywhere, and the people shouted and cheered, and the music played. But neither Selim the Fisherman nor the beautiful statue saw or heard anything.

"I have done all this for you!" said Selim the Fisherman.

"And I have been waiting for you a thousand years!" said the beautiful statue—only she was not a statue any longer.

After that they were married, and Selim the Fisherman and the enchanted statue became king and queen in real earnest.

I think Selim the Fisherman sent for Selim the Baker and made him rich and happy—I hope he did—I am sure he did.

So, after all, it is not always the lucky one who gathers the plums when wisdom is by to pick up what the other shakes down.

THE - LITTLE - MAN - AS - BIG - AS - YOUR - THUMB - WITH - MUSTACHES - SEVEN - MILES - LONG

A Russian Tale

FAR, far behind the blue sea, in the midst of the pleasant meadows, stood a lofty city, and in this city ruled Tsar Wise-Head with his Tsaritsa. There they lived a long time and to their great delight two daughters were born to them, the elder so lovely that they called her Loveliness-That-Shines, and the other no less beautiful whom they named Jewel-Without-A-Price.

In his joy, the Tsar made merry and gladdened his heart. But when all the feastings and junketings were over, he began to be greatly troubled how to train up his beloved daughters. He built for them a white marble palace, with pinnacles of gold and mother-of-pearl that shone like fire in the sun. They were laid to sleep on eiderdown beds, covered with sable coverlets, and fed only with golden spoons. Three nurses took it in turn to drive away the flies when the little Princesses slept, and they were bidden to take care that the lovely sun never peeped into the children's room, that the cold dew never fell on them, and the cold wind never touched them.

Yet with all this care, great was the anxiety of the Tsar concerning his daughters. He built a high wall around their palace to protect them, and then he built a higher wall, and then he built one higher still. And, withal, he was just as anxious as he had been in the beginning, so he placed beside the little ones seventy-seven nurses to watch them indoors and seventy-seven nurses to watch them out doors, and seventy-seven guardians to guard the walls of the palace.

Thus Tsar Wise-Head with his Tsaritsa and his two daughters lived many years. The Princesses began to grow up and become

26

beautiful maidens, and still the Tsar was just as anxious concerning them as he had been in the beginning.

One day he sat thinking and casting over in his mind whether he should build a wall higher than all the other three, when he suddenly heard a great noise and commotion. There was a scampering up and down and to and fro in the courtyard. The outdoor nurses were crying; the indoor nurses were howling, and the guardians were bawling with all their might. The Tsar immediately rushed out and asked, "What is the matter?"

Then the seventy-seven men attendants and the twice seventy-seven women attendants all fell down on their knees before him.

"We are guilty!" they cried. "Look now! the Tsarevnas have been carried off by a whirlwind!"

A strange thing indeed had happened. The Princesses had gone out to walk in the garden to pluck a few sweet peas and a red poppy or two, when suddenly a black cloud rose up above them (whence it came nobody knew) and it blew right into the eyes of the nurses and guardians. Of what use then were all the walls? When the attendants came to themselves and began to rub their eyes, the Princesses had been carried straight up in the air and were almost out of sight in the distance!

Tsar Wise-Head flared up with rage.

"Off to the dungeons with you all!" he cried. "What! seventy-seven indoor nurses, seventy-seven out door nurses, seventy-seven guardians, and you could not all look after two Tsarevnas!"

And now the Tsar was in sore affliction, he neither ate nor drank nor slept; banquets at his court there were none, and the sound of the fiddle and the shawm was heard no more. Only sad grief sat beside him and sang her mournful dirge in his ear.

But in time another child was born to the Tsar, and this time it was not a daughter, but a son. Tsar Wise-Head rejoiced greatly and he called the boy Ivan. But he was wiser now than he had been before, so, though he gave the child wise teachers and valiant voevods to surround him, he commended him to God, and built no high walls to protect him.

And the Tsarevitch Ivan began to grow and grow. He grew not by the day, but by the hour, and what wondrous beauty, what a stately figure was his. One thing only weighed upon the heart of the Tsar; he saw nothing in the boy that he held for heroic valor or knightly skill. He did not tear off the heads of his comrades, nor break their arms and legs; he neither loved to play with lances of damask steel, nor swords of tempered metal.

Good and beauteous was the Tsarevitch Ivan; he amazed all men with his wit and wisdom, and his greatest delight was to play on the harp that needed no harper. Ivan played so well that men forgot all else but the music as they listened, and those who heard him danced for joy. But with all these, his son's gifts, the Tsar could not see that there was one among them that would enable him to hold his kingdom against an evil foe.

So one day he called Ivan before him and thus he spake:

"My beloved son, good art thou and beauteous, and I am well content with thee. One thing only grieves me. I do not see in thee the valor of a warrior, or the skill of a champion. Thou dost not love the clash of steel lances, and the tempered blade has no charm for thee. Look now, if evil foes should come upon us, what couldst thou do to defend us?"

The Tsarevitch Ivan listened to the words of the Tsar, his father, and thus he made answer:

"Dear Tsar and father, both courage and strength are mine, yet do I trust rather in sagacity than in the clash of steel. Not by cudgels but by wisdom will I prevail against the foe. Make trial of me this very day; make trial of my youthful valor. Look now! They tell me that I have two sisters whom the whirlwind carried away, and that the rumor of them vanished as if it were covered with snow. Call together now all thy princes, thy heroes, thy stalwart voevods, and bid them do thee the service of finding the Tsarevnas. And if any one of them with all their damask blades, their iron lances, their glowing darts, and their countless soldiery, shall offer himself to do thee this service, then give to him my tsardom and bid me be unto him a scullion, to clean his pots and pans. But if they cannot render thee this service, then will I render it thee, and thou shalt see that my wits are keener than a damask blade, and stronger than a lance."

The words of the Tsarevitch pleased the Tsar. He called together his boyars, his voevods, his strong and mighty champions, and he said to them:

"Is there any one of you, my strong and mighty champions, hero enough to go seek my daughters? If so, to him will I give to choose which of my daughters he will, to be his wife, and with her he shall have half my tsardom."

The boyars, the voevods and the champions looked one upon another, and hid one behind the other, but not one of them dared to speak. Then the Tsarevitch bowed before his father and said:

"Dear Father! if none will take it upon him to render thee this paltry little service, give me thy blessing on my journey. I will go, I will seek my sisters, nor have I need of any royal gift from thee to urge me forth."

"Good!" replied the Tsar, "my blessing go with thee. Depart in God's name on thy journey. Take what thou wilt of my treasures, silver and gold, and if thou requirest soldiers, take a hundred thousand horse and a hundred thousand foot."

But the Tsarevitch Ivan answered:

"I need neither silver nor gold, neither horse nor foot, neither sword nor lance. I will take with me my sweet-sounding harp, and I will not leave my wits behind. Nothing else do I need. And thou, my Sovereign Tsar, await me these three years, then if I come not again, choose thee my successor."

So Ivan received again his father's blessing, commended himself to God, took his harp under his arm, and went straight on his way whither his eyes led him. He went and went near and far, high and low, and as he went, he played songs upon his harp. When night fell, he laid him down on the silky grass beneath the vast roof of the heavenly dome bright with stars; and when the sun in all his glory chased away the darkness like a flock of birds, he rose again and wended his way along.

At last one evening he came to an opening in a dense forest. All around were enormous oaks and pines lit up by the rays of the setting sun. And in the midst of these, within a railing, stood a little house. It was supported on hen's legs that walked about

and kept twirling it round over the yard. And Ivan cried out:
"Turn round, little house, turn round,
I want to come inside;
Let thy back to the forest be found,
Thy door to me open wide."
The little house turned round, Ivan stepped in at the door,
and there in the hut was sitting Baba Yaga, the bony one.

"Fie! fie! fie! why hast thou come here where no Russian
soul ever enters?" cried Baba Yaga.

"Ask me no questions tonight, little Granny," said Ivan.
"Morning is wiser than evening. Give me food tonight."

At these words Baba Yaga leaped up in the twinkling of an
eye, heated her little stove, and prepared him food and drink.
Then she made him a soft bed, and leaving him in the little house
that went walking about on hen's legs, she passed the night out
of doors. In the morning Ivan spake to her thus:

"I go to seek my sisters, Loveliness-That-Shines, and Jewel-
Without-A-Price. Tell me, my dear little Granny, if thou know-
est, what way must I go and where shall I find them?"

"I know where they are," said Baba Yaga. "They are kept
prisoner by the Little-Man-As-Big-As-Your-Thumb-With-Mustaches-Seven-Miles-Long. And a fierce little man is he. His
strength is as the whirlwind. He can pull up an oak by the roots!"

"Nay," said Ivan. "Be his strength thrice ten times that of
a man, God will not give over a Russian soul to fall before such
a swine as that. Where may I find him?"

"The way to his cave among the rocks is long and difficult,"
said Baba Yaga, "but if thou wilt follow the road before the door,
thou wilt come at length to a little hut with a garden and sheep-
fold that he pulled up and carried away at one swoop from a
little peasant of the Steppes. If thou canst contrive to meet him
there, thou wilt be saved a long journey."

So Ivan thanked Baba Yaga for her bread and salt, bade her farewell and was off. He strode and he strode, striding with great strides. He travelled that day and the next and the third also, with nothing but the blue sky above his head and the broad, wild steppes on every side. At length he came to a little hut with a tiny sheep fold and a tiny garden. He knocked at the door, there was no answer, he peeped in the window—it was quite empty. So he lifted the latch and walked in. Then he sat himself down to think of some way to bring the little man to him. After short consideration, he took the kettle that hung in the fireplace, filled it full of green cabbages and what-not from the garden and set himself to make a savory stew. When

DONN P. CRANE

it was all well a-boiling so the pleasant smell rose up the chimney, and floated off in the air, he hung up his harp by the chimney bench to keep it out of harm's way, and sat down again to wait.

Almost at once there came a rumbling and a thundering from without, the door was nearly torn off its hinges and there stood the Little-Man-As-Big-As-Your-Thumb-With-Mustaches-Seven-Miles-Long. He looked at Ivan from beneath his beetling brows and shrieked with a terrible voice:

"How dare you come into my hut as if you were its lord and master? How dare you make savory stew of my cabbages?"

But Ivan looked at him calmly and said with a smile.

"You ought to grow a little bigger before you shriek so."

At that the Little Man fell into a fury. Seizing hold of both doorposts he shook the whole house like a tempest. Then he flung himself violently on Ivan. But though his strength seemed thrice ten times that of Ivan, Ivan was not afraid. Dodging well out of his reach, he seized the little man by his long mustaches and held on tight. Then he began to drag him around the hut and tumble him about.

The-Little-Man-As-Big-As-Your-Thumb-With-Mustaches-Seven-Miles-Long wriggled and writhed like a serpent. At length with a terrible wrench, he jerked himself loose and was off, leaving the ends of his mustaches clutched tight in Ivan's fists. Ivan made after him swiftly—but whither, pray? All at once the Little Man flew up in the air like fluff and vanished. So Ivan knew no more than before where to search for his sisters.

Henceforth, though he made many a savory stew, the fragrance of which went up the chimney, the Little Man came no more. Then Ivan reflected and said to himself:

"I will go to the river hard by, take a boat and ferry people across. Of each who crosses I will take no money, but will ask that he tell me, if he knows, where I may find the Little-Man-

As - Big - As - Your - Thumb - With - Mustaches - Seven - Miles - Long."

So Ivan took his harp on his back, left the little hut and went to the river. There he took a ferry boat and for one whole year he ferried people back and forth, back and forth, and he took no fare, but asked each one where the Little Man was to be found. Not one among thousands could tell him. But on the very last day of the year, it befell that he had to ferry over three old pilgrims. Once across, the men got out on the bank and began to undo their purses. The first pulled out a handful of gold, the second a roll of pearls, and the third the most precious stones.

"There, that is for thy ferrying, good youth," said the old men.

But Ivan pushed from him all the gold and jewels. "Nay," he said, "I will take nothing from you. Tell me, rather, if you know where I may find the Little-Man-As-Big-As-Your-Thumb-With-Mustaches-Seven-Miles-Long."

"Well for thee, good youth, that thou hast asked this of us," said the eldest of the pilgrims, "for thou hast but to wish thyself where the Little Man is, and we can grant thee thy wish."

"Let me be at once where the Little Man keeps my sisters," cried Ivan, and before he could wink, he found himself in a deep chasm amongst the gloomy rocks by the sea, and near a dark yawning cavern before him the Little Man was sitting.

"Hah! what brings you hither?" he screeched as he saw Ivan.

"I have come for my sisters, the Tsarevnas, and you shall not escape me again!" cried Ivan.

But the Little Man laughed mockingly. Slipping into the cave in the great gray rocks, he came forth dragging with him the two lovely Princesses.

In a flash, while they stretched out their arms imploringly toward Ivan, he had them up the rock far out of Ivan's reach, and on the very edge of the cliff that overhung the sea.

"I'll pitch them into the sea!" he roared.

THE TREASURE CHEST

Ivan used his wits in a twinkling. Seizing his harp, he drew his hands across its strings and struck up a lively tune.

As soon as that tune fell on the little man's ears, whether he would or no, he found his arms akimbo, and suddenly fell a-dancing. He skipped up and down, he stamped with his feet, he danced and he danced, and he could not leave off dancing. So angry was he, he roared and shrieked, but he could not leave off dancing. At the sound of that music too, the fish came up out of the sea, whales and sturgeons and herring and carp, not to speak of crabs and lobsters, and they all began to dance on the shore. They circled and spun and leaped. They hopped and skipped and tripped. And they could not leave off dancing.

So the lovely Princesses fled to their brother, and Ivan, setting down his harp, bade it go on playing of itself while he put an arm about each of his sisters and led them safely away.

And the harp went on harping without a harper, and the little man went on howling and dancing, and the whales and the sturgeons and herrings and carp, not to speak of the crabs and the lobsters, all danced in a circle about him. But Ivan delivered his sisters in safety to their father. The Tsar and Tsaritsa received their daughters with joy and henceforth they commended them to God, but built no more walls around them. As to Ivan, he said to his father:

"Thou seest, O sovereign Tsar, that, not with force and valor alone, may one prevail, but as well with wit and wisdom."

THE SQUIRE'S BRIDE
Peter Christen Asbjörnsen

NCE upon a time there was a rich squire who owned a large farm and had plenty of silver at the bottom of his chest and money in the bank besides; but he felt there was something wanting, for he was a widower.

One day the daughter of a neighboring farmer was working for him in the hay field. The squire saw her and liked her very much, and as she was the child of poor parents, he thought if he only hinted that he wanted her she would be ready to marry him at once. So he told her he had been thinking of getting married again.

"Ay! one may think of many things," said the girl, laughing. In her opinion the old fellow ought to be thinking of something that behooved him better than getting married.

"Well, you see, I thought that you should be my wife!"

"No, thank you all the same," said she, "that's not at all likely."

The squire was not accustomed to be gainsaid, and the more she refused him, the more determined he was to get her. But as he made no progress in her favor, he sent for her father and told him that if he could arrange the matter with his daughter he would forgive him the money he had lent him, and he would also give him the piece of land which lay close to his meadow into the bargain.

"Yes, you may be sure I'll bring my daughter to her senses," said the father. "She is only a child and she doesn't know what's best for her." But all his coaxing and talking did not help matters. She would not have the squire, she said, if he sat buried in gold up to his ears.

The squire waited day after day, but at last he became so angry and impatient that he told the father, if he expected him to stand by his promise, he would have to put his foot down and settle the matter now, for he would not wait any longer.

The man knew no other way out of it but to let the squire get everything ready for the wedding; and when the parson and wedding guests had arrived, the squire should send for the girl as if she was wanted for some work on the farm. When she arrived she would have to be married right away, so that she would have no time to think it over. The squire thought this was well and good, and so he began brewing and baking and getting ready for the wedding in grand style. When the guests had arrived the squire called one of his farm lads and told him to run down to his neighbor and ask him to send him what he had promised.

"But if you are not back in a twinkling," he said, shaking his fist at him, "I'll—"

He did not say more, for the lad ran off as if he had been shot at.

"My master has sent me to ask for what you promised him," said the lad when he got to the neighbor, "but there is no time to be lost for he is terribly busy today."

"Yes, yes! Run down into the meadow and take her with you. There she goes!" answered the neighbor.

The lad ran off and when he came to the meadow he found the daughter there raking hay.

"I am to fetch what your father has promised my master," said the lad.

"Ah, ha!" thought she. "Is that what they are up to?"

"Ah, indeed," she said, "I suppose it's that little bay mare of ours. You had better go and take her. She stands there tethered on the other side of the peas field," said the girl.

The boy jumped on the back of the bay mare and rode home at full gallop.

"Have you got her with you?" asked the squire.

"She is down at the door," said the lad.

"Take her up to the room my mother had," said the squire.

"But master, how can that be managed?" said the lad.

"You must just do as I tell you," said the squire. "If you cannot manage her alone you must get the men to help you," for he thought the girl might turn obstreperous.

When the lad saw his master's face he knew it would be no use to gainsay him. So he went and got all the farm tenants who were there to help him. Some pulled at the head and the forelegs of the mare and others pushed from behind, and at last they got her up the stairs and into the room. There lay all the wedding finery ready.

"Now that's done, master!" said the lad; "but it was a terrible job. It was the worst I have ever had here on the farm."

"Never mind, you shall not have done it for nothing," said his master. "Now send the women up to dress her."

"But I say, master—!" said the lad.

"None of your talk!" said the squire. "Tell them they must dress her and mind and not forget either wreath or crown."

The lad ran into the kitchen.

"Look here, lasses," he said, "you must go upstairs and dress up the bay mare as bride. I expect the master wants to give the guests a laugh!"

The women dressed the bay mare in everything that was there, and then the lad went and told his master that now she was ready dressed, with wreath and crown and all.

"Very well, bring her down!" said the squire. "I will receive her myself at the door."

THE TREASURE CHEST

There was a terrible clatter on the stairs; for that bride, you know, had no silken shoes on. When the door was opened and the squire's bride entered the parlor you can imagine there was a good deal of tittering and grinning.

And as for the squire you may be sure he had had enough of that bride, and they say he never went courting again.

THE MAGIC HORSE

The Arabian Nights

HROUGHOUT all Persia the Nevrouz, or Festival of the New Year, has always been celebrated with extraordinary rejoicings. Strangers are invited to appear at court and liberal rewards are given by the sultan to those who can produce the most wonderful inventions. On one of these feast days, after the most skillful inventors of the country had displayed their devices before the Sultan of Persia at Schiraz, there suddenly appeared at the foot of the throne, just as the assembly was breaking up, a Hindu with an artificial horse. The horse was richly bridled and saddled and so wonderfully made that at first sight he looked like a living creature. The Hindu prostrated himself before the throne, and, pointing to the horse, said to the sultan:

"Sire, of all wonders which you have this day seen, I assure you this horse is the most wonderful. Whenever I mount him, be it where it may, if I wish to transport myself to the most distant part of the world, I can do it in a very short time. This is a marvel which nobody ever heard of, and which I offer to display for your majesty if you command me."

The sultan who was fond of everything that was curious, had indeed never beheld or heard of anything that came up to this, so he bade the Hindu perform what he had promised. The Hindu immediately put his foot into the stirrup, and mounted his horse with agility. When he had fixed himself in the saddle, he asked the sultan where he was pleased to send him.

About three leagues from Schiraz there was a high mountain visible from the large square before the palace, where the sultan and his court and a great concourse of people were then gathered.

"Do you see that mountain?" said the sultan. "Ride your

horse thither and bring me a branch from the palm tree that grows at the bottom of the hill."

The sultan had no sooner declared his will, than the Hindu turned a peg, which was in the hollow of the horse's neck, just by the pummel of the saddle. In an instant the horse rose off the ground and carried his rider into the air like lightning, rising to such a great height that the sultan and all the spectators were struck with admiration. In less than a quarter of an hour they saw him returning with the palm branch in his hand. Before he descended, he took two or three turns in the air amid the acclamations of the people, then alighted on the spot whence he had set off. He dismounted, and prostrated himself before the throne, laying the branch of the palm tree at the feet of the sultan.

The sultan, who had viewed this unheard-of sight with no less admiration than astonishment, conceived a great desire to have the horse, and said to the Hindu: "I will buy him of you."

"Sire," replied the Hindu, "I beg of you not to be angry with me, but I cannot resign to you my horse, except on receiving the hand of the princess, your daughter, as my wife."

The courtiers could not forbear laughing aloud at this extravagant demand of the Hindu; but the Prince Firouz Schah, the sultan's eldest son, and heir to the crown, could not hear it without indignation. "Sire," he said, "I hope you will not hesitate to refuse so insolent a demand, or allow this insignificant juggler to flatter himself for a moment with the idea of being allied to one of the most powerful monarchs in the world."

"Son," replied the sultan, "putting my daughter, the princess out of the question, I may still make another agreement with the Hindu. But before I bargain at all, I should be glad that you would examine the horse, try him yourself and give me your opinion." On hearing this, the Hindu readily ran before the prince to help him mount and show him how to guide and

manage the horse. But the prince mounted without the Hindu's assistance; and as soon as he had his feet in the stirrups, without waiting for the artist's advice, he turned the peg he had seen him use. Instantly the horse darted up in the air quick as an arrow out of a bow. In a few moments neither horse nor prince was to be seen.

The Hindu, alarmed at what had happened, prostrated himself before the throne and cried out: "Sire, your majesty yourself saw that the prince was so hasty he would not permit me to give him the necessary instructions how to govern my horse. He knows not how to turn the horse around and bring him back again. I beg you do not hold me accountable for what may happen to him." But the sultan, perceiving the danger into which his son's impatience had brought him, asked in a passion why the Hindu had not called out instructions to the prince the moment he saw him ascend.

"Sire," answered the Hindu, "your majesty saw as well as I with what rapidity the horse flew away. Surprise deprived me of the use of my tongue. But," he added, "there is reason to hope that the prince when he finds himself at a loss, will perceive another peg; as soon as he turns that the horse will cease to rise, and descend to the ground, when he may turn him to what place he pleases by guiding him with the bridle."

"Your head shall answer for my son's life, if he does not return safe in three days' time," cried the sultan, and he ordered his officers to secure the Hindu and keep him close prisoner; after which he retired to his palace in great affliction.

In the meantime, Prince Firouz Schah was carried through the air with prodigious swiftness, and in less than an hour's time he had got so high that he could not distinguish anything on the earth. Mountains and plains seemed confounded together. It was then he began to think of returning, and thought to do it by turning the same peg he had used before, only the contrary way, pulling the bridle at the same time. But when he found that the horse still continued to ascend, his alarm was great. He turned the peg several times, one way and the other, but all in vain. It was then he saw his fault, and apprehended the great danger he was in, from not having waited to learn how to guide the horse before he mounted. He examined the horse's head and neck with great attention, and at length perceived behind the right ear another peg, smaller than the first. He turned that peg, and immediately the horse began to descend in

43

the same oblique manner as he had mounted, but not so swiftly.

Night had overshadowed that part of the earth over which the prince was flying when he discovered the small peg; and as the horse descended, he by degrees lost sight of the sun till it grew quite dark, insomuch that, instead of choosing what place he would go to, he was obliged to let the bridle lie upon the horse's neck and wait patiently till he alighted, though not without dread lest it should be in the desert, a river or the sea.

At last, after midnight, the horse reached the ground and the prince dismounted very faint and hungry, having eaten nothing since the morning when he came out of the palace with his father, to assist at the festival. He found himself to be on the terrace of a magnificent palace surrounded with a balustrade of white marble breast high, and, groping about, reached a staircase.

None but Prince Firouz Schah would have ventured to go down those stairs, dark as they were, and exposed to danger. But he said to himself; "I do not come to do anybody any harm, so whoever meets me and finds me unarmed will attempt nothing against me without hearing what I have to say for myself." After this reflection he went softly down the stairs, and came to a landing place where he found a door opening into an apartment that had a light in it.

The prince stopped and, listening, heard no other sound within than the snoring of some people who were fast asleep. He advanced a little into the room and by the light of the lamp saw that those persons were black chamberlains with naked sabres laid by them, which was enough to inform him that this was the guardchamber of some queen or princess. Prince Firouz Schah advanced on tip-toe, without waking the chamberlains and drew aside the silken curtain that hung before an inner room. There he saw a magnificent chamber containing many beds, one alone being on a raised dais and the others on the floor.

THE TREASURE CHEST

The princess slept in the first and her women in the others. He crept softly toward the dais and there beheld a beauty so extraordinary that he was charmed at first sight. Gently he woke the princess. She opened her eyes, and seeing a handsome young man, was in great surprise, yet showed no sign of fear.

The prince bowed himself to the ground and said: "Beautiful princess, by the most extraordinary and wonderful adventure, you see at your feet a suppliant prince, son of the Sultan of Persia. Pray afford him your assistance and protection."

The personage to whom Firouz Schah so happily addressed himself was the Princess of Bengal, eldest daughter of the Rajah of that kingdom, who had built this palace at a small distance from his capital, whither she went to enjoy the country. After she had heard the prince, she replied with kindness: "Prince, hospitality, humanity, and politeness are to be met with in the kingdom of Bengal, as well as in Persia. I grant you the protection you ask—you may depend on what I say." The Prince of Persia would have thanked the Princess of Bengal for her kindness, but she would not give him leave. "Notwithstanding my desire," said she, "to know by what miracle you have come hither from the capital of Persia in so short a time and how you have been able to come to my apartment and escape the vigilance of my guards, as you must want some refreshment, I will postpone my curiosity and give orders to my women to regale you, and show you to a room where you may rest after your fatigue."

The princess's women each took a wax candle and after the prince had taken leave very respectfully, they went before him and conducted him into a handsome chamber, where they brought him all sorts of meats. When he had eaten they left him to repose. In the meantime the Princess of Bengal was so struck with the intelligence, politeness, and other good qualities which she had discovered in that short conversation with the prince, that she could not sleep, but when her women came into her room again, she asked them if they had taken care of him, and more particularly what they thought of him.

The women answered: "We do not know what you may think of him, but, for our part, we think you would be very happy if the rajah, your father, would marry you to so amiable a prince, for there is not a prince in all the kingdom of Bengal to compare with him, nor can we hear that any of the neighboring princes are worthy of you."

Nothing went forward for several days following this but concerts of music, accompanied with magnificent feasts in the garden, or hunting parties in the vicinity of the palace, which abounded with all sorts of game, stags and deer, and other beasts peculiar to the kingdom of Bengal. After the chase, the prince and princess met in some beautiful spot, where a carpet was spread, and cushions laid for their accommodation. There, resting themselves, they conversed on various subjects.

For two whole months Prince Firouz Schah remained the guest of the Princess of Bengal, taking part in all the amusements she arranged for him. But after that time, he declared seriously that he could not stay any longer, and begged her to give him leave to return to his father, repeating a promise he had made to her to return soon in a style worthy of her and of himself to demand her in marriage of the rajah.

"And, princess," observed the Prince of Persia, "that you may not doubt the truth of my affection, I would presume, were I not afraid you would be offended at my request, to ask the favor of taking you along with me to visit my father, the sultan."

The princess returned no answer to this address of the Prince of Persia; but her silence and down-cast eyes were sufficient to inform him that she had no reluctance to accompany him into Persia. The next morning, therefore, a little before daybreak,

THE TREASURE CHEST

they went upon the terrace of the palace. The prince turned
the horse's head towards Persia, and the princess was no sooner
up behind him with her arms about his waist for better security,
than he turned the peg, when the horse mounted into the air.
In two hours' time, the prince discovered the capital of Persia.

The prince would not alight in the palace of his father, but
directed his course toward a small kiosk at a little distance from
the capital. He led the princess into a handsome apartment
where he told her that to do her all honor, he would go and
inform his father of their arrival, and return to her immediately.
He ordered the attendants of the palace whom he summoned
to provide the princess with whatever she had occasion for.

Having then taken leave of the princess, he left the artificial
horse and ordered a real one to be brought. This he mounted
and set out for the palace. As he passed through the streets
he was received with acclamations by the people, who were
overjoyed to see him again. The sultan his father was in the
midst of his council when his son appeared before him. He

received the prince with tears of joy and, embracing him, asked what had been his adventures. This question gave the prince an opportunity of describing what had happened to him and the affection he and the Princess of Bengal entertained for each other; also how he had persuaded her to accompany him into Persia and desired his father's consent to their marriage.

After these words the sultan embraced his son a second time and said: "Son, I not only consent to your marriage with the Princess of Bengal, but will go and meet her myself, thank her for the obligation I am under to her, bring her to my palace and celebrate your wedding this day."

The sultan now ordered that the Hindu should be fetched out of prison and brought before him, when he said: "Thanks be to God, my son is returned again. Go, take your horse and never let me see your face more."

As the Hindu had learned that Prince Firouz Schah was returned with a princess whom he had left at the kiosk, he thought he would just be beforehand with the prince and the sultan and have the princess for himself. So, without losing any time, he went direct to the kiosk, and addressing himself to the Captain of the Guard, told him he came from the Prince of Persia to fetch the Princess of Bengal on the horse to the sultan, who waited in the great square of the palace to gratify the whole court and the city of Schiraz with that wonderful sight.

The Captain of the Guard credited what the Hindu said and presented him to the Princess of Bengal, who no sooner understood that he came from the Prince of Persia, than she consented to what the prince, as she thought, desired of her.

The Hindu, overjoyed at the ease with which he had accomplished his villainy, mounted his horse, took the princess before him and turned the peg, whereat the horse mounted instantly into the air.

THE TREASURE CHEST

At the same time, the sultan, with his entire court, was on the way from his palace to the kiosk, and the Prince of Persia had ridden on before to prepare the princess to receive his father. To defy them both and revenge himself for the ill-treatment he had received, the Hindu appeared directly over their heads with his prize. When the Sultan of Persia saw the Hindu he stopped. His surprise and affliction were keen. He loaded him with a thousand imprecations, as did also all his courtiers. But the Hindu, little moved by their curses, continued his way, while the sultan went back to his palace in rage and vexation.

But what was Prince Firouz Schah's grief to see the Hindu carry away the princess whom he loved so dearly! At so unexpected a sight he was thunderstruck, and before he could make up his mind what to do the horse was out of sight. He continued his way therefore to the kiosk where he had left the princess. When he arrived, the Captain of the Guard, who had learned how he had been deceived, threw himself at the prince's feet, and, with tears in his eyes, accused himself of the crime which he had unintentionally committed.

"Rise up," said the prince to him, "I do not impute the loss of my princess to you, but to my own want of precaution. But lose no more time; fetch me a dervish's robe at once and take care that you do not give the least hint it is for me."

Not far from this place there stood a convent of dervishes, the superior of which was the particular friend of the Captain of the Guard. From him the Captain readily obtained a complete dervish's habit, and carried it to Prince Firouz Schah. The prince immediately put it on, and being so disguised, left the palace, uncertain which way to go, but resolved never to return until he had found out his princess.

Meantime, the Hindu, mounted on his enchanted horse with the princess before him, arrived early that evening at the capital of the kingdom of Cashmere. Being hungry, he alighted in an open part of the wood, and left the princess on a grassy spot, close to a rivulet of fresh water, while he went to seek for food. During the Hindu's absence, the princess, knowing that she was in the power of a base deceiver, whose violence she dreaded, thought of getting away from him and seeking a sanctuary. But the Hindu discovered her, and dragged her back with great violence. The princess made stout resistance and her cries and shrieks soon drew to the spot the Sultan of Cashmere and his attendants who chanced to be passing.

The sultan, addressing himself to the Hindu, demanded who he was and wherefore he ill-treated the lady. The Hindu, with great impudence, replied that she was his wife, and what had anyone to do with his quarrel with her?

The princess, who knew neither the rank nor the quality of the person who came so seasonably to her relief, exclaimed: "Sir, whoever you are whom Heaven has sent to my assistance, have compassion on a princess, and give no credit to that impostor. He is a wicked magician who has stolen me away from the Prince of Persia to whom I was going to be married, and has brought me hither on the enchanted horse you behold there."

The Princess of Bengal had no occasion to say more. Her beauty, majestic air and tears, declared that she spoke the truth. Justly enraged at the insolence of the Hindu, the sultan ordered his guards to surround him and strike off his head, which sentence was immediately executed. The sultan then conducted the princess to his palace, where he lodged her in the most magnificent apartment and commanded a great number of women slaves to attend her.

The Princess of Bengal's joy was inexpressible at finding herself delivered from the Hindu, of whom she could not think without horror. She flattered herself that the Sultan of Cashmere would complete his generosity by sending her back to the Prince of Persia when she should have told him her story and asked that favor of him. But she was much deceived in these hopes, for her deliverer had resolved to marry her himself the next day; and to that end had issued a proclamation, commanding the general rejoicing of the inhabitants of the capital. At the break of day, drums were beaten, trumpets sounded and the whole palace echoed with music and joy.

When the Sultan of Cashmere came to wait upon the Princess of Bengal, he informed her that all those rejoicings were in honor of their wedding; and at the same time, desired her to agree to the marriage. This declaration threw her into such a state of agitation that, rather than break the promise she had made to Prince Firouz Schah, by consenting to marry the Sultan of Cashmere, she resolved to feign madness. She began to utter the most extravagant expressions before the sultan and ever rose off her seat as if to fly at him; insomuch that the sultan was very

much surprised and greatly afflicted that he should have made
his proposal so unseasonably.

When he found that her frenzy rather increased than abated,
he left her with her women, charging them never to leave her
alone, but to take great care of her. He sent often that day,
to inquire how she did, but received no other answer than that
she was rather worse than better. So the sultan was induced
to send for all the physicians about his court to ask if they could
cure her. When he saw that they could not, he called in the
most celebrated and experienced physicians of the city who had
no better success. He then sent for the most famous in the
kingdom and to neighboring courts, but all with no effect.

During this interval, Firouz Schah disguised in the habit of
a dervish, had traveled through a great many provinces and
towns, full of grief and having endured much fatigue, not knowing which way to direct his course. He made diligent inquiry
after his lost princess at every place he came to. At last, passing
through a city of Hindustan, he heard the people talk much
of a Princess of Bengal who had become mad on the day of her
intended marriage to the Sultan of Cashmere. Supposing that
there could exist no other Princess of Bengal, he had hastened
toward the kingdom of Cashmere, and upon his arrival at the
capital, took up his lodging at a khan, where, the same day, he
was informed of the story of the princess and the fate of the
Hindu magician. The prince was convinced he had at last
found the beloved object whom he had sought so long.

Being informed of all particulars, he provided himself with
a physician's habit and went boldly to the palace, announcing
to the chief of the officers his wish to be allowed to undertake
the cure of the princess. Some time had elapsed since any
physician had offered himself; and the Sultan of Cashmere had
begun to lose all hope of ever seeing the princess restored to

herself. Therefore he lost no time in ordering the officer to introduce the new physician. The sultan then told the prince that the Princess of Bengal could not bear the sight of a physician without falling into the most violent transports. Accordingly, he conducted the prince into a closet whence he might see her without being observed. There Firouz Schah beheld his lovely princess looking very melancholy and singing an air in which she deplored the unhappy fate which had deprived her perhaps forever of the prince whom she loved so tenderly.

The prince was much affected at the melancholy condition in which he found his beloved princess, but he at once comprehended that her madness was but a pretence. When he came away, he told the sultan that he had discovered the nature of her ailment, but added that, in spite of the manner in which she took on at sight of a physician, he must speak to her in private.

The sultan ordered the princess's door to be opened and Firouz Schah went in. As soon as the princess saw him, she resorted to her old practice of violence on meeting physicians, but he made directly toward her, and when he was nigh enough for her to hear, and no one else, he said in a low voice: "Princess, I am not a physician, but the Prince of Persia."

The princess, who knew the sound of his voice and recognized his features, notwithstanding he had let his beard grow long, became calm at once and a secret joy and pleasure overspread her face. Firouz Schah then told her as briefly as possible his own adventures and she informed him of all that had happened

to her—how she had feigned to be mad because she saw no other way to preserve herself for a prince to whom she had given her heart and faith. The Prince of Persia then asked her if she knew what had become of the horse, to which she answered that she did not, but she supposed, after the account she had given the sultan of it, he would preserve it as a curiosity.

The Sultan of Cashmere was overjoyed when the Prince of Persia stated to him how calmly the princess had received him and what effect his first visit had had toward her recovery. In order to introduce the subject of the horse, the prince then inquired of the sultan how the princess had come into the kingdom of Cashmere thus alone, when her own country was so far distant. The sultan at once informed him; adding that he had ordered the horse to be kept safe, though he knew not how to use it.

"Sire," replied Firouz Schah, "the information which your majesty has given me, affords me a means of restoring the princess. As she was brought hither on this horse and the horse is enchanted she hath contracted somewhat of the enchantment, which can be dissipated only by a certain incense I know of. If your majesty would entertain yourself, your court, and the people of your capital with the most surprising sight that ever you beheld, let the horse be brought tomorrow into the great square before the palace, and leave the rest to me. I promise to show you and all that assembly in a few moments, the Princess of Bengal completely recovered."

The sultan would have undertaken much more difficult things to have secured his marriage with the princess, moreover he was greatly encouraged by the improvement already made, so, the next day, the enchanted horse was by his order taken out of the treasury, and placed in the great square before the palace. A report was spread through the town that there was something extraordinary to be seen, and crowds of people flocked thither from all parts, insomuch that the sultan's guards were placed about to prevent disorder, and to keep space enough round the horse.

The Sultan of Cashmere, surrounded by all his nobles and ministers of state, was placed in a gallery erected on purpose. The Princess of Bengal, attended by a number of women whom the sultan had assigned to her, went up to the enchanted horse, and the women helped her to mount. When she was fixed in the saddle and had the bridle in her hand, the Prince of Persia placed round the horse, at a proper distance, many vessels full of lighted charcoal, which he had ordered to be brought, and going round them with a solemn pace, cast in handfuls of incense. Then, with downcast eyes and his hands upon his breast, he ran three times about the horse, making as if he pronounced some mystical words. The moment the pots sent forth a dark cloud of smoke accompanied with a pleasant smell,—which so surrounded the princess that neither she nor the horse was to be discerned,—the prince, watching his opportunity, jumped nimbly up behind her, and reaching his hand to the peg, turned it. Just as the horse rose with them into the air, he pronounced these words which the sultan heard distinctly: "Sultan of Cashmere, when you would marry a princess who implores your protection, learn first to obtain her consent."

Thus the prince delivered the Princess of Bengal, and carried her the same day to the capital of Persia, where he alighted in the midst of the palace before the window of the sultan, his father.

The sultan deferred the marriage only so long as was required to make preparations to render the ceremony magnificent.

After the days appointed for the rejoicing were over, the Sultan of Persia at once sent an ambassador to the Rajah of Bengal, to give him an account of what had happened and ask his approval of the marriage. This the Rajah of Bengal took as an honor and was pleased to grant with great satisfaction.

RECOLLECTIONS OF THE ARABIAN NIGHTS
Alfred Tennyson

When the breeze of a joyful dawn blew free
In the silken sail of infancy,
The tide of time flowed back with me,
The forward-flowing tide of time;
And many a sheeny summer-morn,
Adown the Tigris I was borne,
By Bagdad's shrines of fretted gold,
High-walled gardens green and old;
True Mussulman was I and sworn,
For it was in the golden prime
Of good Ha-roun' Al-rasch'id.

Anight my shallop, rustling through
The low and bloomed foliage, drove
The fragrant, glistening deeps, and clove
The citron-shadows in the blue:
By garden porches on the brim,
The costly doors flung open wide,
Gold glittering through lamp light dim,
And broidered sofas on each side;
In sooth it was a goodly time,
For it was in the golden prime
Of good Ha-roun' Al-rasch'id.

THE STORY OF THE TALKING BIRD
The Arabian Nights

There were once two brothers named Bah'man and Per'viz, who lived in Persia in the closest and most pleasant friendship with their only sister Par'i-zade. They had never known their father, the Sultan Khos'roo Shah, nor he them, for they had been stolen away from the palace one after the other when they were but a day old. Now, on the occasion when the sultan had asked to see his first babe, two wicked aunts, who lived in the palace, and had a spite against their sister, the sultaness, told him that the sultaness had in the cradle but a puppy, which she was trying to pass off as a child; on the second occasion that she had a cat, on the third a log of wood and no real infant at all, which ridiculous tale the sultan was foolish enough to believe, conceiving, finally, such indignation against the sultaness that he ordered her to be imprisoned in a shed with iron bars to the windows near one of the great mosques. But the truth of the matter was that the aunts had stolen the real babes, substituting for each in turn a dog, a cat, and a log of wood. They placed the children each in a basket, and sent them, one after the other, adrift down the canal.

It so happened that, just after the first babe was sent adrift, the keeper of the sultan's gardens, a powerful but kind-hearted officer, who lived on the canal bank some way below the palace, was walking along the path and saw something floating in the water. He called to the gardener, who came with his rake, reached out toward the floating object, and drew it to land. To their great surprise they found it to be a basket containing a beautiful little boy. The keeper, to his sorrow, had no children of his own, so he immediately determined to adopt this foundling, and picking up the basket, carried the babe to his wife, who received the child with great joy and named him Bahman.

The following year, the keeper while walking on the canal banks, saw another floating basket, containing another babe, whom he and his wife adopted in exactly the same way, and named Perviz. The third year there appeared a third basket containing the little princess, whom they called Parizade and brought up with the boys. The keeper and his wife grew so extremely fond of these children, that they determined not to make any inquiries into the mystery of their origin, nor to tell them that they were not really their own. All of them were so quick and clever and good that the keeper had them taught by the very best masters, and although the sister was the youngest, she was soon as proficient in all learning, in riding, running, bending the bow and darting the javelin as her brothers, whom indeed she oftentimes outdid in the race or other contest of agility.

The keeper was so overjoyed to find his adopted children so accomplished in body and mind, and so well justifying the care and expense he had bestowed upon them, that he determined to build them a country house at some distance from the city, and to furnish it most magnificently. He then asked permission of the sultan to be released from his service as he wished to end his days in peace and tranquillity. The sultan granted this request, with the more pleasure because he was satisfied with his long services, and the keeper retired with the two princes and the princess to the country retreat he had built. His wife had now been dead some years, and the keeper himself had not lived above six months with his charges, before he, too, suddenly died without ever giving the princes and the princess any account of the manner in which he had found them.

The Princes Bahman and Perviz, and the Princess Parizade, who knew no other father and loved the keeper as such, paid his memory all the honors which love and filial gratitude required of them. Content with the plentiful fortune he had left them, they lived together in perfect union, free from any ambition for places of honor and dignity at court.

One day when the two princes were hunting, and the Princess Parizade stayed at home, an old woman came to the gate and desired leave to come in and say her prayers, it being then the hour. The servants asked the princess's permission, who ordered them to show her into the oratory.

The old woman went into the oratory and when she came out, two of the princess's women invited her to see the residence, which civility she accepted, following them from one apartment to another and observing the nice arrangement of everything. Afterward she was brought before the princess in the great hall.

As soon as the princess saw the old woman, she said to her: "My good mother, come near and sit down by me. I am overjoyed at the opportunity of profiting for a few moments by the conversation of such a wise woman as you."

"Madame," said the good woman, "I ought not to have such respect shown me, but since you command me, I will obey."

When she had sat down, before they entered into any conversation, one of the princess's women brought a little low table of mother-of-pearl and ebony, with a china dish full of cakes, and a great many others full of fruits in season and sweetmeats. While they were eating the princess asked the good woman a great many questions, all of which she answered with modesty. At last the princess asked her what she thought of the house.

"Madame," answered the devout woman, "I should certainly

have very bad taste to disapprove of anything in it, since it is furnished with remarkably good judgment; yet if you will give me leave to speak my mind freely, I will say that this house would be incomparable if it had three things which are lacking in it."

"My good mother," replied the princess, "I implore you to tell me what are those things. I will spare no trouble to get them."

"Madame," replied the devout woman, "the first of these three things is the Talking Bird called Bul-bul-ke'zer, which is so singular a creature that it can draw around it all the singing birds of the neighborhood. The second is the Singing Tree, the leaves of which form an harmonious concert of different voices and never cease. The third is the Golden Water, a single drop of which being poured into a vessel increases so as to fill the vessel immediately, and rises up in the middle like a fountain, which continually plays, and yet the basin never overflows."

"Ah! my good mother," cried the princess, "how much am I obliged to you! I never before heard that there were such curious and wonderful things in the world; but as I am sure you know where they are, do me the favor to tell me."

"Madame," replied the good woman, "I should be unworthy the hospitality you have shown me if I should refuse to satisfy your curiosity on this point, and am glad to tell you that these rarities are all to be met with in the same spot on the confines of this kingdom, towards India. The road lies before your house, and whoever you send needs but follow it for twenty days, and on the twentieth only let him ask the first person he meets where the Talking Bird, the Singing Tree, and the Golden Water are, and he will be informed." After saying this, she rose from her seat, took her leave and went her way.

The Princess Parizade's thoughts were so taken up with the Talking Bird, the Singing Tree, and the Golden Water, that she never perceived the old woman's departure, till she wanted to ask her some further questions. However, she would not send after her visitor, but endeavored to remember all the directions she had given. It seemed to her that she could only be satisfied now if she could get these things into her possession, yet she feared there would be plenty of difficulties and dangers on the way.

She was lost in these thoughts when her brothers returned from hunting, who, when they entered the great hall, instead of finding her lively and gay as she was wont to be, were amazed to see her pensively hanging her head as if something troubled her.

"Sister," said Prince Bahman, "what is become of all your mirth and gaiety? Has some misfortune befallen you? Tell us, that we may know how to act and give you some relief."

The Princess Parizade remained for some time without speaking, but at last she lifted up her eyes to her brothers and said:

"We always thought this house which our late father built for us was so complete that it needed nothing. But this day I have learned that it lacks three things in order to render it the most perfect country seat in the world. These three things are the Talking Bird, the Singing Tree, and the Golden Water." Then she told them all about the visit of the religious woman. "You," she added, "may not think this a matter of great importance, but I am persuaded these rarities are absolutely nec-

essary and I shall not be happy without them. Therefore, whether you value them or not, I desire you to consider what person you may think proper for me to send on this expedition."

"Sister," replied Prince Bahman, "whatever concerns you, concerns us also. It is enough that you have an earnest desire for the things you mention; but even if it were otherwise, we should be anxious to go and search for them on our own account. Only tell me where the place is and I will set out tomorrow."

"Brother," said Prince Perviz," it is not fitting that you who are the head of the family should be absent so long. I beg you will abandon your design and let me undertake it."

"I am sure of your good will, brother," replied Prince Bahman, "but I have resolved on it and will do it. You shall stay home with our sister and I need not recommend her to your care."

He spent the remainder of that day in making preparations for his journey and in learning from the princess the directions the devout woman had left her, that he might not miss his way.

Early the next day, Prince Bahman mounted his horse and Prince Perviz and the Princess Parizade embraced him and wished him a pleasant journey. But in the midst of their farewells, it suddenly came over the princess into what dangers and difficulties she was letting her brother go forth; whereupon she cried out to him, "Ah, brother, I had quite forgotten the difficulties that may lie in the way. Alight, I beseech you, and give up this journey. I would rather never possess the Talking Bird, the Singing Tree and the Golden Water than run the risk of losing you."

"Sister," replied Prince Bahman, "my resolution is fixed and you must allow me to excute it. Neverless, as events are uncertain and I may fail, all I can do is to leave you this knife." At that he drew a knife out of his pocket and, presenting it to his sister, said; "Take this knife, sister, and sometimes pull it out of its sheath. While you see it clean as it is now, it shall be a sign that I am alive; but if you find it stained with blood, then you may believe me dead and favor me with your prayers."

The Princess Parizade could obtain nothing more from Prince Bahman. He bade farewell to her and Prince Perviz for the last time, and rode away, well mounted, armed and equipped. When he got into the road, he never turned to the right nor to the left but went straight forward towards India. On the twentieth day he perceived by the roadside a hideous old man, who sat under a tree at some small distance from a thatched house, which was his retreat from the weather. His eyebrows were white as snow, and so was the hair of his head; his whiskers covered his mouth, and his beard and hair reached down to his feet. The nails of his hands and feet were extremely long, and a flat broad hat, like an umbrella, covered his head. He had no clothes but only a mat thrown round his body. This old man was a dervish who had for many years retired from the world, and so neglected himself that at last he had become what we have described.

Prince Bahman stopped when he came near the dervish for here was the first person he had met on the twentieth day.

"God prolong your days, good father, and grant you the fulfilment of your desires," said he.

The dervish returned the prince's salutation, but so unintelligibly that he could not understand one word he said. Prince Bahman perceived that the reason for this was that the dervish's whiskers hung over his mouth. Being unwilling to go any further without the instruction he wanted, he pulled out a pair of scissors, and having tied his horse to a tree, said: "Good dervish, I want to have a talk with you, but your whiskers prevent my understanding what you say. If you consent, I will cut off part of them, for they disfigure you so much, that you look more like a bear than a man."

The dervish did not oppose the prince, but let him do it;

63

and when the prince had cut off as much hair as he thought fit, he said: "Good dervish, you look now like a man."

The kind behavior of Prince Bahman made the dervish smile. "I am greatly obliged to you," said he, "and am ready to show my gratitude by doing anything in my power for you."

"Good dervish," said Prince Bahman, "I have come a long way and am in search of the Talking Bird, the Singing Tree, and the Golden Water. I beg you to tell me where they may be found, that I may not lose my labor after so long a journey."

While the prince was speaking, he observed that the dervish changed countenance, looked very serious, and remained silent. At last he said: "I know the way you ask, but the friendship which I feel for you keeps me in suspense as to whether I should tell you what you desire."

"What can hinder you?" asked the prince.

"The danger to which you are going to expose yourself is greater than you believe. A great many brave gentlemen have passed by here and asked me the same question. Though I used all my power to persuade them to desist, they would not believe me. At last I was compelled to show them the way, and I have

never seen one come back again. I assure you they have all perished. Therefore, if you have any regard for your life, take my advice. Go no further, but return home."

But Prince Bahman persisted in his resolution. "Whatever the danger," said he, "nothing shall make me change my mind. If any one attacks me, I am well armed, and as brave as any."

"But they who will attack

you are not to be seen," replied the dervish, "and there are a great many of them. How will you defend yourself against foes you cannot see?"

"It is no matter," answered the Prince, "all you say shall not persuade me to do anything contrary to my duty. Since you know the way I beg you once more to tell me."

When the dervish found that he was absolutely bent on pursuing his journey, he put his hand into a bag that lay by him, and pulled out a bowl which he gave to him. "Since I cannot prevail on you to take my advice," said he, "take this bowl. When you are on horse-back throw it before you, and follow it to the foot of a mountain, where it will stop. As soon as it stops, alight, and leave your horse with the bridle thrown over his neck; he will stand in the same place till you return. As you go up the hill, you will see right and left a great quantity of large black stones, and will hear on all sides of you a confusion of voices, which will say a thousand irritating things to discourage you and prevent your climbing to the top of the hill. But take care and be not afraid; and, above all things, do not turn your head to look behind you, for at that instant you will be turned into a black stone like those you see, which are all so many gentlemen who have failed. If you escape the danger of which I give you but a slight description, and get to the top of the mountain, you will see a cage, and in that cage is the Bird you seek. Ask him where are the Singing Tree and Golden Water and he will tell you. I have nothing more to say."

"I am very much obliged to you," said Prince Bahman. "I will endeavor to follow your instructions and not to look behind as I go up and I hope to come and thank you further when I have got what I am in search of." After these words to which the dervish made no answer, he mounted his horse, took leave of the dervish with a low bow, and threw the bowl before him.

The bowl rolled away with such swiftness that Prince Bahman was obliged to spur his horse to follow without losing sight of it. When it came to the foot of the mountain it stopped. The prince alighted and threw the bridle on his horse's neck. Having surveyed the mountain and seen the black stones, the prince began to climb it, but had not gone four steps when he heard the voices mentioned by the dervish, though he could see nobody. Some said, "Where is that fool going? What does he want? Don't let him pass." Others, "Stop him, catch him, kill him," and others with a voice like thunder, "Thief, assassin, murderer!" while some in a gibing tone, cried, "No, no; do not hurt him, let the pretty fellow pass; the cage and bird are kept for him."

Notwithstanding all those troublesome voices, Prince Bahman mounted with courage and resolution for some time, but the voices increased with so loud a din, both in front and behind, that at last he was seized with fear, his legs trembled under him, he staggered, and presently finding that his strength failed, he forgot the dervish's advice, turned about to run down the hill, and was at that instant turned into a black stone as had happened to so many before him. His horse was likewise transformed.

From the time of Prince Bahman's departure, the Princess Parizade always wore the knife and sheath in her girdle, and pulled it out several times a day to know how her brother was faring. For some time she had the consolation of seeing the knife clean and shining. But on the fatal day that Prince Bahman was changed into a stone, the princess perceived blood running down the point, and was so seized with horror and grief that she threw it down. "Ah, my dear brother," cried she, "why did I ever tell you of the Talking Bird, the Singing Tree, and the Golden Water. Of what importance was it to me to know whether the religious woman thought this house ugly or handsome, complete or not? I wish to heaven I had never seen her."

Prince Perviz was as much afflicted at what had occurred to Prince Bahman as the princess, but not to waste time in needless regret, he said: "Sister, our regret for our brother is vain. It ought not to prevent us from pursuing our object. I offered to go on this journey. His example has no effect on my resolution. Tomorrow I will go myself."

The Princess did all she could to dissuade Prince Perviz, but all she could urge had no effect upon him. Before he went, that she might know what success he had, he left her a string of a hundred pearls, telling her that if they would not run when she told them upon the string, but remained fixed, that would be a certain sign that he had met the same fate as his brother.

Prince Perviz on the twentieth day from the setting out, met with the dervish. After he had saluted him, he asked if he could tell him where he should find the Talking Bird, the Singing Tree, and the Golden Water. The dervish remonstrated as before, but he could not persuade the prince to give up his resolution. At last, therefore, he took a bowl out of his bag and gave it to the young man, with the same directions as he had given Prince Bahman, warning him never to turn around at the voices but to continue his way up the hill.

Prince Perviz thanked the dervish and when he had taken leave, he threw the bowl before his horse and followed it. When the bowl came to the bottom of the hill, it stopped and the prince got off his horse. He encouraged himself, and began to walk up with a resolution to reach the top; but before he had gone six steps, he heard a voice, which seemed to be that of a man behind him, saying in an insulting tone, "Stay, rash youth, that I may punish you for your boldness."

At this affront, the prince forgot the dervish's advice, clapped his hand upon his sword and drew it, and turned about to revenge himself. But scarcely had he time to see that nobody followed him when he and his horse were changed into black stones.

The day that Prince Perviz was changed to stone, the Princess Parizade was pulling over as usual the pearls which he had left her, when all of a sudden she could not stir them, and never doubted that the prince, her brother, was dead. As she had determined beforehand what to do in case it should so happen, she lost no time in outward show of grief, but, disguising herself in man's apparel, she mounted her horse the next morning, and took the road her brothers had taken before her. The princess who was used to riding on horseback, supported the fatigue of so long a journey well, and she also met the dervish on the twentieth day. When she came near him, she alighted off her horse, and leading him by the bridle, she went and sat down by the dervish. "Good dervish," she said, "give me leave to rest by you; and do me the favor to tell me if there are somewhere hereabouts a Talking Bird, a Singing Tree, and Golden Water."

"Madame," answered the dervish, "for by your voice I know you to be a woman disguised in man's apparel, I thank you for the honor you do me. I know very well the place where these things you speak of are to be found, but doubtless you have not been told of the difficulties and dangers which must be surmounted in order to obtain them. Take my advice. Go no further; return and do not urge me to contribute to your ruin."

"Good father," said the princess, "I have come a long way and should be sorry to return home without accomplishing my purpose. You talk of difficulties and dangers, but pray tell me wherein these consist, that I may consider and judge whether I can trust my courage and strength to undertake the journey."

Then the dervish repeated to the Princess Parizade what he had said to the Princes Bahman and Perviz. When he had done, the princess replied: "I own the voices you speak of are capable of striking terror into the most undaunted, but as in all enterprises and dangers every one may use contrivances, I desire to know if I may make use of one."

"And what do you intend to do?" asked the dervish.

"To stop my ears with cotton," said the princess, "that, however loud and terrible the voices may be, they may make less impression upon me."

"Madame," replied the dervish, "of all the persons who have addressed themselves to me to ask the way, I do not know that anyone has made use of the plan you propose. All I know is, they all perished. If you persist, you can make the experiment, but I would advise you not to expose yourself to the danger."

"My good father," replied the princess, "nothing prevents my persisting. I am sure I shall succeed."

The dervish exhorted her again for the last time to consider well what she was doing, but finding her resolute he gave her a bowl. After the princess had thanked the dervish and taken leave of him, she mounted her horse, threw the bowl before her, and followed it till it stopped at the foot of the mountain.

The princess alighted, and stopped her ears with cotton wool. After she had well examined the way by which she was to get to the top, she began at a moderate pace and walked up with undaunted courage. She heard the voices in spite of the cotton, and the higher she went, the louder they seemed; but they could not make any impression on her. She heard a great many affronting speeches and jeering very disagreeable to a woman, which she only laughed at. "I mind not," said she to herself, "all that can be said, were it even worse. I shall pursue my way." At last she got so high that she began to perceive the cage and Bird which also tried to frighten her, crying in a thundering voice, notwithstanding the smallness of its size, "Retire, fool, and approach no nearer."

The princess nevertheless redoubled her haste and by effort gained the summit of the mountain. Running straight to the cage she clapped her hands upon it and cried: "Bird, I have you in spite of yourself, and you shall not escape me."

While the Princess Parizade was pulling the cotton-wool out of her ears, the Bird said to her: "Heroic princess, I would rather be your slave than any other person's in the world since you have obtained me so courageously. From this instant I swear entire submission to all your commands. The time will come when I shall do you a great service. I know who you are though you do not know yourself and some day I will tell you. As a proof of my sincerity now, tell me what you desire at this moment and I will obey you."

"Bird," said the princess, "I have been told that there is not far off, Golden Water. Before all things, I ask you to tell me where it is." The Bird showed her the place which was close by, and she went and filled a little silver flagon which she had brought with her. Then she returned to the Bird and said: "Bird, this is not enough, I want also the Singing Tree."

"Turn round," said the Bird," and you will see behind you a wood where you will find this tree." The princess went into the wood and by the harmonious sounds she heard, soon knew the tree among many others, but it was very large and high. She came back to the bird and said: "Bird, I have found the Singing Tree, but I can neither pull it up by the roots nor carry it."

The Bird replied: "It is not necessary that you should take it up by the roots. Break off a branch and carry it to plant in your garden. It will grow as fine a tree as this you see."

When the Princess Parizade had in her hand all the three things which she had set out to obtain, she said to the Bird: "Bird, all you have done for me as yet is not enough. My two brothers must be among the black stones which I saw as I came up the hill. I wish to take them home with me."

"What you now ask of me is more difficult than all the rest," said the Bird, "yet I will do it for you. Cast your eyes around and see if you do not find a little pitcher."

"I see it already," said the princess.

"Take it then," said he, "and as you go down the hill, spill a little of the water that is in it on every black stone, and that will be the way to find your brothers again."

The Princess Parizade took up the pitcher, and carried with her the cage and the Bird, the flagon of Golden Water and the branch of the Singing Tree. As she went down the hill, she spilt a little of the water on every black stone, which was changed immediately into a man; and as she did not miss one stone, all of the horses also resumed their former shape. She presently recognized Prince Bahman and Prince Perviz, and they ran to embrace her. Prince Bahman and Prince Perviz perceived how greatly they were indebted to the Princess, their sister, as did all the other gentlemen who had collected round.

"Gentlemen," said the princess, "I rejoice with you for the happiness which has come to you by my means. Let us however stay no longer where we have nothing to detain us; but mount our horses and return to our respective homes."

71

When the princes and all the gentlemen had mounted their horses, the Princess Parizade waited for some of them to lead the way. The two princes waited for the gentlemen, and they again for the princess, who, finding that none of them would accept the honor, but that it was reserved for her, said: "Gentlemen, I do not deserve the honor you do me, and accept it only because you desire it." So she led the way, and the two princes and the gentlemen followed her all together.

As soon as the princess reached home, she placed the cage in the garden just by the hall; and the Bird no sooner began to sing, than he was surrounded by nightingales, chaffinches, larks, linnets, goldfinches, and a great many other birds of the country. As for the branch of the Singing Tree, it was no sooner set in the midst of the garden than it took root, and in a short time became a large tree, the leaves of which gave as harmonious a concert as those of the tree from which it was gathered. For the Golden Water a large basin of beautiful marble was made in the midst of the garden, and when it was finished the princess poured into it all the water from the flagon. This increased and swelled so much that it soon reached up to the edges of the basin, and afterwards formed in the middle a fountain twenty feet high, which fell again into the basin without running over.

Some days afterwards, when the Princes Bahman and Perviz had resumed their usual diversion of hunting, they chanced to  meet the Sultan of Persia in so narrow a path that they could not turn away nor retreat without being seen. In their surprise they had only time to alight and prostrate themselves before the sultan, who seeing they were well mounted and dressed as if they belonged to his court, had some curiosity to see their faces. He stopped and commanded them to rise. The princes rose up and stood before him with an easy and graceful air, and respectful, modest countenances. The sultan then asked them who they were and where they lived.

The princes made him such polished and prudent answers that the sultan was charmed with them and asked them at once to join him in the hunt. They therefore mounted their horses again and followed the sultan. They had not gone very far before they saw a great many wild beasts together. Prince Bahman chose a lion and Prince Perviz a bear and the young men pursued them with such vigor that the sultan was surprised. They came up with their game and darted their javelins with so much skill, that they pierced, the one the lion and the other the bear, through and through. At that the sultan felt so kindly disposed towards the two that he invited them to pay him a visit, to which Prince Bahman replied: "Your majesty does us an honor we do not deserve and we beg you will excuse us."

The sultan, who was astonished that the princes should refuse this token of his favor, pressed them to tell him why they excused themselves. "Sire," said Prince Bahman, "we have a younger sister, with whom we live in such perfect union that we undertake nothing before we consult her, nor she without our advice."

"I commend your brotherly affection," answered the sultan. "Consult your sister, and give me your answer here tomorrow."

The Princess Parizade was somewhat surprised at the news her brothers brought her. "It was on my account, I know, that you refused the sultan," said she, "and I am infinitely obliged to you for it. I perceive by this how strong is your love for me, since you would rather be guilty of incivility towards the sultan than break the bond that unites us to one another. You judged rightly that if you had once gone, you would by degrees have been led to leave me altogether to devote yourselves to him. Nevertheless, do you think it an easy matter to refuse the sultan what he seems so eagerly to desire? Sultans will be obeyed and it may be dangerous to oppose him. Before we decide on anything, let us consult the Talking Bird. He is wise and has promised to assist us."

The Princess Parizade sent for the Bird and asked him what they should do in their perplexity. The Bird answered: "The princes, your brothers, must conform to the sultan's pleasure, and in their turn ask him to come and see your house."

"But, Bird," replied the princess, "my brothers and I love one another. Will not this step be injurious to our friendship?"

"Not at all," replied the Bird. "It will become stronger."

Next morning the princes met the sultan hunting, who asked them if they had spoken to their sister. Prince Bahman made answer: "Sire, your majesty may dispose of us as you please; we are ready to obey you, for our sister has agreed."

Presuming that the princes possessed minds equal to their courage and bravery, the sultan longed with impatience to converse with them more at liberty, and made them ride to the palace on each side of him. When the sultan entered his capital, the eyes of the people who stood in crowds in the streets, were fixed only upon the two princes, Bahman and Perviz; and they were anxious to know who they were. All agreed in wishing that the sultan had been blessed with two such princes and said: "He might have had children just their age if he had been more fortunate."

The first thing the sultan did when he arrived was to show the princes over his palace. Afterwards a magnificent repast was served. The sultan was a clever and learned man, but in whatever way he turned the conversation, they showed so much judgment and discernment, that he was struck with admiration. "Were these my own children," said he to himself, "and I had improved their talents by suitable education, they could not be better informed."

Before they went out of the sultan's presence that night, Prince Bahman said: "Sire, may we presume to request that your majesty will do us and our sister the favor to pass by our house and rest and refresh yourself the first time you go hunting?"

"Gentlemen," replied the sultan, "you and your sister are already dear to me. I will call early tomorrow morning."

When the Princes Bahman and Perviz went home, they gave the Princess Parizade an account of what had passed.

"We must think at once of preparing a repast fit for his majesty," said the princess. "I will consult the Talking Bird. He will tell us perhaps what dishes the sultan likes best." The princes approved and after they retired, she consulted the Bird alone.

"Good mistress," replied the Bird, "you have excellent cooks; let them do the best they can. But above all, let them prepare a dish of cucumbers stuffed with pearls, which must be set before the sultan in the first course."

"Cucumbers with pearls!" cried the princess in amazement. "Surely, you know not what you say. It is an unheard-of dish."

"Mistress," said the Bird, "do what I say, and be not uneasy. Nothing but good will follow."

As soon as the princess got into the house she called for the head cook; and after she had given him directions about the entertainment, she bade him prepare a dish of cucumbers stuffed with pearls. The chief cook who had never heard of such a dish started back and showed his thoughts by his looks. The princess said, "I see you take me to be mad to order such a dish, nevertheless I give you these orders with the utmost sincerity."

Next day the two princes went to escort the sultan and when the latter entered the courtyard and alighted at the portico, the Princess Parizade came and threw herself at his feet. The sultan stooped to pick her up, and, struck with her good person, and noble air, he said: "The brothers are worthy of the sister and she of them; I am not surprised that the brothers would do nothing without their sister's consent."

The princess then led the sultan through the various rooms of the house, all of which he considered attentively and admired excessively. At last she opened a door which led into the garden; and the first object which presented itself to the sultan's view was the Golden Fountain. Surprised at so rare a sight, he asked whence came such wonderful water, where was its source, and by what art it was made to play so high.

"Sire," replied the princess, "this water has no communication with any spring; the basin is one single stone, so that the water cannot come in at the sides or underneath. It all proceeded from one flagon, which I emptied into the basin."

Then the princess led him to the spot where the harmonious Tree was planted; and there the sultan heard a concert that was different from all the concerts he had ever heard in his life. Stopping to see where the musicians were, he could discern nobody far or near.

"My fair one," said he to the princess, "where are the musicians? Are they underground or invisible in the air?"

"Sire," answered the princess, smiling. "It is not musicians, but the Tree your majesty sees which makes this concert."

The sultan went nearer and was so charmed with the sweet harmony that he would never have been tired of hearing it.

As he went towards the hall he perceived a prodigious number of singing birds in the trees thereabouts, filling the air with their songs and warblings, and asked why there were so many and none on the other trees in the garden. "The reason, Sire," answered the princess, "is because they all come to accompany the song of the Talking Bird, which your majesty may perceive in the cage; and if you listen you will hear that his notes are sweeter than those of all the other birds, even the nightingale."

The sultan went into the hall, and the princess said to the Bird, "My slave, here is the sultan; pay your respects to him."

The Bird left off singing that instant and when all the other birds had ceased one after another, he said: "The sultan is welcome here. Heaven prosper him, and prolong his life."

As the meal was served by the sofa near the window where the Bird was, the sultan replied: "Bird, I thank you and am over-joyed to find in you the Sultan of Birds."

As soon as the sultan saw the dish of cucumbers set before him, thinking they were stuffed in the ordinary manner, he reached out his hand and took one; but when he cut it, he was extremely surprised to find it stuffed with pearls. "What is this?" cried he in great astonishment; "why are these cucumbers stuffed with pearls? Pearls are not to be eaten!" But the Bird, interrupting, demanded of him: "Can your majesty stop and question at such a small matter as cucumbers stuffed with pearls, when you accepted altogether without question the state-ment that the sultaness your wife, had passed off a dog, a cat, and a piece of wood as your children?"

"Ah!" replied the sultan, "I believed it, because the two aunts assured me of it."

"The sultaness's two sisters," replied the Bird, "were envious of her happiness in being preferred by your majesty before them, and so they deceived you. If you question them, they will confess their crime. The two brothers and the sister whom you see before you are your own children, whom they sent adrift, and who were taken in and reared by the keeper of your gardens."

This speech of the Bird's illumined the sultan's understanding. "Bird," cried he, "I believe the truth of what you tell me. Come, then, my children: come, my daughter, let me embrace you." Then he rose up, and having embraced the two princes and the princess and mingled his tears with theirs, he said: "I am persuaded you are such children as will maintain the royal glory of the Sultans of Persia, and am deeply grateful to the keeper of my gardens for the care he has taken of you."

After this, he sat down again and finished his meal, and when he had done, he said, "My children, tomorrow I will bring to you the sultaness, your mother. Therefore prepare to receive her."

Afterwards the sultan mounted his horse and returned in great haste to his capital. The first thing he did as soon as he alighted and entered his palace, was to command the grand vizier to try the sultaness's two sisters. They were taken from their homes separately, convicted, and condemned to be executed; which sentence was carried out within the hour.

In the meantime, the sultan, followed by all the lords of his court, went to fetch the sultaness out of the miserable confinement in which she had languished, and embracing her, he said with tears in his eyes: "I come, madame, to ask your pardon for the injustice I have done you, and to make you the reparation I ought. I have begun by punishing the unnatural wretches who put this abominable cheat upon me; and I hope you will look upon it as complete when I present to you two accomplished princes and a charming lovely princess, our children. Come and resume your former rank and all the honors which are your due." All this was done and said before great crowds of people who immediately spread the news through the town.

Early the next morning, the sultan and sultaness went with all their court to the house built by the keeper, where the sultan presented the Princes Bahman and Perviz, and the Princess Parizade to the sultaness. "These, madame," said he, "are the two princes, your sons, and the princess, your daughter; embrace them with the same tenderness that I have done, since they are worthy both of you and of me." The tears flowed plentifully down their cheeks at these tender embraces, especially the sultaness's, so great was the comfort and joy of having two such princes for her sons, and such a princess for her daughter, on whose account she had endured affliction so long.

The two princes and the princess had prepared a magnificent repast for the sultan and sultaness and their court. As soon as that was over the sultan led the sultaness into the garden and showed her the Singing Tree and the Golden Fountain. As for the Bird she had already seen and admired him in his cage.

When there was nothing to detain the sultan any longer, he took horse again, and with the Princes Bahman and Perviz on his right hand, and the sultaness and the princess at his left, surrounded by all the officers of his court, he returned to his capital. Crowds of people came out to meet them, and with acclamations of joy ushered them into the city, where all eyes were fixed, not only on the sultaness, the two princes, and the princess, but also upon the Bird which the princess carried before her in his cage. He was singing the sweet notes that drew all the other birds after him, flying from tree to tree in the country, and from one house-top to another in the city. The Princes Bahman and Perviz and the Princess Parizade were at length brought to the palace, and nothing was heard or seen all that night and for many days thereafter but illuminations and rejoicings both in the palace and in the utmost parts of the city.

THE THREE SILLIES*
Joseph Jacobs

ONCE upon a time there was a farmer and his wife who had one daughter, and she was courted by a gentleman. Every evening he used to come and see her, and stop to supper at the farmhouse, and the daughter used to be sent down into the cellar to draw the ale for supper. So one evening she had gone down to draw the ale, and she happened to look up at the ceiling while she was drawing, and she saw a mallet stuck in one of the beams. It must have been there a long, long time, but somehow or other she had never noticed it before, and she began a-thinking. And she thought it was very dangerous to have that mallet there, for she said to herself, "Suppose him and me was to be married, and we was to have a son, and he was to grow up to be a man, and come down into the cellar to draw the ale, like as I'm doing now, and the mallet was to fall on his head and kill him, what a dreadful thing it would be!" And she put down the candle and the jug, sat herself down and began a-crying.

Well, they began to wonder upstairs how it was that she was so long drawing the ale, and her mother went down to see after her, and she found her sitting on the settle crying, and the ale running over the floor. "Why, whatever is the matter?" said her mother. "Oh, mother!" says she, "look at that horrid mallet! Suppose we was to be married, and was to have a son, and he was to grow up, and was to come down to the cellar to draw the ale, and the mallet was to fall on his head and kill him, what a dreadful thing it would be!" "Dear, dear! what a dreadful thing it would be!" said the mother, and she sat her down aside of the daughter and started a-crying too. Then after a bit the father began to wonder that they didn't come back, and he went down into the cellar to look after them himself, and there they two sat a-crying, and the ale running all

*From *English Fairy Tales*. Used by permission of the publishers, G. P. Putnam's Sons.

over the floor. "Whatever is the matter?" says he. "Why," says the mother, "look at that horrid mallet. Just suppose if our daughter and her sweetheart was to be married, and was to have a son, and he was to grow up, and was to come down into the cellar to draw the ale, and the mallet was to fall on his head and kill him, what a dreadful thing it would be!" "Dear, dear, dear! so it would!" said the father, and he sat himself down aside of the other two, and started a-crying.

Now the gentleman got tired of stopping up in the kitchen by himself, and at last he went down into the cellar too, to see what they were after; and there they three sat a-crying side by side, and the ale running all over the floor. And he ran straight and turned the tap. Then he said: "Whatever are you three doing, sitting there crying, and letting the ale run all over the floor?" "Oh," says the father, "look at that horrid mallet! Suppose you and our daughter was to be married, and was to have a son, and he was to grow up, and was to come down into the cellar to draw the ale, and the mallet was to fall on his head and kill him!" And then they all started a-crying worse than before. But the gentleman burst out a-laughing, and reached up and pulled out the mallet, and then he said: "I've

travelled many miles, and I never met three such big sillies as you three before; and now I shall start out on my travels again, and when I can find three bigger sillies than you three, then I'll come back and marry your daughter." So he wished them good-bye, and started off on his travels, and left them all crying because the girl had lost her sweetheart.

Well, he set out, and he travelled a long way, and at last he came to a woman's cottage that had some grass growing on the roof. And the woman was trying to get her cow to go up a ladder to the grass, and the poor thing durst not go. So the gentleman asked the woman what she was doing. "Why, lookye," she said, "look at all that beautiful grass. I'm going to get the cow on to the roof to eat it. She'll be quite safe, for I shall tie a string round her neck, and pass it down the chimney, and tie it to my wrist as I go about the house, so she can't fall off without my knowing it." "Oh, you poor silly!" said the gentleman, "you should cut the grass and throw it down to the cow!" But the woman thought it was easier to get the cow up the ladder than to get the grass down, so she pushed her and coaxed her and got her up, and tied a string round her neck, and passed it down the chimney, and fastened it to her own wrist. And the gentleman went on his way, but he hadn't gone far when the cow tumbled off the roof, and hung by the string tied round her neck, and it strangled her. And the weight of the cow tied to her wrist pulled the woman up the chimney, and she stuck fast half-way and was smothered in the soot.

Well, that was one big silly.

And the gentleman went on and on, and he went to an inn to stop the night, and they were so full at the inn that they had to put him in a double-bedded room, and another traveller was to sleep in the other bed. The other man was a very pleasant fellow, and they got very friendly together; but in the morning, when they were both getting up, the gentleman was surprised to see the other hang his trousers on the knobs of the chest of drawers and run across the room and try to jump into them, and he tried over and over again, and couldn't manage it; and the gentleman wondered whatever he was doing it for. At last he stopped and wiped his face with his handkerchief. "Oh, dear," he says, "I do think trousers are the most awkwardest kind of clothes that ever were. I can't think who could have invented such things. It takes me the best part of an hour to get into mine every morning, and I get so hot! How do you manage yours?" So the gentleman burst out a-laughing, and showed him how to put them on; and he was very much obliged to him, and said he never should have thought of doing it that way.

So that was another big silly.

Then the gentleman went on his travels again; and he came to a village, and outside the village there was a pond, and round the pond was a crowd of people. And they had got rakes, and brooms, and pitchforks, reaching into the pond; and the gentleman asked what was the matter. "Why," they say, "matter enough! Moon's tumbled into the pond, and we can't rake her out anyhow!" So the gentleman burst out a-laughing, and told them to look up into the sky, the moon was there and it was only the shadow in the water. But they wouldn't listen to him, and abused him shamefully, and he got away as quick as he could.

So there was a whole lot of sillies bigger than the three sillies at home. So the gentleman turned back home again and married the farmer's daughter, and if they didn't live happily ever after, that's nothing to do with you or me.

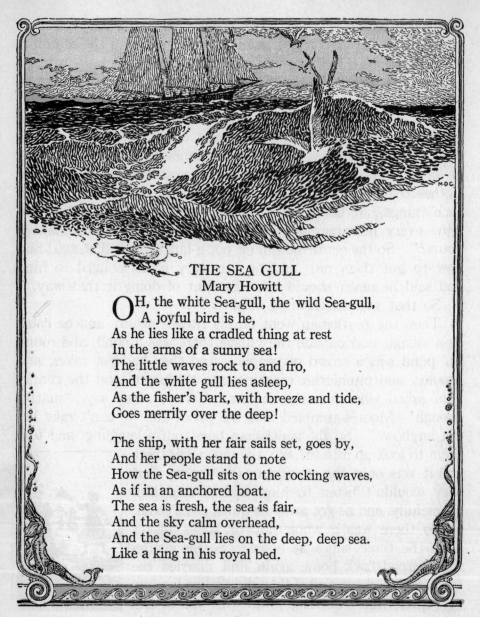

THE SEA GULL
Mary Howitt

OH, the white Sea-gull, the wild Sea-gull,
　A joyful bird is he,
As he lies like a cradled thing at rest
In the arms of a sunny sea!
The little waves rock to and fro,
And the white gull lies asleep,
As the fisher's bark, with breeze and tide,
Goes merrily over the deep!

The ship, with her fair sails set, goes by,
And her people stand to note
How the Sea-gull sits on the rocking waves,
As if in an anchored boat.
The sea is fresh, the sea is fair,
And the sky calm overhead,
And the Sea-gull lies on the deep, deep sea,
Like a king in his royal bed.

THE TREASURE CHEST

LITTLE GULLIVER*
Louisa M. Alcott

Up in the light-house lived Davy, with Old Dan, the keeper. Most boys would have found it very lonely; but Davy had three friends, and was as happy as the day was long. One of Davy's friends was the great lamp, which was lighted at sunset, and burnt all night, to guide the ships into the harbor. To Dan it was only a lamp; but to the boy it seemed a living thing, and he loved and tended it faithfully. Every day he helped clear the big wick, polish the brass work, and wash the glass lantern which protected the flame. Every evening he went up to see it lighted, and always fell asleep, thinking, "No matter how dark or wild the night, my good Shine will save the ships that pass, and burn till morning."

Davy's second friend was Nep, the Newfoundland, who was washed ashore from a wreck, and had never left the island since. Nep was rough and big, but had such a loyal and loving heart that no one could look in his soft brown eyes and not trust him. He followed Davy's steps all day, slept at his feet all night, and more than once had saved his life when Davy fell among the rocks, or got caught by the rising tide.

*From *Aunt Jo's Scrap Bag*. Used by permission of the publishers, Little, Brown & Co.

But the dearest friend of all was a sea-gull. Davy found him, with a broken wing, and nursed him carefully till he was well; then let him go, though he was very fond of "Little Gulliver," as he called him in fun. But the bird never forgot the boy, and came daily to talk with him, telling all manner of wild stories about his wanderings by land and sea, and whiling away many an hour that otherwise would have been very lonely.

Old Dan was Davy's uncle,—a grim, gray man, who said little, did his work faithfully, and was both father and mother to Davy, who had no parents, and no friends beyond the island. That was his world; and he led a quiet life among his playfellows,—the winds and waves. He seldom went to the main land, three miles away; for he was happier at home. He watched the sea-anemones open below the water, found curious and pretty shells, and sometimes more valuable treasures, washed up from some wreck. He saw little yellow crabs, ugly lobsters, and queer horse-shoes with their stiff tails. Sometimes a whale or a shark swam by, and often sleek black seals came up to bask on the warm rocks. He gathered lively sea-weeds of all kinds, from tiny red cobwebs to great scalloped leaves of kelp, longer than himself. He heard the waves dash and roar unceasingly; the winds howl or sigh over the island; and the gulls scream shrilly as they dipped and dived, or sailed away to follow the ships that came and went from all parts of the world.

With Nep and Gulliver he roamed about his small kingdom, never tired of its wonders; or, if storms raged, he sat up in the tower, safe and dry, watching the tumult of sea and sky. Often in long winter nights he lay awake, listening to the wind and rain, that made the tower rock with their violence; but he never was afraid, for Nep nestled at his feet, Dan sat close by, and overhead the great lamp shone far out into the night, to cheer and guide all wanderers on the sea.

THE TREASURE CHEST

Close by the tower hung the fog-bell, which, being wound up, would ring all night, warningly. One day Dan found that something among the chains was broken; and, having vainly tried to mend it, he decided to go to the town, and get what was needed. He went once a week, usually, and left Davy behind, for in the daytime there was nothing to do, and the boy was not afraid to stay.

"A heavy fog is blowing up: we shall want the bell tonight, and I must be off at once. I shall be back before dark, of course; so take care of yourself, boy," said Dan.

Away went the little boat; and the fog shut down over it, as if a misty wall had parted Davy from his uncle. As it was dull weather, he sat and read for an hour or two; then fell asleep, and forgot everything till Nep's cold nose on his hand waked him up. It was nearly dark; and, hoping to find Dan had come, he ran down to the landing-place. But no boat was there, and the fog was thicker than ever.

Dan never had been gone so long before, and Davy was afraid something had happened to him. For a few minutes he was in great trouble; then he cheered up, and took courage.

"It is sunset by the clock; so I'll light the lamp, and, if Dan is lost in the fog, it will guide him home," said Davy.

Up he went, and soon the great star shown out above the black-topped light-house, glimmering through the fog, as if eager to be seen. Davy had his supper, but no Dan came. He waited hour after hour, and waited all in vain. The fog thickened, the lamp was hardly seen; and no bell rung to warn the ships of the dangerous rocks. Poor Davy could not sleep, but all night long wandered from the tower to the door, watching, calling, and wondering; but Dan did not come.

At sunrise he put out the light, and, having trimmed it for the next night, ate a little breakfast, and roved about the island

hoping to see some sign of Dan. The sun drew up the fog at last; and he could see the blue bay, the distant town, and a few fishing-boats going out to sea. But nowhere was the island-boat with gray Old Dan in it. Davy's heart grew heavier and heavier, as the day passed, and still no one came. In the afternoon Gulliver appeared; to him Davy told his trouble, and the three friends took counsel together.

"I'd gladly swim to town, if I could; but it's impossible to do it, with wind and tide against me. I've howled all day, hoping some one would hear me; but no one does, and I'm discouraged," said Nep, with an anxious expression.

"I can do something for you; and I will, with all my heart. I'll fly to town, if I don't see him in the bay, and try to learn what has become of Dan. Then I'll come and tell you, and we will see what is to be done next. Cheer up, Davy dear: I'll bring you tidings, if any can be had." With these cheerful words, away sailed Gulliver, leaving Nep and his master to watch and wait again.

The wind blew hard, and the broken wing was not quite well yet, else Gulliver would have been able to steer clear of a boat that came swiftly by. A sudden gust drove the gull so violently against the sail that he dropped breathless into the boat; and a little girl caught him, before he could recover himself.

"Oh, what a lovely bird! See his black cap, his white breast, down-colored wings, red legs and bill, and soft, bright eyes. I wanted a gull; and I'll keep this one."

Poor Gulliver struggled, pecked and screamed; but little Dora held him fast, and shut him in a basket till they reached the shore.

THE TREASURE CHEST

Then she put him in a lobster pot,—a large wooden thing, something like a cage,—and left him on the lawn, where he could catch glimpses of the sea, and watch the light-house tower, as he sat alone in this dreadful prison. If Dora had known the truth, she would have let him go, and done her best to help him; but she could not understand his speech, as  Davy did, for very few people have the power of talking with birds, beasts, insects, and plants. To her, his prayers and cries were only harsh screams; and, when he sat silent, with drooping head and ruffled feathers, she thought he was sleepy: but he was mourning for Davy, and wondering what his little friend would do.

For three long days and nights he was a prisoner, and suffered much. The house was full of happy people, but no one took pity upon him. Ladies and gentlemen talked learnedly about him; boys poked and pulled him; little girls admired him. Cats prowled about his cage; dogs barked at him; hens cackled over him; and a shrill canary jeered at him from the pretty pagoda

JOHN P. CRANE

in which it was hung, high above danger. In the evening there was music; and the poor bird's heart ached as the sweet sounds came to him, reminding him of the airier melodies he loved. Through the stillness of the night, he heard the waves break on the shore; the wind came singing up from the sea; the moon shone kindly on him, and he saw the water-fairies dancing on the sand. But for three days no one spoke a friendly word to him, and he pined away with a broken heart.

On the fourth night, when all was quiet, little Gulliver saw a black shadow steal across the lawn, and heard a soft voice say:

"Poor bird, I'se gwine to let yer go. Specs little missy'll scold dreffle; but Moppet'll take de scolding for yer. Hi, dere! you is pert nuff now, kase you's in a hurry to go; but jes wait till I gits de knots out of de string dat ties de door, and away den you flies."

"But, Moppet, wont you be hurt for doing this? Why do you care so much for me? I can only thank you, and fly away."

As Gulliver spoke, he looked up at the little black face bent over him, and saw tears in the child's sad eyes; but she smiled at him, and shook her fuzzy head, as she whispered kindly:

"I don't want no tanks, birdie: I loves to let you go, kase you's a slave, like I was once; and it's a dreffle hard ting, I knows. I got away, and I means you shall. I'se watched you, deary, all dese days and I tried to come 'fore, but dey didn't give me no chance."

"Do you live here? I never saw you playing with the other children," said the gull, as Moppet's nimble fingers picked away at the knots.

"Yes: I lives here, and helps de cook. You didn't see me, kase I never plays, de chil'en don't like me."

"Why not?" asked Gulliver, wondering.

"I'se black," said Moppet, with a sob.

"But that's silly in them," cried the bird, who had never heard of such a thing. "Color makes no difference; the peeps are gray, the seals black, and the crabs yellow; but we don't care, and are all friends. Haven't you any friends to love you?"

"Nobody in de world keres fer me. De oder chil'en has folks to lub and kere fer em, but Moppet's got no friends"; and here the black eyes grew so dim with tears that the poor child couldn't see that the last knot was out.

Gulliver saw it, and, pushing up the door, flew from his prison with a glad cry; and, hopping into Moppet's hand, looked into the little dark face with such grateful confidence that it cleared at once, and the brightest smile it had worn for months broke over it as the bird nestled its soft head against her cheek, saying gently: "I'm your friend; I love you, and I never shall forget what you have done for me to-night. How can I thank you before I go?"

For a minute, Moppet could only hug the bird, and cry; for these were the first kind words she had heard for a long time, and they went straight to her lonely little heart.

"O my deary! I'se paid by dem words, and I don't want no tanks. Jes lub me, and come sometimes to see me ef you can; it's so hard livin' in dis yere place. I don't tink I'll bar it long. I wish I was a bird to do as I's amind."

"I wish you could go and live with Davy on the island; he is so kind, so happy, and as free as the wind. Can't you get away, Moppet?" whispered Gulliver, longing to help this poor, friendless little soul. He told her all his story; and they agreed that he should fly at once to the island, and see if Dan was there; if not, he was to come back, and Moppet would try to get some one to help find him. When this was done, Davy and Dan were to take Moppet, if they could, and make her happy on the island. Full of hope and joy, Gulliver said good-by, and spread his wings; but alas for the poor bird! he was too weak to fly. For three days he had hardly eaten anything, had found no salt water to bathe in, and had sat moping in the cage till his strength was gone.

"What shall I do? what shall I do?" he cried, fluttering his feeble wings, and running to and fro in despair.

"Hush, birdie, I'll take kere ob you till you's fit to fly. I knows a nice, quiet little cove down yonder, where no one goes; and dare you kin stay till you's better. I'll come and feed you, and you kin paddle, and rest, and try your wings, safe and free, honey."

As Moppet spoke, she took Gulliver in her arms, and stole away in the dim light, over the hill, down to the lonely spot where nothing went but the winds and waves, the gulls, and little Moppet, when hard words and blows made heart and body ache. Here she left the bird, and, with a loving "Good-night," crept home to her bed in the garret, feeling as rich as a queen, and much happier; for she had done a kind thing, and made a friend.

Next day, a great storm came; the wind blew a hurricane, the rain poured, and the sea thundered on the coast. If he had been well, Gulliver wouldn't have minded at all; but, being sad, he spent an anxious day, sitting in a cranny of the rock, thinking of Davy and Moppet. It was so rough, even in the cove, that he could neither swim nor fly, and he could find no food but such trifles as he could pick up among the rocks. At nightfall the storm raged fiercer than ever, and he gave up seeing Moppet; for he was sure she wouldn't come through the pelting rain to feed him. So he put his head under his wing, and tried to sleep; but he was so hungry and anxious, no sleep came.

"What has happened to Davy alone on the island all this while? The lamp won't be lighted, the ships will be wrecked, and many people will suffer. O Dan, Dan, if we could only find you, how happy we would be!"

As Gulliver spoke, a voice cried through the darkness:

"Is you dere, honey?" and Moppet came climbing over the

rocks, with a basket full of such bits as she could get. "Poor birdie, is you starvin'? Here, jes go at dis, and joy yourself. Dere's fish and tings I tink you'd like. How is you now, dear?"

"Better, Moppet; but, it's so stormy, I can't get to Davy; and I worry about him," began Gulliver, pecking away at his supper; but he stopped suddenly, for a faint sound came up from below, as if some one called, "Help, help!"

"Hi! what's dat?" said Moppet, listening.

"Davy, Davy!" called the voice.

"It's Dan. Hurrah, we've found him!" and Gulliver dived off the rocks so recklessly that he went splash into the water. But that didn't matter to him; and he paddled away, like a little steamer with all the engines in full blast. Down by the seaside, between two stones, lay Dan, so bruised he couldn't move, and so faint with hunger he could hardly speak. As soon as Gulliver called, Moppet scrambled down, and fed the poor man with her scraps, brought him rainwater from a crevice near by, and bound up his wounded head with her little apron. Then Dan told them how his boat had been run down by a ship in the fog; how he was cast ashore in the lonely cove; how he had lain there, for no one heard his shouts, and he couldn't move; how the

sound of Moppet's voice told him at last that help was near.

How glad they all were then! Moppet danced for joy; Gulliver screamed and flapped his wings; and Dan smiled, to think he should see Davy again. He couldn't understand Gulliver; but Moppet told him all the story, and, when he heard it, he was more troubled for the boy than for himself.

"What will he do? He may try to come ashore. Is the lamp alight?" he cried.

Gulliver flew up to the highest rock, and looked out across the dark sea. Yes, there it was,—the steady star shining through the storm, and saying plainly, "All is well."

"Thank heaven! if the lamp is burning, Davy is alive. Now, how shall I get to him?" said Dan.

"Never you fret, massa; Moppet'll see to dat. You jes lay still till I comes. Dere's folks in de house as'll tend to you, ef I tells em who and where you is."

Off she ran, and soon came back with help. Dan was taken to the house and carefully tended; Moppet wasn't scolded for being out so late; and, in the flurry, no one thought of the gull. Next morning, the cage was found blown over, and every one fancied the bird had flown away. Dora was already tired of him; so he was soon forgotten by all but Moppet.

In the morning it was clear; and Gulliver flew gladly to the tower where Davy still watched and waited, with a pale face and heavy heart, for the three days had been very hard to bear, and, but for Nep and Shine, he would have lost his courage entirely. Gulliver flew straight into his bosom, and, sitting there, told his adventures; while Davy laughed and cried, and Nep stood by, wagging his tail for joy, while his eyes were full of sympathy. The three had a very happy hour together, and then came a boat to carry Davy ashore, while another keeper took charge of the light till Dan was well.

THE TREASURE CHEST

Nobody ever knew the best part of the story but Moppet, Davy, and Gulliver. Other people didn't dream that the boy's pet gull had anything to do with the finding of the man, or the good fortune that came to Moppet. While Dan lay sick, she tended him, like a loving little daughter; and, when he was well, he took her for his own. He did not mind the black skin; he only saw the loneliness of the child, the tender heart, the innocent, white soul; and he was as glad to be a friend to her as if she had been as blithe and pretty as Dora.

It was a happy day when Dan and Davy, Moppet, Gulliver, and Nep sailed away to the island; for that was still to be their home, with stout young Ben to help.

The sun was setting; and they floated through the waves as rosy as the rosy sky. A fresh wind filled the sail, and ruffled Gulliver's white breast as he sat on the mast-head crooning a cheery song to himself. Dan held the tiller, and Davy lay at his feet, with Nep bolt upright beside him, but the happiest face of all was Moppet's. Kneeling at the bow, she leaned forward, with her lips apart, her fuzzy hair blown back, and her eyes fixed on the island which was to be her home. Like a little black figure-head of Hope, she leaned and looked, as the boat flew on, bearing her away from the old life into the new.

As the sun sunk, out shone the lamp with sudden brightness, as if the island bade them welcome. Dan furled the sail; and, drifting with the tide, they floated in, till the waves broke softly on the shore, and left them safe at home.

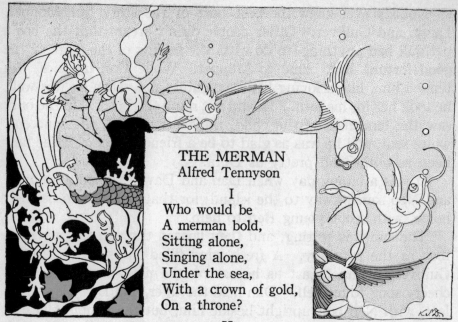

THE MERMAN
Alfred Tennyson

I

Who would be
A merman bold,
Sitting alone,
Singing alone,
Under the sea,
With a crown of gold,
On a throne?

II

I would be a merman bold,
I would sit and sing the whole of the day;
I would fill the sea-halls with a voice of power;
But at night I would roam abroad and play
With the mermaids in and out of the rocks,
Dressing their hair with the white sea-flower;
And holding them back by their flowing locks
Laughingly, laughingly;
And then we would wander away, away,
To the pale-green sea-groves straight and high,
Chasing each other merrily.

III

There would be neither moon nor star;
But the wave would make music above us afar—
Low thunder and light in the magic night—
Neither moon nor star.

THE TREASURE CHEST

We would call aloud in the dreamy dells,
Call to each other and whoop and cry
    All night, merrily, merrily.
They would pelt me with starry spangles and
      shells,
Laughing and clapping their hands between,
    All night, merrily, merrily,
But I would throw to them back in mine
Turkis and agate and almondine;
    Laughingly, laughingly.
O, what a happy life were mine
Under the hollow-hung ocean green!
Soft are the moss-beds under the sea;
We would live merrily, merrily.

DAVID COPPERFIELD AND LITTLE EM'LY*
Charles Dickens

 Y good nurse, Peggotty, and I were sitting alone one evening (my mother being out), in company with Peggotty's darning, and the little piece of candle with which she waxed her thread, and the little house with a thatched roof where the yard measure lived, and Peggotty's work box with a view of St. Paul's cathedral painted on the top. I had been reading aloud about crocodiles, when Peggotty, after looking at me several times and opening her mouth as if she were going to speak without doing it—said coaxingly: "Master Davy, how should you like to go along with me and spend a fortnight at my brother's at Yarmouth? Wouldn't *that* be a treat?"

"Is your brother an agreeable man, Peggotty?" I inquired.

"Oh what an agreeable man he is!" cried Peggotty, holding up her hands. "Then there's the sea; and the boats and ships; and the fishermen; and the beach; and Am to play with—"

Peggotty meant her nephew Ham, but she spoke of him as a morsel of English grammar.

I was flushed by her summary of delights, and replied that it would indeed be a treat, but what would my mother say?

"Why then I'll as good as bet a guinea," said Peggotty, "that she'll let us go. I'll ask her, if you like, as soon as ever she comes home."

"But what's she to do while we're away?" said I, putting my small elbows on the table. "She can't live by herself."

"Oh bless you!" said Peggotty, looking at me again. "Don't you know? She's going to stay for a fortnight with Mrs. Grayper."

Oh! If that was it, I was quite ready to go. I waited, in the utmost impatience until my mother came home, to ascertain if we could get leave to carry out this great idea. Without being nearly so much surprised as I had expected, my mother

*Arranged from *David Copperfield.*

entered into it readily. It was all arranged that night, and my board and lodging during the visit were to be paid for.

The day soon came for our going. It was such an early day that it came soon, even to me, who was in a fever of expectation, and half afraid that an earthquake or a fiery mountain, or some other great convulsion of nature might interpose to stop the expedition. We were to go in a carrier's cart which departed in the morning after breakfast. I would have given any money to have been allowed to wrap myself up over night, and sleep in my hat and boots.

I am glad to recollect that when the carrier's cart was at the gate, and my mother stood there kissing me, a grateful fondness for her and for the old place I had never turned my back upon before, made me cry. I am glad to know that my mother cried too, and that I felt her heart beat against mine. I am glad to recollect that when the carrier began to move, my mother ran out at the gate, and called to him to stop, that she might kiss me once more. I am glad to dwell upon the earnestness and love with which she lifted up her face to mine and did so.

The carrier's horse was the laziest horse in the world, I should hope, and shuffled along with his head down, as if he liked to keep the people waiting to whom the packages were directed. I fancied, indeed, that he sometimes chuckled over this reflection, but the carrier said he was only troubled with a cough.

The carrier had a way of keeping his head down, like his horse, and of drooping sleepily forward as he drove, with one of his arms on each of his knees. I say "drove," but it struck me that the cart would have gone to Yarmouth quite as well without him, for the horse did all that—and as to conversation, he had no idea of it but whistling.

Peggotty had got a basket of refreshments on her knee, which would have lasted us out handsomely, if we had been going to

London by the same conveyance. We ate a good deal, and slept a good deal. Peggotty always went to sleep with her chin upon the handle of the basket, her hold of which never relaxed, and I could not have believed unless I had heard her do it, that one woman could have snored so much.

We made so many turns up and down lanes, and were such a long time delivering a bedstead at a public house, and calling at other places, that I was quite tired, and very glad, when we saw Yarmouth. It looked rather spongy and soppy, I thought, as I carried my eye over the great dull waste that lay across the river; and I could not help wondering, if the world were really as round as my geography-book said, how any part of it came to be so flat. As we drew a little nearer, and saw all the land round about lying a straight low line under the sky, I hinted to Peggotty that a mound or so might have improved it. But Peggotty said, with greater emphasis than usual, that we must take things as we found them, and that, for her part, she was proud to call herself a Yarmouth Bloater.

When we got into the street (which was strange enough to me) and smelt the fish, and pitch, and oakum, and tar, and saw the sailors walking about, and the carts jingling up and down over the stones, I felt that I had done so busy a place an injustice, and said as much to Peggotty, who heard my expressions of delight with great satisfaction, and told me it was well known (I suppose to those who had the good fortune to be born Bloaters) that Yarmouth was, upon the whole, the finest place in the universe.

"Here's my Am!" screamed Peggotty, "growed out of knowledge!"

He was waiting for us, in fact, at the public-house, and asked me how I found myself, like an old acquaintance. I did not feel, at first, that I knew him as well as he knew me. But our friendship was much advanced by his taking me on his back to carry me home. He was a huge, strong fellow of six feet high, broad in proportion, and round-shouldered; but with a simpering boy's face, and curly light hair, that gave him quite a sheepish look. He was dressed in a canvas jacket, and a pair of such very stiff trousers that they would have stood quite as well alone, without any legs in them.

Ham carrying me on his back and a small box of ours under his arm, and Peggotty carrying another small box of ours, we turned down lanes littered with bits of chips and little hillocks of sand, and went past gas-works, rope-walks, boat-builders' yards, shipwrights' yards, ship-breakers' yards, calkers' yards riggers' lofts, smiths' forges, and a great many of such places, until we came out upon the dull waste I had already seen at a distance; when Ham said, "Yon's our house, Master Davy!"

I looked in all directions, as far as I could stare over the wilderness, and away at the sea, and away at the river, but no house could I make out. There was a barge, or some other kind of old boat, not far off, high and dry on the ground, with an iron funnel sticking out of it for a chimney and smoking very cosily, but nothing else in the way of a house that was visible to *me*.

"That's not it?" said I, "that ship-looking thing?"

"That's it, Master Davy," returned Ham.

If it had been Aladdin's Palace, roc's egg and all, I suppose I could not have been more charmed with the romantic idea of living in it. There was a delightful door cut in the side, and it was roofed in, and there were little windows in it; but the wonderful charm of it was, that it was a real boat which had no doubt been upon the water hundreds of times, and which had never been intended to be lived in, on dry land. That was the captivation of it to me. If it had ever been meant to be lived in, I might have thought it small, or inconvenient, or lonely, but never having been designed for any such use, it became a perfect dwelling.

It was beautifully clean inside, and as tidy as possible. There was a table, and a Dutch clock, and a chest of drawers, and on the chest of drawers there was a tea-tray with a painting on it of a lady with a parasol, taking a walk with a military-looking child who was trundling a hoop. The tray was kept from tumbling down, by a Bible, and the tray, if it had tumbled down, would have smashed a quantity of cups and saucers and a teapot that were grouped around the book. On the walls there were some common colored pictures, framed and glazed, of Scripture subjects;—Abraham in red going to sacrifice Isaac in blue, and Daniel in yellow cast into a den of green lions. Over the little mantel-shelf, was a picture of the Sarah Jane Lugger, built at Sunderland, with a real little wooden stern stuck on to it. There were some hooks in the beams of the ceiling, the

THE TREASURE CHEST

use of which I did not understand then; and some lockers and boxes, which served for seats, and filled out the shortage of chairs.

All this I saw in the first glance after I crossed the threshold, and then Peggotty opened a little door and showed me my bedroom. It was the completest and most desirable bedroom ever seen, in the stern of the vessel. It had a little window where the rudder used to go through; a little looking-glass, just the right height for me, nailed against the wall, and framed with oyster shells; a little bed which there was just room enough to get into; and a nosegay of seaweed in a blue mug on the table. The walls were whitewashed as white as milk, and the patchwork counterpane made my eyes quite ache with its brightness. One thing I particularly noticed in this delightful house, was the smell of fish; which was so searching that when I took out my pocket-handkerchief to wipe my nose, I found it smelt exactly as if it had wrapped up a lobster. On my telling Peggotty of this discovery, she informed me that her brother dealt in lobsters, crabs, and crawfish; and I afterwards found that a heap of these creatures, wonderfully jumbled up together, and never leaving off pinching whatever they laid hold of, were usually to be found in a little out-house where the pots and kettles were kept.

We were welcomed by a very civil woman in a white apron, whom I had seen curtseying at the door when I was on Ham's back, about a quarter of a mile off. Likewise by a most beautiful little girl (or I thought her so) with a necklace of blue beads on, who wouldn't let me kiss her when I offered to, but ran away and hid herself. By and by, when we had dined in a sumptuous manner off boiled dabs, melted butter, and potatoes, with a chop for me, a hairy man with a very good-natured face, came home. As he called Peggotty "Lass," and gave her a hearty smack on the cheek, I had no doubt that he was her brother; and so he turned out; being presently introduced to me as Mr. Peggotty.

"Glad to see you, Sir," said Mr. Peggotty. "You'll find us rough, Sir, but you'll find us ready."

I thanked him, and replied that I was sure I should be happy in such a delightful place.

"How's your Ma, Sir," said Mr. Peggotty. "Did you leave her pretty jolly?"

I gave Mr. Peggotty to understand that she was as jolly as I could wish.

"Well, Sir, if you can make out here, fur a fortnut, 'long wi' her," nodding at his sister, "and Ham, and little Em'ly, we shall be proud of your company."

Having done the honors of his house in this hospitable manner, Mr. Peggotty went out to wash himself in a kettlefull of hot water, remarking that "cold would never get *his* muck off." He soon returned, greatly improved in appearance, but so ruddy, that I couldn't help thinking his face had this in common with the lobsters, crabs, and crawfish;—that it went into the hot water very black, and came out very red.

After tea, when the door was shut and all was made snug (the nights being cold and misty now) it seemed to me the most

delicious retreat that could ever be imagined. To hear the wind getting up out at sea, to know that the fog was creeping over the desolate flat outside, and to look at the fire, and think that there was no house near but this one, and this one a boat, was like enchantment. Little Em'ly had overcome her shyness, and was sitting by my side upon the lowest and least of the lockers, which was just large enough for us two, and just fitted into the chimney corner. Mrs. Peggotty with the white apron, was knitting on the opposite side of the fire. Peggotty at her needle-work was as much at home with Saint Paul's and the bit of wax-candle as if they had never known any other roof. Ham was trying to recollect a scheme of telling fortunes with the dirty cards, and printing off fishy impressions of his thumb on all the cards he turned. Mr. Peggotty was smoking his pipe. I felt it was a time for conversation.

"Mr. Peggotty!" says I.

"Sir," says he.

"Did you give your son the name of Ham, because you lived in a sort of Ark?"

Mr. Peggotty seemed to think it a deep idea, but answered: "No, Sir. I never giv him no name."

"Who did give him that name, then?" said I.

"Why, Sir, his father giv it him," said Mr. Peggotty.

"I thought you were his father!"

"My brother Joe was *his* father," said Mr. Peggotty.

"Dead, Mr. Peggotty?" I hinted, after a respectful pause.

"Drowndead," said Mr. Peggotty.

I was very much surprised that Mr. Peggotty was not Ham's father, and began to wonder whether I was mistaken about his relationship to any body else there. I was so curious to know, that I made up my mind to have it out with Mr. Peggotty.

"Little Em'ly," I said, glancing at her. "She is your daughter, isn't she, Mr. Peggotty?"

"No, Sir. My brother-in-law Tom, was *her* father."

I couldn't help it. "—Dead, Mr. Peggotty?" I hinted, after another respectful silence.

"Drowndead," said Mr. Peggotty.

"Haven't you *any* children, Mr. Peggotty?

"No, master," he answered, with a short laugh. "I'm a bacheldore."

"A bachelor!" I said, astonished. "Why, who's that, Mr. Peggotty?" pointing to the person in the apron who was knitting.

"That's Missis Gummidge," said Mr. Peggotty.

"Gummidge, Mr. Peggotty?"

But at this point, Peggotty—I mean my own peculiar Peggotty—made such impressive motions to me not to ask any further questions, that I could only sit and look at all the silent company, until it was time to go to bed. Then, in the privacy of my own little cabin, she informed me that Ham and Em'ly were an orphan nephew and niece, whom my host had at different times adopted in their childhood when they were left destitute; and that Mrs. Gummidge was the widow of his partner in a boat, who had died very poor. He was but a poor man himself, said Peggotty, but as good as gold and as true as steel. The only subject, she informed me, on which he ever showed a violent temper or swore an oath, was this generosity of his; and if it were ever referred to, by any one of them, he struck the table a heavy blow with his right hand (had split it on one such occasion), and swore a dreadful oath that he would be "gormed" if he didn't cut and run away for good, if it was ever mentioned again. It appeared, in answer to my inquiries, that nobody had the least idea of the meaning of this terrible word "to be gormed;" but that they all regarded it as a most solemn oath.

I was very sensible of my entertainer's goodness, and listened to the women's going to bed in another little crib like mine at the opposite end of the boat, and to him and Ham hanging up two hammocks for themselves on the hooks I had noticed in the roof. As slumber gradually stole upon me, I heard the wind howling out at sea and coming on across the flat so fiercely, that I had a lazy apprehension of the great deep rising in the night. But I be-thought myself that I was in a boat, after all, and that a man like Mr. Peggotty was not a bad person to have on board if any thing did happen. Nothing happened, however, worse than morning. Almost as soon as it shone upon the oyster shell frame of my mirror, I was out of bed, and out with little Em'ly, picking up stones upon the beach.

"You're quite a sailor, I suppose?" I said to Em'ly. I don't know that I supposed any thing of the kind, but I felt it an act of gallantry to say something.

"No," replied Em'ly, shaking her head. "I'm afraid of the sea."

"Afraid!" I said, with an air of boldness, and looking very big at the mighty ocean. "*I* ain't."

"Ah! but it's cruel," said Em'ly. "I have seen it tear a boat as big as our house, all to pieces."

"I hope it wasn't the boat that—"

"That father was drownded in?" said Em'ly. "No. Not that one, I never see that boat."

"Nor him?" I asked her.

Little Em'ly shook her head. "Not to remember!"

Here was a point of likeness in our two lives! I immediately went into an explanation how I had never seen my own father, and how my mother and I had always lived by ourselves in the happiest state imaginable, and always meant to live so.

"But," said Em'ly, as she looked about for shells and pebbles, "your father was a gentleman and your mother is a lady; and my father was a fisherman, and my mother was a fisherman's daughter, and my uncle Dan is a fisherman."

"Dan is Mr. Peggotty, is he?" said I. "He must be very good, I should think?"

"Good?" said Em'ly. "If I was ever to be a lady, I'd give him a sky-blue coat with diamond buttons, nankeen trousers, a red velvet waistcoat, a cocked hat, a large gold watch, a silver pipe, and a box of money."

I said I had no doubt that Mr. Peggotty well deserved these treasures. I must acknowledge that I felt it difficult to picture him quite at his ease in the raiment proposed for him by his grateful little niece, and that I was particularly doubtful about the cocked hat; but I kept these sentiments to myself.

"You would like to be a lady?" I said.

Emily looked at me, and laughed, and nodded "yes."

"I should like it very much. We would all be gentle-folks together, then, me, and uncle, and Ham, and Mrs. Gummidge, and we'd help the poor fishermen with money when they come to any hurt."

This seemed to me to be a very satisfactory picture. I expressed my pleasure in it, and little Em'ly was emboldened to say, shyly: "Don't you think you are afraid of the sea, now?"

It was quiet enough to reassure me, but I have no doubt if I had seen a moderately large wave come tumbling in, I should have taken to my heels. However, I said, "No," and I added, "You don't seem to be, either, though you say you are;"—for she was walking much too near the brink of a sort of old jetty or wooden causeway we had strolled upon, and I was afraid of her falling over.

"I'm not afraid in this way," said little Em'ly. "But I wake when it blows, and tremble to think of uncle Dan and Ham, and believe I hear 'em crying out for help. But I'm not afraid in this way. Not a bit. Look here!"

THE TREASURE CHEST

She started from my side, and ran along a jagged timber which protruded from the place we stood upon, and overhung the deep water at some height, without the least defence, springing forward to her destruction (as it appeared to me). I uttered a cry, but directly the light, bold, fluttering little figure turned and came back safe to me, and I soon laughed at my fears.

We strolled a long way, and loaded ourselves with things that we thought curious, and put some stranded star-fish carefully back into the water, then made our way home to Mr. Peggotty's dwelling. We stopped under the lee of the lobster out-house to exchange an innocent kiss, and went in to breakfast glowing with health and pleasure.

"Like two young mavishes," Mr. Peggotty said. I knew this meant, in our local dialect, like two young thrushes, and received it as a compliment.

Of course I was in love with little Em'ly. My fancy raised up something round that blue-eyed mite of a child, which made a very angel of her. If, any sunny forenoon, she had spread a little pair of wings and flown away before my eyes, I don't think I should have regarded it as much more than I had had reason to expect. We used to walk about that dim old flat at Yarmouth in a loving manner, hours and hours. The days sported by us, as if Time had not grown up himself yet, but were a child too, and always at play.

We were the admiration of Mrs. Gummidge and Peggotty, who used to whisper of an evening when we sat, lovingly, on our little locker side by side, "Lor! wasn't it beautiful!" Mr. Peggotty smiled at us from behind his pipe, and Ham grinned all the evening and did nothing else.

I soon found out that Mrs. Gummidge did not always make herself so agreeable as she might have been expected to do, in consideration of the kindness with which Mr. Peggotty had taken her in. Mrs. Gummidge's was rather a fretful disposition, and she whimpered more sometimes than was comfortable for other parties in so small an establishment. I was very sorry for her, but there were moments when it would have been more agreeable, I thought, if Mrs. Gummidge had had a convenient apartment of her own to retire to, and had stopped there until her spirits revived.

Mr. Peggotty went occasionally to a public house called The Willing Mind. I discovered this, by his being out on the second or third evening of our visit, and by Mrs. Gummidge's looking up at the Dutch clock, between eight and nine, and saying he was there, and that, what was more, she had known in the morning he would go there.

Mrs. Gummidge had been in a low state all day, and had burst into tears in the forenoon, when the fire smoked. "I am a lone lorn creetur'," were Mrs. Gummidge's words, when that unpleasant occurrence took place, "and every think goes contrairy with me."

"Oh, it'll soon leave off," said Peggotty—I again mean our Peggotty—"and besides, it's not more disagreeable to you than to us."

"I feel it more," said Mrs. Gummidge.

It was a very cold day, with cutting blasts of wind. Mrs. Gummidge's peculiar corner of the fireside seemed to me to be the warmest and snuggest in the place, as her chair was certainly the easiest, but it didn't suit her that day at all. She was constantly complaining of the cold, and of its occasioning what she called "the creeps in her back." At last she shed tears on that subject, and said again that she was "a lone lorn creetur' and every think went contrairy with her."

"It is certainly very cold," said Peggotty. "Everybody must feel it."

"I feel it more than other people," said Mrs. Gummidge.

So at dinner, when Mrs. Gummidge was always helped immediately after me, to whom the preference was given as a visitor of distinction. The fish were small and bony, and the potatoes were a little burnt. We all acknowledged that we felt this something of a disappointment; but Mrs. Gummidge said she felt it more than we did, and shed tears again.

Accordingly, when Mr. Peggotty came home about nine o'clock, this unfortunate Mrs. Gummidge was knitting in her corner in a very wretched and miserable condition. Peggotty had been working cheerfully. Ham had been patching up a great pair of water-boots, and I, with little Em'ly by my side, had been reading to them. Mrs. Gummidge had never made any other remark than a forlorn sigh, and had never raised her eyes since tea.

"Well, Mates," said Mr. Peggotty, taking his seat, "and how are you?"

We all said something, or looked something, to welcome him, except Mrs. Gummidge, who shook her head over her knitting.

"What's amiss?" said Mr. Peggotty, with a clap of his hands. "Cheer up, old Mawther" (Mr. Peggotty meant old girl.)

Mrs. Gummidge did not appear to be able to cheer up. She took out an old black silk handkerchief and wiped her eyes, but instead of putting it in her pocket, kept it out, and wiped them again, and still kept it out ready for use.

"What's amiss, dame?" said Mr. Peggotty.

"Nothing," returned Mrs. Gummidge. "You've come from The Willing Mind, Dan'l?"

"Why yes, I've took a short spell at The Willing Mind to-night," said Mr. Peggotty.

"I'm sorry I should drive you there," said Mrs. Gummidge.

"Drive! I don't want no driving," returned Mr. Peggotty, with an honest laugh. "I only go too ready."

"Very ready," said Mrs. Gummidge, shaking her head, and wiping her eyes. "Yes, yes, very ready. I am sorry it should be along of me that you're so ready."

"Along o' you. It an't along o' you!" said Mr. Peggotty. "Don't ye believe a bit on it."

"Yes, yes, it is," cried Mrs. Gummidge. "I know what I am. I know that I'm a lone lorn creetur, and not only that every think goes contrairy with me, but that I go contrairy with everybody. Yes, yes. I feel more than other people do, and I show it more. It's my misfortun'."

I really couldn't help thinking as I sat taking in all this, that it was a misfortune for other members of that family besides Mrs. Gummidge. But Mr. Peggotty made no such retort, only answering with another entreaty to Mrs. Gummidge to cheer up.

"I an't what I could wish myself to be," said Mrs. Gummidge. "I am far from it. I know what I am. My troubles has made me contrairy. I feel my troubles, and they make me contrairy. I wish I didn't feel 'em, but I do. I wish I could be hardened to 'em, but I an't. I make the house uncomfortable. I've made your sister so all day, and Master Davy."

Here I was suddenly melted, and roared out, "No, you haven't, Mrs. Gummidge," in great mental distress.

"It's far from right that I should do it," said Mrs. Gummidge. "It an't a fit return. I had better go into the Poorhouse and die. I am a lone lorn creetur, and had much better not make myself contrairy here!"

Mrs. Gummidge retired with these words, and betook herself to bed. When she was gone, Mr. Peggotty, who had not exhibited a trace of any feeling but the profoundest sympathy, looked round upon us, and nodding his head with a lively expression of pity still animating his face,

said in a whisper: "She's been thinking of the old 'un."
I did not quite understand what Old One Mrs. Gummidge
was supposed to have fixed her mind upon, until Peggotty, on
seeing me to bed, explained that it was the late Mr. Gummidge,
and that her brother always took that for a received truth on
such occasions, and that it always had a moving effect upon him.
Some time after he was in his hammock that night, I heard him
myself repeat to Ham, "Poor thing! She's been thinking of the
old 'un!" And whenever Mrs. Gummidge was overcome in a
similar manner during the remainder of our stay (which happened
some few times) he always said the same thing in explanation
of the circumstance, and always with the tenderest pity.

So the fortnight slipped away, varied by nothing but the
variation of the tide, which altered Mr. Peggotty's times of
going out and coming in, and altered Ham's engagements also.
When the latter was unemployed, he sometimes walked with
us to show us the boats and ships, and once or twice he took
us for a row. I never hear the name, or read the name, of Yarmouth, but I am reminded of a certain Sunday morning on the
beach, the bells ringing for church, little Em'ly leaning on my
shoulder, Ham lazily dropping stones into the water, and the
sun, away at sea, just breaking through the heavy mist, and
showing us the ships, like their own shadows.

At last the day came for going home. I bore up against
the separation from Mr. Peggotty and Mrs. Gummidge, but
my sorrow at leaving little Em'ly was piercing. We went arm
in arm to the public house where the carrier put up, and I promised, on the road, to write to her. (I kept that promise afterwards in letters larger than those in which apartments are usually
announced as being to let.) We were greatly overcome at
parting, and if ever, in my life, I have had a void made in my
heart, I had one made that day.

THE TREASURE CHEST

THE SANDPIPER
Celia Thaxter

Across the narrow beach we flit,
One little sandpiper and I;
And fast I gather, bit by bit,
The scattered driftwood, bleached and dry.
The wild waves reach their hands for it,
The wild wind raves, the tide runs high,
As up and down the beach we flit,—
One little sandpiper and I.

Above our heads the sullen clouds
Scud black and swift across the sky;
Like silent ghosts in misty shrouds
Stand out the white lighthouses high.
Almost as far as eye can reach
I see the close-reefed vessels fly,
As fast we flit along the beach,—
One little sandpiper and I.

I watch him as he skims along,
Uttering his sweet and mournful cry;
He starts not at my fitful song,
Or flash of fluttering drapery.
He has no thought of any wrong;
He scans me with a fearless eye;
Stanch friends are we, well tried and strong,
The little sandpiper and I.

Comrade, where wilt thou be to-night
When the loosed storm breaks furiously?
My driftwood fire will burn so bright!
To what warm shelter canst thou fly?
I do not fear for thee, though wroth
The tempest rushes through the sky;
For are we not God's children both,
Thou, little sandpiper, and I?

THE SWITCH YARD*
John Curtis Underwood

Out of the glimmer of arc lights and spaces of shade,
Far on the frontier the city has won from the dark,
Rails in the moonlight in ribbons of silver are laid;
Eyes that are watchful the loom of the switch yard shall mark;
Ears that are keen to its music shall hark.

Red, green, and gold are the signals that mark the design,
Black is the ground where the work of the weaver is spread,
Bright in the night is the glittering length of the line,
Swiftly and strongly and surely the shuttles are sped,
Bringing and braiding and breaking the thread.

Clicking of switches and resonant rolling of wheels
Mix in the midnight with stifled escape of steam.
Down the long siding a shadowed shape silently steals;
Sudden it checks; and the grind of the brakes is a scream,
The sound of a rent in the stuff of the dream.

*Used by permission of the publishers, G. P. Putnam's Sons.

THE STEAMBOAT AND THE LOCOMOTIVE*
Gelett Burgess

ON the railway that ran through the City o' Ligg there was once an English-made locomotive, who was always discontented and grumbling. Nothing in the world was good enough for him; or, at least, nothing in the City o' Ligg.

His coal was too hard or too soft; it was never just right. He hated to pull passenger trains because he had to go so fast, and he didn't like to pull freight trains because they were too heavy. He was always complaining that he was out of order, so that he might stay in the Round House, and not work. He would shunt himself on sidings in hopes he might be forgotten; he was afraid to go over bridges, for fear they would break down; and he hated tunnels because they were so dark and cold. He thought iron rails were too soft to get good hold on, and he said that steel rails were altogether too slippery. Sometimes he declared that he wouldn't run where there were not modern metal ties, and at other times he asserted that the old fashioned wooden sleepers made a much better road bed. He quarrelled with his tender, and he refused to be coupled up to one that he didn't fancy. He snorted and hissed at the semaphores and point signals, and he was a nuisance to the railway in more ways than can be told.

But if he were bad there was a young steamboat on the river who was worse. She was a very pretty craft, but that was no reason why she should insist on having a new set of paddle-wheels *every* year. She was absurdly particular about her funnel, and if it were not painted the exact color that she fancied, she would declare that she would scuttle herself. She would roll and pitch with anger if they tried to back her. She would dig up the muddy

* Taken from *The Lively City o' Ligg*. Used by permission of the publishers, Frederick A. Stokes Company.

bottom of the river with her paddles, and she gave a deal of trouble about steering.

When these ill-natured creatures came together at the dock in the river, below the fortifications, they used to complain to each other till the cannon above them would cry, "Oh, I *say!*" and the bridge told them that they ought to be ashamed of themselves.

One day, after the steamboat had been carrying a load of noisy excursionists up from the harbor, she found the locomotive on the pier in a very gloomy state of mind.

"I'm not going to stand this any longer!" he said. "They've put me to hauling coal, and it's no work for a machine like me, especially when I can't burn any of it myself. I'm going to run away!"

"Well, that's a good idea; suppose I go with you, and we'll set out together to seek our fortunes!" said the steamer.

They talked it all over, and finally decided to start that very night. The steamboat was to help the locomotive on the water,

BERT R. ELLIOTT

and the locomotive was to help the steamboat on the land. They were to share their wood and coal and water together, and have a jolly good time as long as they could.

At midnight the locomotive got on board the boat, and she steamed softly up the river. "This is fun!" said the locomotive.

"It's all right for you," said the boat; "but I must say you're heavier than I thought. Wait till it's *your* turn to give *me* a ride. I can't go much farther, anyway, the water is getting shallow. There's a dam up above here, so I think we'd better go ashore now."

She climbed up the bank with the locomotive's assistance, and he then hoisted her up on top of his cab, and set out across the fields. She was a little boat but she was heavy, and the locomotive puffed away with all his might through the grass, stopping to rest once in a while. So they went on for several days, turn and turn about, for they had to cross several lakes on the way.

After awhile they began to approach a line of hills, and the ground grew steeper and steeper, till at last the locomotive could go no further with the steamboat on his back. So she got off and scrambled along for a few miles with her paddle wheels while the locomotive pushed her from behind. But the time came when neither of them could go a step further, and they lay on the ground exhausted. To make matters worse, they grew short of water and fuel. They cut down their rations to a ton of coal and a barrel of water a day, and even then they didn't have enough to take them back to either a forest or a lake.

It seemed likely that they would have to perish there on the hillside, and they quarrelled with each other peevishly, each accusing the other of being at fault for suggesting this terrible journey. The old river Wob and the railway of the City o' Ligg had never seemed so pleasant before, but, alas! it was many days' journey away.

Just as they had begun to think that all hope was gone, one

of them espied a dot in the sky. It grew slowly larger and larger.

"It is a *balloon!*" they cried together, and they both began to blow their whistles with all the strength of the little steam that was left in their boilers.

The balloon came nearer and nearer, till it had got within hailing distance, and then they saw it was laughing almost hard enough to split its sides. It was a very fat, pink, round balloon, and as it shook with merriment, its basket swung wildly above them.

"Well, I *declare!*" it cried out, "this is the queerest thing I ever saw! What in the world are you doing away up in these mountains? I never saw a locomotive or a steamboat on top of a hill before!"

"For heaven's sake, please don't laugh like that," cried the steamer, "but come and help us, before we perish!"

The balloon finally consented to give them assistance over the mountains, and let down a rope, which the two tied around their waists. The balloon then rose, and the locomotive and steamboat were hoisted high in the air, and they all sailed away towards the East, across the range of mountains. They had floated for half a day in this way, when the balloon gave a pull up, a little harder than usual, and the rope suddenly broke!

Down went the two, falling faster and faster through the air, and they both thought that their last moment had come. But by good luck they happened to fall in the middle of a large forest, and landed safely in an oak tree, without breaking a piece of machinery.

Yet they had, after all, escaped one danger only to fall into another. They were lost in an immense wilderness, and did not know in which direction to turn.

The locomotive finally succeeded in climbing a tall tree, and made out smoke rising in the distance.

To this they painfully made their way, and after a terrible struggle, they drew near—rusty, scratched, and smoky—and came to an old saw-mill by the side of a little stream. It was a hideous old mill, of a villainous aspect, that alarmed them both. But here was their only hope, and though they were far from any assistance in case of danger, the two unfortunate machines found themselves obliged to apply to the mill for shelter and fuel.

The mill welcomed them very hospitably, but there was something in his dusty, oily manner that the locomotive did not trust, and he resolved to stay awake and watch. The little delicate steamboat was, by this time, too exhausted to notice anything. After they had drunk many barrels of water each, they revived a little, and the mill offered them a few tons of sawdust, which, he said, was the only fuel he could give them. At the first trial the steamer whispered to the locomotive that it tasted queerly, but they decided it was only the oil in which it was soaked. At any rate they had to eat that or nothing, and they made a meal of it without more ado.

Hardly had they burned the last mouthful, however, before they both fell into a heavy sleep, and knew nothing for many hours. The locomotive was awakened by a sudden pain, and he was terrified to find the teeth of a buzz-saw cutting through his side. He sprang up with a roar, but it was too late, his left side wheel had been bitten off! He charged furiously at the sides of the mill, and tore open a great hole, then dragged out the steamboat, and ran her into the forest as fast as his five wheels could carry him. The mill screamed and shrieked after them as they hurried away.

As they stood trembling in the forest, and thanked their stars for such a narrow escape, a sudden glare of light attracted their attention. The mill was on fire, set, no doubt, from some sparks dropped by the locomotive in its terrible struggle for escape.

By the light of the burning mill they made their way through the forest all night. With new fuel and water their strength had been partially renewed, and terror increased their efforts.

In the morning, after a short sleep, they awoke to find themselves by the side of a wide river, to which they had hobbled during the night, but had not seen in the dark. Alongside the bank of the stream ran a beautiful level railway line. They looked and looked, hardly able to believe their windows. It was too good to be true!

It did not take them long to decide what to do. The little steamboat gave one leap into the river, and whistled long and merrily. The locomotive crawled on to the line, and rang its bell in a joyous peal. For they knew by the looks of the country that they had been travelling in a huge semi-circle, and that the river and the railway led directly into the City o' Ligg.

So they steamed along, side by side, together, the lame loco-

THE TREASURE CHEST

motive and the sorrowful, shamefaced steamboat. That day one laid her head at last alongside the dock, and one puffed timidly into the station; both decided never to complain of any work that they should have to do in the future.

THE TRAIN★
C. H. Crandall
Hark!
It comes!
It hums!
With ear to ground
I catch the sound,
The warning courier-roar
That runs along before.
The pulsing, struggling, now is clearer!
The hillsides echo "nearer, nearer,"
Till like a drove of rushing, trampling
    cattle,
With dust and wind and clang and
    shriek and rattle,
Passes the cyclops of the train!
I see a fair face at the pane,—
Like a piano string
The rails, unburdened, sing;
The white smoke flies
Up to the skies;
The sound
Is drowned—
Hark!

★ From *Wayside Music*, published by G. P. Putnam's Sons. Used by the courteous permission of the author.

THE BOOMS*
Stewart Edward White

AT nine o'clock one morning Bobby Orde, following an agreement with his father, walked sedately to the Proper Place, where he kept his cap and coat and other belongings. The Proper Place was a small, dark closet under the angle of the stairs. He called it the Proper Place just as he called his friend Clifford Fuller, or the saw-mill town in which he lived Monrovia—because he had always heard it so called. At the door a beautiful black and white setter solemnly joined him.

"Hello, Duke!" greeted Bobby.

The dog swept back and forth his magnificent feather tail, and fell in behind his young master.

Bobby knew the way perfectly. You went to the fire-engine house; and then to the left after the court-house was Mr. Proctor's; and then, all at once, the town. Father's office was in the nearest square brick block, where Bobby turned in to the straight, broad stairway that led to the office above. The stairway, and the hall to which it mounted were dark and smelled of old coco-matting and stale tobacco. Bobby liked this smell very much. He liked, too, the echo of his footsteps as he marched down the hall to the door of his father's offices.

Within were several long, narrow desks burdened with large ledgers and flanked by high stools. On each stool sat a clerk—five of them. An iron "base burner" stove occupied the middle of the room. Its pipe ran in suspension here and there through the upper air until it plunged unexpectedly into the wall. A capacious wood-box flanked it. Bobby was glad he did not have to fill that wood-box at a cent a time.

Against the walls at either end of the room and next the windows

*Taken from *Adventures of Bobby Orde*. Used by permission of the publishers, Doubleday Page & Company.

were two roll-top desks at which sat Mr. Orde and his partner.

"Hullo, Bobby," called Mr. Orde, who was talking earnestly to a man; "I'll be ready in a few minutes."

Nothing pleased Bobby more than to wander about the place with its delicious "office smell." At one end of the room, nailed against the wall, were rows and rows of beautifully polished models of the firm's different tugs, barges and schooners. Bobby surveyed them with both pleasure and regret. It seemed a shame that such delightful boats should have been built only in half and nailed immovably to boards. Against another wall were maps, and a real deer's head. Everywhere hung framed photographs of logging camps and lumbering operations. From any one of the six long windows he could see the street below, and those who passed along it. Time never hung heavy at the office.

When Mr. Orde had finished his business, he put on his hat, and the big man, the ten-year old boy and the grave, black and white setter dog walked down the long dark hall, down the steps and around the corner to the livery stable.

Here they climbed into one of the light and graceful buggies which were at that time a source of such pride to their owners, and flashed out into the street behind Mr. Orde's celebrated team.

Duke's gravity at this juncture deserted him completely. Ears back, mouth wide, body extended, he flew away. Faster and faster he ran, until he was almost out of sight; then turned with a whirl of shingle dust and came racing back. When he reached the horses he leaped vigorously from one side to the other, barking ecstatically; then set off on a long even lope along the sidewalks and across the street, investigating everything.

Mr. Orde took the slender whalebone whip from its socket.

"Come, Dick!" said he.

The team laid back their pointed delicate ears, shook their heads from side to side, snorted and settled into a swift stride.

Bobby leaned over to watch the sunlight twinkle on the wheel-spokes. The narrow tires sunk slightly in the yielding shingle fragments. *Brittle! Brittle! Brittle!* the sound said to Bobby.

At the edge of town they ran suddenly out from beneath the maple trees to find themselves at the banks of the river. A long bridge crossed it. The team clattered over the planks so fast that hardly could Bobby get time to look at the cat-tails along the bayous before blue water was beneath him.

But here Mr. Orde had to pull up. The turn-bridge was open; and Bobby to his delight was allowed to stand up in his seat and watch the wallowing, churning little tug and the three calm ships pass through. He could not see the tug at all until it had gone beyond the bridge, only its smoke; but the masts of the ship passed stately in regular procession.

"Three-masted schooner," said he.

Then when the last mast had scarcely cleared the opening, the ponderous turn-bridge began slowly to close. Bobby could now make out the two bridge tenders walking around and around, pushing on the long lever that operated the mechanism. In a moment more the bridge came into place with a clang. The team, tossing their heads impatiently, moved forward.

On the other side of the bridge was no more town; but instead, great lumber yards, and along the river a string of mills with many smokestacks. The road-bed at this point changed abruptly to sawdust, springy and odorous with the sweet smell of pine that now perfumed all the air. To the left Bobby could see the shipyards and the skeleton of a vessel well under way. From it came the irregular *Block! Block! Block!* of mallets; and it swarmed with little, black, ant-like figures of men.

Mr. Orde drove rapidly and silently between the shipyards and the rows and rows of lumber piles, arranged in streets and alleys like an untenanted city. Overhead ran tramways **on**

which dwelt cars and great black and bay horses. The wild exultant shriek of the circular saw rang out. White plumes of steam shot up against the intense blue of the sky. Beyond the piles of lumber Bobby could make out the topmasts of more ships. At the end of the lumber piles the road turned sharp to the right. It passed in turn the small building which Bobby knew to be another delightful office, and the huge cavernous mill with its shrieks and clangs, its blazing, winking eyes beneath, and its long incline up which the dripping, sullen logs crept in unending procession to their final disposition. And then came the "booms" or pens, in which the logs floated like a patterned brown carpet. Men with pike poles were working there; and even at a distance Bobby caught the dip and rise, and the flash of water as the rivermen ran here and there over the unstable footing.

Next were more lumber yards and more mills, for five miles or so, until at last they emerged into an open, flat country divided by the old-fashioned snake fences; dotted with blackened stumps of the long-vanished forest; eaten by sloughs and bayous from the river. As far as the eye could reach were marshes grown with wild rice and cat-tails. Occasionally one of these bayous would send an arm in to cross the road. Then Bobby was delighted, for that meant a float-bridge through the cracks of which the water spurted up in jets at each impact of the horse's hoofs. On either hand the bayou, filmed with green weeds and the bright scum of water, offered surprises to the watchful eye. One could see many mud-turtles floating lazily, feet outstretched; and bull-frogs and little frogs; and, in the clear places, trim and self-sufficient mud hens. From the reeds at the edges flapped small green herons and thunder pumpers. And at last——

"Oh, look, papa!" cried Bobby, excited and awed. "There's a snap'n' turtle!"

Indeed, there he was in plain sight, the boys' monster of the marshes, fully two feet in diameter, his rough shell streaming with long green grasses, his wicked black eyes staring, his hooked, powerful jaws set in a grim curve. If once those jaws clamped—so said the boys—nothing could loose them but the sound of thunder, not even cutting off the head.

Ten of the twelve miles to the booms had already been passed. The horses continued to step out freely. Duke, the white of his coat soiled and muddied by frequent and grateful plunges, loped alongside, his pink tongue hanging from one corner of his mouth. Occasionally he rolled his eyes up at his master's in sheer enjoyment of the expedition.

"Papa," asked Bobby suddenly, "what makes you have the booms so far away? Why don't you have them down by the bridge?"

"It's this way, Bobby," explained Mr. Orde carefully. "The logs are cut 'way up the river—ever so far—and then they float down the river. Now everybody has logs in the river—Mr. Proctor and Mr. Heinzman and Mr. Welton and lots of people, and they're all mixed up together. When they get down to the mills where they are to be sawed up into boards, the logs belong-ing to the different owners have to be sorted out. Papa's com-pany is paid by all the others to do the floating down the stream and the sorting out. The sorting out is done in the booms; and we put the booms up stream from the mills because after the logs have been sorted it is easier to float them down the stream than to haul them back up the stream."

Bobby said nothing for some time, then he demanded:

"Papa, I don't see how you tell your logs from Mr. Proctor's or Mr. Heinzman's or any of the rest of them."

"Why, you see, each log is stamped on the end with a mark," answered Mr. Orde. "Mr. Proctor's mark is one thing; and Mr. Heinzman's is another; and all the rest have different ones."

"I see," said Bobby.

The road now led them through a small grove of willows. Emerging thence they found themselves in full sight of the booms.

For fifty feet Bobby allowed his eyes to run over a scene already familiar and always of the greatest attraction to him. Then came what he called, after his Malory, the Stumps Perilous. Between them there was but just room to drive. Bobby loved to imagine them as the mighty guardians of the land beyond, and he always held his breath until they had been passed in safety.

Shying gently toward each other, ears pricked toward the two obstacles, the horses shot through with pace undiminished and drew up proudly before the smallest of the group of buildings. Thence emerged a tall, spare, keen-eyed man in slouch hat, flannel shirt, shortened trousers and spiked boots.

"Hullo, Jim," said Mr. Orde.

"Hullo, Jack," said the other.

"Where's your chore boy to take the horses?"

"I'll rustle him," replied the River Boss. Bobby drew a deep breath of pleasure, and looked about him.

From the land's edge extended a wide surface of logs. Near at hand little streaks of water lay between some of them, but at a short distance they appeared brown and uniform, until far away a narrow flash of blue marked the open river. Here and there ran the boundaries of the various booms included in the monster main boom. Those boundaries consisted of long heavy timbers floating on the water, and joined end to end by means of strong links. They were generally laid in pairs, and hewn on top, so that they constituted a network of floating sidewalks threading the expanse of saw-logs. At intervals they were anchored to bunches of piles driven deep, and bound at the top. An unbroken palisade of piles constituted the outer boundaries of the main boom. At the upper end of them perched a little house whence was operated the mechanism of the heavy swing boom, capable of closing entirely the river channel. Thus the logs, floating or driven down the river, encountered this obstruction; were shunted into the main booms, where they were distributed into the various pocket booms; and later were released at the lower end, one lot at a time, to the river again. Thence they were taken up by the mill to which they belonged.

Bobby did not as yet understand the mechanism of all this. He saw merely the brown logs, and the distant blue water, and the hut wherein he knew dwelt machinery and a good natured, short, dark man with a short, dark pipe, and the criss-cross floating sidewalks, and the men with long pike poles and shorter peavies moving here and there about their work. And he liked it.

But now the chore boy appeared to take charge of the horses. Mr. Orde immediately walked away with the River Boss, leaving Bobby the parting command not to go out on the booms.

Bobby, left to himself, climbed laboriously, one steep step at a time, to the elevation of the roofless porch before the mess house. The sun proving hot, he peeped within. There long tables flanked each by two benches of equal extent, stretched down the dimness. They were covered with dark oil-cloth, and at intervals on them arose irregular humps of cheese cloth. Beneath the cheese cloth, which Bobby had seen lifted, were dishes containing stewed fruit, sugar, salt, pepper, catsup, molasses and the like. Innumerable tin plates and cups laid upside down were guarded by iron cutlery. It was very dark and still, and the flies buzzed.

Beyond, Bobby could hear the cook and his helpers, called cookees. He decided to visit them; but he knew better than to pass through the dining room. Until the bell rang, that was sacred from the boss himself.

Therefore he descended from the porch, one step at a time, and climbed around to the kitchen. Here he found preparations for dinner well under way.

"'Llo, Bobby," greeted the cook, a tall white-moustached lean man with bushy eyebrows. The cookees grinned, and one of them offered him a cooky as big as a pie-plate. Bobby accepted the offering, and seated himself on a cracker box.

Food was being prepared in quantities to stagger the imagination of one used only to private kitchens. Prunes stewed away in galvanized iron buckets; meat boiled in washboilers; coffee was made in fifty-pound lard tins; pies were baking in racks of ten; mashed potatoes were handled by the shovelful; a barrel of flour was used every two and a half days, in this camp of hungry hard-working men. It took a good man to plan and organize; and a good man Corrigan was. His meals were never late, never scant, and never wasteful. Consequently, in his own domain he was autocrat. The dining room was sacred, the kitchen was sacred, meal hours were sacred. Each man was fed at half-past five, at twelve, and at six. No man could get a bite

even of dry bread between those hours, save occasionally a team-ster in the line of duty. Bobby himself had once seen Corrigan chase a would-be forager out at the point of a carving knife. As for Bobby, he was an exception, and a favorite.

The place held one's interest spell-bound, with its two stoves, each as big as the dining room table at home, its shelves and barrels of supplies, its rows of pies and loaves of bread, and all the crackle and bustle and aroma of its preparations. Time passed on wings. At length Corrigan glanced up at the square wooden clock and uttered some command to his two subordi-nates. The latter immediately began to dish into large recep-tacles of tin the hot food from the stove—boiled meat, mashed potatoes, pork and beans, boiled corn. These they placed at regular intervals down the long tables of the dining room. Bobby descended from his cracker box to watch them. Between the groups of hot dishes they distributed many plates of pie, of bread and of cake. Finally the two-gallon pots of tea and coffee, one for each end of each table, were brought in. The window cov-erings were drawn back. Corrigan appeared for final inspection.

"Want to ring the bell, Bobby?" he asked.

They proceeded together to the front of the house where hung the bell cord. Bobby seized this and pulled as hard as he was able. But his weight could not bring the heavy bell over. Corrigan, smiling grimly under his moustache, gave him advice.

"Pull on her, Bobby, hang yer feet off'n the ground. Now let up entire! Now pull again! Now let up! That's the bye! You'll get her goin' yit widout the help of any man."

Sure enough, the weight of the bell did give slightly under Bobby's frantic efforts. Nevertheless, Corrigan took opportunity to reach out secretly above the boy's head to add a few pounds to the downward pull. At last the clapper reached the side.

Cling! it broke the stillness.

"There you got her goin', Bobby!" cried Corrigan. "Now all you got to do is to keep at her."

The bell, started swinging, was now easy enough to manage. Bobby was delighted at the noise he was producing, and still more delighted at its results. For from the maze of his toil he could see men coming—men from the logs near at hand, men from the booms far away—all coming to the bell. By now the bell was turning entirely over. Bobby was becoming enthusiastic. He tugged and tugged. Sometimes when he did not let go the rope in time, he was lifted slightly off his feet. The sun was hot, but he had no thought of quitting. His hat fell off backward, his towseled hair wetted at the edges, clung to his forehead, his dull red cheeks grew redder behind his freckles, his eyes fairly closed in an ecstasy of enjoyment. He did not hear Corrigan laughing, nor the gleeful shouts of the men as they leaped ashore and with dripping boots advanced to the expected meal. All he knew was that wonderful *clang! clang! clang!* over him; the only thought in his head was that he, *he*, Bobby Orde, was making all this noise himself!

How long he would have continued before giving out entirely it would be hard to say, but at this moment Mr. Orde and Jim Denning came around the corner with some haste. Both looked worried and a little angry until they caught sight of the small bell-ringer. Then they too laughed with the men.

"That'll do," advised Mr. Orde, "we're all here. Lord, Corrigan! I thought you were afire at least."

"You got to show us up a reg'lar Christmas dinner to match that noise," said one of the men to Corrigan.

After the meal, which Bobby enjoyed thoroughly, because it was so different from what he had at home, he had a request to proffer.

"Papa," he demanded, "I want to go out on the booms."

"Haven't time to-day, Bobby," replied Mr. Orde. "You just play around."

But Jim Denning would not have this.

"Can't start 'em in too early, Jack," said he. "I bet you'd been fished out from running logs before you were half his age."

Mr. Orde laughed.

"Right you are, Jim, but we were raised different in those days."

"Well," said Jim, "work's slack. I'll let one of the men take him."

At that moment a youth not more than fifteen years of age was passing from the cook house to the booms. He had the slenderness of his years, but was toughly knit, and already possessed in eye and mouth the steady unwavering determination the river life develops. In all details of equipment he was a riverman complete; the narrow-brimmed black felt hat, pushed back from a tangle of curls; the flannel shirt crossed by the broad bands of the suspenders; the kersey trousers; the heavy knit socks; and the strong shoes armed with thin half-inch needlesharp caulks.

"Jimmy Powers!" called the River Boss after this boy, "Come here!"

The youth approached, grinning cheerfully.

THE TREASURE CHEST

"I want you to take Bobby out on the booms," commanded Denning, "and be careful he don't fall in."

The older men moved away. Bobby and Jimmy Powers looked a little bashfully at each other, and then turned to where the first hewn logs gave access to the booms.

"Ever been out on 'em afore?" asked Jimmy Powers.

"Yes," replied Bobby; "I been out to the swing with Papa."

They walked out on the floating booms, which tipped and dipped ever so slightly under their weight. Bobby caught himself with a little stagger, although his footing was a good three feet in width. On either side of him nuzzled the great logs, like patient beasts, and between them were narrow strips of water, the color of steel that has just cooled.

"How deep is it here?" asked Bobby.

"'Bout six feet," replied Jimmy Powers.

They passed an intersection, and came to an empty enclosure over which the water stretched like a blue sheet. Bobby looked back. Already the shore seemed far away. Through the cracks between the piles the wavelets went lap, lap, slap, lap! Beyond were men working the reluctant logs down toward the lower end of the booms. Some jabbed the pike poles in and then walked forward along the boom logs. Others ran quickly over the logs themselves until they had gained timbers large enough to sustain their weight, whence they were able to work with greater advantage. The supporting log rolled and dipped under the burden of the man pushing mightily against his implement; but always the riverman trod it, first one way, then the other, in entire unconsciousness of the fact that he was doing so.

"Can you walk on the logs?" asked Bobby of his companion.

"Sure," laughed Jimmy Powers.

"Let's see you," insisted Bobby.

Jimmy Powers leaped lightly from the boom to the nearest

log. It was a small one, and at once dipped below the surface. If the boy had attempted to stand on it even a second he would have fallen in. But all Jimmy Powers needed was a foothold from which to spring. Hardly had the little timber dipped before he had jumped to the next and the next after. Behind him the logs, bobbing up and down, churned the water white. Jimmy moved rapidly across the enclosure on an irregular zig-zag. The smaller logs he passed over as quickly as possible; on the larger he paused. Bobby was interested to see how he left behind him a wake of motion. The little logs bobbed furiously; the larger bowed in more stately fashion and rolled slowly in dignified protest. In a moment Jimmy was back again, grinning.

"Look here," said he.

He took his station sideways on a log of about twenty inches diameter, and began to roll it beneath him by walking rapidly forward. As the timber gained its momentum, the boy increased his pace, until finally his feet were fairly twinkling beneath him, and the side of the log rising from the river was a blur of white water. Then suddenly with two quick strong stamps of his caulked feet the young riverman brought the whirling timber to a standstill. "That's birling a log," said he to Bobby.

They walked out on the main boom still farther.

"How deep is it here?" asked Bobby again.

"'Bout thirty feet," replied Jimmy Powers.

Bobby for an instant felt a little dizzy, as though he were on a high building. As he looked back, the buildings of the river camp, lying low among the trees, had receded to a great distance; apparently at another horizon was the dark row of piling that marked the outer confines of the booms; up and down stream, as far as he could see, were the logs. Bobby suddenly felt very much alone, with the blue sky above him, and the deep black water beneath, and about him nothing but the quiet sullen monsters herded from the wilderness. He gripped very tightly Jimmy Power's hand as they walked along.

But shortly they turned to the left; and after a brief walk, mounted the rickety steps to the floor of the hut where dwelt old man North, and the winch for operating the swinging boom. Old man North was short, dark, heavy and bearded; he smoked perpetually a small black clay pipe which he always held upside down in his mouth, but his black eyes twinkled at Bobby, so the boy was not afraid of him. When he saw the two approaching, he reached over in the corner and handed out a hickory fish pole peeled to a beautiful white.

"The wums is yonder," said he. Bobby put a fat worm on his hook and sat down in the opposite doorway where he could dangle his feet directly over the river. Where the shadow of the cabin fell, he could see far down in the water, which there became a transparent fair green. Close to the piles, on the tops of which the hut was built, were various fish. Jimmy leaned over.

"Mostly suckers," he advised. "Yan's a perch, try him."

Bobby cautiously lowered his baited hook until it dangled before the perch's nose. The latter paid absolutely no attention to it. Bobby juggled it up and down. No results. At last he fairly plumped the worm on top of the fish's nose. The perch, with an air of annoyance, spread his gills and, with the least perceptible movement of his tail, sank slowly until he faded from sight.

"Better let down your hook and fish near bottom?" suggested Jimmy Powers.

Bobby did so. The peace of warm afternoon settled upon him. He dangled his chubby legs, and watched the waving green current slip silently beneath his feet. Beside him sat Jimmy Powers.

"I'd like to walk on logs," proffered Bobby at last, "It looks like lots of fun."

"Oh, that's nothin'," said Jimmy Powers. "You ought to be on drive."

The boys fell into conversation. Jimmy told of the drive, and the log-running. Bobby listened with the envy of one whose imagination cannot conceive of himself permitted in such affairs. And then all at once the peace was shattered.

"Yank him, Bobby, yank him!" yelled Jimmy.

"Christmas, he's a whale!" said old North.

For, without wavering, the tip of the hickory pole had been ruthlessly jerked below the water's surface, and the butt nearly pulled from Bobby's hands.

Bobby knew the proper thing to do. In such cases you heaved strongly. The fish flew from the water, described an arc over your head, and lit somewhere behind you. He tried to accomplish this, but his utmost strength could but just lift the wriggling, jerking end of the pole from the water.

"Give her to me!" cried Jimmy Powers.

"Le' me 'lone," grunted Bobby.

He planted the butt of the pole in the pit of his stomach, and lifted as hard as ever he could with both hands. His face grew red, his ears rang, but, after a first immovable resistance, to his great joy the tip of the bending, wriggling pole began to give. Slowly, little by little, he pulled up the fish, until he could make out the flash of its body darting to and fro far down in the depths.

"Black bass!" murmured Jimmy Powers breathlessly.

And then just as his size and beauty were becoming clearly visible, the line came up with a sickening ease. The interested spectators caught a glimpse of white as the fish turned.

"*Oh, gee*, that's hard luck!" cried Jimmy Powers.

"Bet he weighed four pounds," proffered North curtly.

But at this instant a faint clear whistle sounded from about the wooded bend of the river above.

"Boat coming," said North. "Clear out of the way, boys."

He began at once to operate the winch which drew the long slanting swing boom out of the channel, for the river must not be obstructed. In a moment appeared the *Lucy Belle*, a flimsy-looking double decker, with two slim smokestacks side by side connected by a band of fancy grill-work, two huge paddle boxes and much white paint. She sheered sidewise with the current and headed down upon them accompanied by a vast beating of paddle wheels. Almost immediately she was passing, within ten feet or so of the hut. The water boiled and eddied among the piles, rushing in and sucking back. A ruddy-faced man in official cap and citizen's clothes leaned over the rail.

"Well, you made her to-day," shouted North.

"Bet ye," called the man with a grin. "Only aground once."

The *Lucy Belle* swept away with an air of pride. She made the trip to and from Redding, forty miles up the river, twice a week. Sometimes she came through in a day. Oftener she ran aground.

Now Bobby went back to his original idea.

"I'd like to walk on the logs," said he.

"Well, come on, then," said Jimmy Powers.

They retraced their steps along the booms until near the shore.

"You don't want to try her where she's deep," explained Jimmy Powers. "Cause if you should fall in, the logs would close right together over your head, and then where'd you be?"

Bobby shuddered at this idea, which in the event continued to haunt him for some days.

"There's a big one," said Jimmy Powers. "Try her."

Bobby stepped out on a big solid-looking log, which immediately proved to be not solid at all. It dipped one way, Bobby tried to tread the other. The log promptly followed his suggestion—too promptly. Bobby soon found himself about two moves behind in this strange new game. He lost his balance, and the first thing he knew, he found himself waist deep in the water. Jimmy Powers laughed heartily; but to Bobby this was no laughing matter. The penalties attached both by nature, and his mother were dire in the extreme. In any other surroundings or with any other company he would have wept bitterly. Even in the presence of Jimmy Powers his lower lip quivered; and his soul filled to the very throat with dismay.

"You're all right, kid," announced Jimmy Powers at last. "Your collar's all right, and your hair ain't wet. The rest'll dry out so nobody will know the diff'. You rustle in to the cook shanty and get Corrigan to let you sit by the stove."

Bobby said farewell to his guide, and presented himself to the cook.

"I fell in," he announced, "can I sit by the stove?"

"Sure," said Corrigan, hospitably. "Take a cracker-box and go over by the wood box. Tryin' to ride a log?"

"Yes," confessed Bobby.

"Well, you want to look out for them!" warned Corrigan a little vaguely. He produced the customary cooky. Bobby sat and steamed, and munched and told about the fish he had almost caught. In a moment Duke thrust his muzzle in the door. Bobby looked hastily down. His clothes were quite dry.

After a moment Mr. Orde appeared.

"Bobby here?" he inquired. "Oh, yes! Come on, youngster."

Bobby showed himself with considerable trepidation; but apparently Mr. Orde noticed nothing wrong, and the boy's spirits rose. The team was waiting, and they mounted the buggy at once. Duke fell in behind them soberly.

Bobby talked busily all the way in. He told principally of the fish, although the *Lucy Belle* and Jimmy Powers came in for a share. From time to time Mr. Orde said, "That's good," or, "Yes," which sufficed Bobby.

Under the maples the sun slanted low and golden and mote-laden. Bobby suddenly felt a little tired, and more than a little hungry. He descended from the buggy with alacrity. The wetting was forgotten in the home-coming. Only when washing for dinner did he remember that even his mother had noticed nothing. For the first time it occurred to him that he possessed the ability to meet an emergency without the aid of his parents—that was the good of his experience.

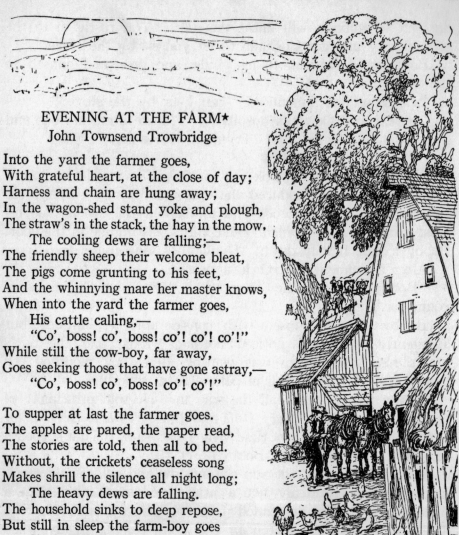

EVENING AT THE FARM★
John Townsend Trowbridge

Into the yard the farmer goes,
With grateful heart, at the close of day;
Harness and chain are hung away;
In the wagon-shed stand yoke and plough,
The straw's in the stack, the hay in the mow,
    The cooling dews are falling;—
The friendly sheep their welcome bleat,
The pigs come grunting to his feet,
And the whinnying mare her master knows,
When into the yard the farmer goes,
    His cattle calling,—
    "Co', boss! co', boss! co'! co'! co'!"
While still the cow-boy, far away,
Goes seeking those that have gone astray,—
    "Co', boss! co', boss! co'! co'!"

To supper at last the farmer goes.
The apples are pared, the paper read,
The stories are told, then all to bed.
Without, the crickets' ceaseless song
Makes shrill the silence all night long;
    The heavy dews are falling.
The household sinks to deep repose,
But still in sleep the farm-boy goes
    Singing, calling,—
    "Co', boss! co', boss! co'! co'! co'!"
And oft the milkmaid, in her dreams,
Drums in the pail with the flashing streams,
    Murmuring "So, boss! so!"

★Used by permission of, and special arrangement with, Houghton Mifflin Company, the Publishers.

THE SUGAR CAMP*
Charles Dudley Warner

I THINK there is no part of farming the boy enjoys more than the making of maple sugar; it is better than "blackberrying," and nearly as good as fishing. And one reason he likes this work is that somebody else does the most of it. It is a sort of work in which he can appear to be very active, and yet not do much.

In my day maple-sugar-making used to be something between picnicking and being shipwrecked on a fertile island, where one should save from the wreck tubs and augurs, and great kettles and pork, and hen's-eggs and rye-and-Indian bread, and begin at once to lead the sweetest life in the world.

As I remember the New England boy (and I am very intimate with one), he used to be on the qui vive in the spring for the sap to begin running. I think he discovered it as soon as anybody. Perhaps he knew it by a feeling of something starting in his own veins,—a sort of spring stir in his legs and arms, which tempted him to stand on his head, or throw a handspring, if he could find a spot of ground from which the snow had melted. The sap stirs early in the legs of a country boy, and shows itself in uneasiness in the toes, which get tired of boots, and want to come out and touch the soil just as soon as the sun has warmed it a little. The country boy goes barefoot just as naturally as the trees burst their buds, which were packed and varnished over in the fall to keep the water and the frost out. Perhaps the boy has been out digging into the maple trees with his jack-knife; at any rate, he is pretty sure to announce the discovery as he comes running into the house in a great state of excitement—as if he had heard a hen cackle in the barn—with, "Sap's runnin'!"

And then, indeed, the stir and excitement begin. The sap-buckets, which have been stored in the garret over the wood-house,

*Taken from *Being a Boy*. Used by permission of, and by special arrangement with, Houghton, Mifflin Company, the publishers.

and which the boy has occasionally climbed up to look at with another boy, for they are full of sweet suggestions of the annual spring frolic,—the sap-buckets are brought down and set out on the south side of the house and scalded. The snow is still a foot or two feet deep in the woods, and the ox-sled is got out to make a road to the sugar camp, and the campaign begins. The boy is everywhere present, superintending everything, asking questions, and filled with a desire to help the excitement.

It is a great day when the cart is loaded with the buckets and the procession starts into the woods. The sun shines almost unobstructedly into the forest, for there are only naked branches to bar it; the snow is soft and beginning to sink down, leaving the young bushes spindling up everywhere; the snow-birds are twittering about, and the noise of shouting and of the blows of the ax echoes far and wide. This is spring, and the boy can scarcely contain his delight that his out-door life is about to begin again.

In the first place the men go about and tap the trees, drive in the spouts, and hang the buckets under. The boy watches all these operations with the greatest interest. He wishes that some time when a hole is bored in a tree the sap would spout out in a stream as it does when a cider-barrel is tapped; but it never does, it only drops, sometimes almost in a stream, but on the whole slowly, and the boy learns that the sweet things of the world have to be patiently waited for, and do not usually come otherwise than drop by drop.

Then the camp is to be cleared of snow. The shanty is re-covered with boughs. In front of it two enormous logs are rolled nearly together, and a fire is built between them. Forked sticks are set at each end, and a long pole is laid on them, and on this are hung the great caldron kettles. The huge hogsheads are turned right side up, and cleaned out to receive the sap that is gathered. And now, if there is a good "sap run," the establishment is under full headway.

The great fire that is kindled up is never let out, night or day, as long as the season lasts. Somebody is always cutting wood to feed it; somebody is busy most of the time gathering in the sap; somebody is required to watch the kettles that they do not boil over, and to fill them. It is not the boy, however; he is too busy with things in general to be of any use in details. He has his own little sap-yoke and small pails, with which he gathers the sweet liquid. He has a little boiling-place of his own, with small logs and a tiny kettle. In the great kettles the boiling goes on slowly, and the liquid, as it thickens, is dipped from one to another, until in the end kettle it is reduced to sirup, and is taken out to cool and settle, until enough is made to "sugar off." To "sugar off" is to boil the sirup until it is thick enough to crystallize into sugar. This is the grand event, and is only done once in two or three days.

But the boy's desire is to "sugar off" perpetually. He boils his kettle down as rapidly as possible; he is not particular about chips, scum, or ashes; he is apt to burn his sugar; but if he can get enough to make a little wax on the snow, or to scrape from the bottom of the kettle with his wooden paddle, he is happy. A good deal is wasted on his hands, and the outside of his face, and on his clothes, but he does not care; he is not stingy.

To watch the operations of the big fire gives him constant pleasure. Sometimes he is left to watch the boiling kettles, with a piece of pork tied on the end of a stick, which he dips into the boiling mass when it threatens to go over. He is constantly tasting of it, however, to see if it is not almost sirup. He has a long round stick, whittled smooth at one end, which he uses for this purpose, at the constant risk of burning his tongue. The smoke blows in his face; he is grimy with ashes; he is altogether

C. H. LAWRENCE

such a mass of dirt, stickiness, and sweetness, that his own mother wouldn't know him.

He likes to boil eggs with the hired man in the hot sap; he likes to roast potatoes in the ashes, and he would live in the camp day and night if he were permitted. Some of the hired men sleep in the bough shanty and keep the fire blazing all night. To sleep there with them, and awake in the night and hear the wind in the trees, and see the sparks fly up to the sky, is a perfect realization of all the stories of adventures he has ever read. He tells the other boys afterwards that he heard something in the night that sounded very much like a bear. The hired man says that he was very much scared by the hooting of an owl.

The great occasions for the boy, though, are the times of "sugaring-off." Sometimes this used to be done in the evening and it was made the excuse for a frolic in the camp. The neighbors were invited; sometimes even the pretty girls from the village, who filled all the woods with their sweet voices and merry laughter and little affectations of fright. The white snow still lies on all the ground except the warm spot about the camp. The tree branches all show distinctly in the light of the fire, which sends its ruddy glare far into the darkness, and lights up the bough shanty, the hogsheads, the buckets on the trees, and the group about the boiling kettles, until the scene is like something taken out of a fairy play. If Rembrandt could have seen a sugar party in a New England wood he would have made out of its strong contrasts of light and shade one of the finest pictures in the world.

At these sugar parties every one was expected to eat as much sugar as possible; and those who are practised in it can eat a great deal. It is a peculiarity about eating warm maple sugar, that though you may eat so much of it one day as to loathe the thought of it, you will want it the next day more than ever. At the "sugaring-off" they used to pour the hot sugar upon the snow, where it congealed, without crystallizing, into a sort of wax, which I do suppose is the most delicious substance that was ever invented. And it takes a great while to eat it. If one should close his teeth firmly on a ball of it, he would be unable to open his mouth until it dissolved. The sensation while it is melting is very pleasant, but one cannot converse.

The boy used to make a big lump of it and give it to the dog, who seized it with great avidity, and closed his jaws upon it, as dogs will on anything. It was funny the next moment to see the expression of perfect surprise on the dog's face when he found that he could not open his jaws. He shook his head; he sat down in despair; he ran round in a circle; he dashed into the woods and back again. He did everything except climb a tree, and howl. It would have been such a relief to him if he could have howled. But that was the one thing he could not do.

GOING A-NUTTING★
Edmund Clarence Stedman

No clouds are in the morning sky,
    The vapors hug the stream,—
Who says that life and love can die
    In all this northern gleam?
At every turn the maples burn,
    The quail is whistling free,
The partridge whirs, and the frosted burrs
    Are dropping for you and me.
        Ho! hilly ho! heigh O!
        Hilly ho!
In the clear October morning.

Along our path the woods are bold,
    And glow with ripe desire;
The yellow chestnut showers its gold,
    The sumachs spread their fire;
The breezes feel as crisp as steel,
    The buckwheat tops are red.
Then down the lane, love, scurry again,
    And over the stubble tread!
        Ho! hilly ho! heigh O!
        Hilly ho!
In the clear October morning.

★ Used by permission of, and by special arrangement with, Houghton Mifflin Company, the publishers.

THE MOCK TURTLE'S SONG*
Lewis Carroll

"Will you walk a little faster?" said a whiting to a
      snail,
"There's a porpoise close behind us, and he's treading
      on my tail!
See how eagerly the lobsters and the turtles all
      advance!
They are waiting on the shingle—will you come and
      join the dance?
Will you, won't you; will you, won't you; will you
      join the dance?
Will you, won't you; will you, won't you; won't you
      join the dance?

"You can really have no notion how delightful it
      will be,
When they take us up and throw us, with the lobsters,
      out to sea!"
But the snail replied: "Too far, too far!" and gave
      a look askance—
Said he thanked the whiting kindly, but he would not
      join the dance.
Would not, could not; would not, could not; would not
      join the dance.
Would not, could not; would not, could not; could not
      join the dance.

★From *Alice In Wonderland*. The Mock Turtle sings the song to Alice and the Gryphon.

THE TREASURE CHEST

"What matters it how far we go?" his scaly friend
    replied;
There is another shore you know upon the other
    side.
The further off from England, the nearer is to
    France,
Then turn not pale, beloved snail, but come and
    join the dance.
Will you, won't you; will you, won't you; will you
    join the dance?
Will you, won't you, will you, won't you; won't you
    join the dance?"

MY BOOK HOUSE

THE MEMOIRS OF A WHITE ELEPHANT*
Judith Gautier

I WAS born in the forest of Laos, and regarding my youth I have retained only very confused memories; occasional punishments inflicted by my Mother, when I refused to take my bath, or to follow her in search of food; some gay frolics with elephants of my own age; pillage of the enemy's fields—and long beatitudes on the borders of streams, and in the silent glades of the forest. That is all.

When I grew large I perceived with surprise that the Elders of the Herd of which I was a member regarded me with disfavour. This pained me, and I would have been glad to think that I was mistaken; but it was evident that no matter what advances were made by me, I was avoided by all. I sought for some cause of this aversion, and soon discovered it by observing my reflection in a pool. *I was not like the others!*

My skin instead of being like theirs, gray and dingy, was white, and in spots of a pinkish colour. How did that happen? Mortification overwhelmed me. And I formed the habit of retiring from the Herd which despised me, and of remaining by myself.

One day when I was thus alone, and sad, and humiliated, at a distance from the Herd, I noticed a slight noise in the thicket, near me. I parted the branches with my trunk, and saw a singular being, who walked on two legs—and yet was not a bird. He wore neither feathers nor fur; but on his skin there shone brilliant stones, and bits of bright colours that made him look like a flower! *I beheld for the first time a Man.*

An extreme terror seized me; but a curiosity equally intense kept me motionless in the presence of this creature—so small that without the slightest effort I could have crushed him, and who yet

*From *Memoirs of a White Elephant.* Copyrighted by Duffield & Company.

in some way appeared to me more formidable and powerful than I.

While I was gazing at him he saw me, and instantly threw himself on the ground, making extraordinary motions, of which I did not comprehend the meaning, but which did not seem to me to be hostile.

After a few moments he rose and retired, bowing at every step, till I lost sight of him.

I returned next day to the same spot, in the hope of seeing him again; the man was there, but this time he was not alone. On seeing me his companions, like himself, performed the same singular movements, throwing themselves on their faces upon the ground, and doubling their bodies backwards and forwards.

My astonishment was great, and my fears diminished. I thought the men so pretty, so light and graceful in their motions, that I could not tire of watching them.

After a while they went away, and I saw them no more.

One day soon after, when, alone as usual, I descended to the Lake to drink, I saw upon the opposite shore an elephant who looked over at me and made friendly signals. It flattered me that he did not seem to feel repelled by my appearance, but on the contrary seemed to admire me, and was disposed to make my acquaintance. But he was a stranger to me, and certainly did not belong to our Herd.

He gathered some delicate roots, of a kind that we elephants greatly enjoy, and held them out to me, as though to offer them for my acceptance. I hesitated no longer, but began to swim across the Lake.

On reaching the other side I gave the polite stranger to understand that I was attracted, not so much by the sight of the delicacies, as by the wish to enjoy his company. He insisted upon my accepting a portion of his hospitality, and began, very sociably, to eat up the rest.

★ The white elephant is regarded as very sacred in Siam and treated with the utmost respect. The Siamese never willingly permit a white elephant to be taken out of the country. The only one ever seen in the United States was brought here by P. T. Barnum.

Then, after some gambols, which seemed to me very graceful, he moved off, inviting me by his looks to follow. I did not need urging, and we plunged into the Forest, running, frolicking, pulling fruits and flowers. I was so delighted with the companionship of my new friend that I took no notice of the direction in which he was leading me. But suddenly I stopped. I saw with uneasiness that I was quite lost. We had come out into a plain that was strange to me, and where, in the distance, singular objects showed against the sky—tall points the colour of snow, and brilliant red mounds, and smoke—things that seemed to me not natural!

Seeing my hesitation, my companion gave me a friendly blow with his trunk, of sufficient force, however, to show more than ordinary strength.

My suspicions were not allayed by this blow, under which my flank smarted; I refused to go further.

The stranger then uttered a long call, which was answered by similar calls. Seriously frightened now, I turned abruptly towards the Forest. A dozen elephants barred the way.

He who had so duped me (for what reason I could not imagine), fearing the effects of my indignation, now promptly retired. He set off running; but I was so much larger than he that it seemed easy to overtake him. I rushed in pursuit, but just as I caught up with him I was obliged to stop short. He had entered the open door of a formidable stockade, made of the trunks of giant trees. It was *inside* that he wished to lead me, *to make me a prisoner!*

I tried to draw back and escape, but I was surrounded by the accomplices of my false friend, who beat me cruelly with their trunks, and at last forced me into the enclosure—the door being at once shut behind me.

Seeing myself caught, I uttered my war-cry, and charged the palisades, throwing all my weight against them, in the hope of breaking through. I ran madly round the enclosure, thrusting my tusks into the walls, and seizing the timbers with my trunk, endeavouring to wrench them apart. It was against the door that I strove most furiously. But all was useless. My enemies had prudently disappeared; they did not return till I was exhausted, paralyzed by my impotent rage, and until, motionless and with drooping head, I owned myself *vanquished!*

Then he who had lured me into this *trap* reappeared and approached me, dragging enormous chains, which he wound around my feet. Groaning deeply, I reproached him with his perfidy; but he gave me to understand that I was in no danger, and that if I would be submissive I would have no cause to regret my lost liberty.

The night came. I was left alone, chained in this manner. I strove with desperation to break my manacles, but without success. At last, worn out with grief and fatigue, I threw myself on the ground and after a time fell asleep.

When I opened my eyes the sun was up, and I saw, all standing around the stockade, the elephants of the day before—but out of

my reach! They were fastened by the foot, by means of a rope which they could have broken without the slightest effort. They were eating with great relish the fine roots and grasses piled up in front of them.

I was too sad and mortified to feel hungry, and I looked gloomily at these prisoners, whose happiness and contentment I could not understand.

After they had finished eating some men arrived, and far from showing fear, they saluted them by flapping their ears—giving every sign of joy. Each man seemed to be welcomed by one special elephant to whom he gave his sole attention. He loosened the rope from the foot, and rubbed the rough skin with an ointment, and then, upon a signal, the captive bent back one of his fore-legs to enable the man to mount upon his colossal back. I looked at all this with such astonishment that I almost for the moment forgot my own sufferings.

And now, each man being seated upon the neck of an elephant, they, one after another, fell into line and marched out of the enclosure, and the gate was shut behind them.

I was alone; abandoned. The day was long and cruel. The sun scorched me, and hunger and thirst began to cause me suffering.

I struggled no more. My legs were lacerated by the vain efforts I had made. I was prostrate—hopeless!—and considered myself as one already dead!

At sunset the elephants returned, each one bearing a ration of food; and again I saw them eat joyously, while hunger gnawed my stomach and no one noticed me.

The night again descended. I could no longer suppress my screams, which were more of misery than of rage. Hunger and thirst prevented me from sleeping, even for a moment.

In the morning a man came towards me. He stopped at some distance, and began to speak to me. I could not, of course, understand what he said to me, but his voice was gentle, and he did not appear to threaten me.

When he had finished speaking he uncovered a bowl that he carried filled with some unfamiliar food, the appetizing odor of which made me fairly quiver!

Then he came near, and kneeling, held out the bowl to me.

I was so famished that I forgot all pride, and even all prudence. I never had tasted anything so delicious; and when the basin was empty I carefully picked up the smallest crumbs that had fallen on the ground.

The elephant who had captured me now drew near, bearing a man on his back; he made me understand by little slaps of his trunk that I should bend back one of my fore-legs to allow the man who had fed me to get upon my neck. I obeyed, resigned to anything, and the man sprang up very lightly and placed himself near my head. Then he pricked me with an iron—but very gently—just to let me know that he was armed, and that he could hurt me terribly at this point, so sensitive with us, at the least sign of rebellion.

Sufficiently warned, I allowed myself to show no impatience. Then they removed my manacles; the other elephant took up the march, and I followed quietly.

We left the stockade, and they led me to a pool in which I was permitted to bathe and drink. After the privations I had suffered the bath seemed so delightful that I could not make up my mind to leave it when the time came; but a prick on the ear told me plainly that I must obey, and I was so afraid of being deprived of food and drink that I rushed out of the water, determined to do all I was bid.

We now went towards the strange objects that I had seen in the distance on the plain, on the day I was made prisoner. I learned later that it was the city of Bangkok, the capital of

Siam. I had never yet beheld a city, and my curiosity was so aroused that I was anxious to reach it. As we drew near men appeared on the sides of the road, more and more numerously, so that the way was crowded. They stood on each side of the pathway, and to my great surprise, I at last discovered that it was I whom they were expecting, and had come out to see!

At my approach they uttered shouts of joy; and when I passed before them they threw themselves, face-downward, upon the earth, with extended arms, then rose and followed me.

At the gates of the city a procession appeared, with cloth of gold, and arms, and streamers of silk on long poles.

All at once there was a noise—so wonderful that I stopped short. One would have said it was composed of shrieks and groans, and claps of thunder, and whistling winds, mingled with the songs of birds! I was so terrified that I turned to escape, but found myself trunk to trunk with my companion who was following me. His perfect tranquility, and the roguish wink that he gave me, reassured me, and I felt *mortified* to have exhibited less courage than others before so many spectators, and I wheeled about so promptly that the man on my head did not have time to prick my ear.

I was ordered to stop in front of the leader of the Procession, who saluted me, and made an address.

The great and fearful noise had ceased, but began again as soon as this personage had finished his speech. The Procession turned around now and preceded me, and we again moved on. I then saw that it was men who were *making* all this noise. They struck various objects—they tapped them—they whistled into them—and seemed to take the greatest trouble! That which they made was called *"Music."* I grew used to it in time, and even came to think it agreeable. I was no longer afraid, and all that I saw interested me, and delighted me greatly.

In the city the crowds were even denser, and the rejoicings more noisy. They spread carpets on the route I was to traverse; the houses were wreathed with garlands of flowers, and from the windows they threw phials of perfume, which my rider caught, flying and sprinkled over me.

Why were they so glad to see me? Why were all these honors showered upon me? I, who in my own Herd had been repulsed and disdained!

I could find no reply at the time, but later on I learned that it was the whiteness of my skin which alone was responsible for all this enthusiasm. That which seemed to elephants a defect, seemed admirable to men, and made me more valuable than a treasure. They believed my presence was a sign of Happiness—of Victory—of Prosperity to the Kingdom—and they treated me accordingly.

We had now reached a great square in front of a magnificent building which might well cause amazement to a "wild" elephant.

Often since then I have seen this Palace, and with better understanding, but always with the same astonishment and admiration. It was like a mountain of snow, carved into domes and great stairways, with painted statues, and columns encrusted with jewels, and tipped with globes of crystal that dazzled their eyes. The tall golden points rose higher than the domes, and in many places red standards floated, and on all of them there was the figure of a *White Elephant!*

All the Court, in costume of ceremony was assembled on the lower steps of the stairway. Above, on the platform, on either side of a doorway of red and gold, elephants covered with superb housings were ranged—eight to the right, eight to the left, all standing motionless.

They summoned me to the foot of the stair, and there I was told to stop. A great silence fell upon all. One would have said that there was nobody there. The crowd which had been so noisy now was mute.

The red and gold doorway was opened wide, and all the people prostrated themselves, resting their foreheads upon the earth.

The King of Siam appeared.

He was borne by four porters in a pavilion of gold, in which he sat with crossed legs. His robe was covered with jewels, and scattered blinding rays. Before him walked young boys dressed in crimson, who waved great bunches of feathers attached to long sticks; others carried silver basins out of which came clouds of perfumed smoke.

I am able to describe all this now, with words which I have learned since then; but at that time I admired without understanding, and I felt as if I was looking upon all the *Stars of Heaven*, and the *Sun at Noonday*, and all the *Flowers of the loveliest Spring—* at one and the same time!

The bearers of the King descended the steps in front of me.

THE TREASURE CHEST

His Majesty approached. Then my conductor pricked my ear, and my companion struck my leg with his trunk, indicating that I was to kneel.

I did so voluntarily, in the presence of such splendor, which seemed to me as if it might burn any one who should touch it!

The King inclined his head slightly—*The King of Siam had saluted me!* (I learned afterwards that I was the only one who had ever been honored in such fashion. And I was soon able to return the King's salute, or rather to anticipate it.)

His Majesty addressed me with a few words which had an agreeable sound. He bestowed on me the name of "*King Mag-nanimous*" with the rank of *Mandarin of the First Class*. He

placed upon my head a chaplet of pearls set with gold and precious stones, and then retired to his Palace.

The multitude, who until now had remained prostrated, now rose up, and with shouts and cries of joy, accompanied me to my own palace, where I was to dwell. It was in a garden, in the midst of an immense lawn. The walls were of sandal wood, and the great roofs extended far out on all sides; they were lacquered in red and glistened in the sunlight, with here and there globes of copper, and carved likenesses of elephants' heads. I was taken into an immense Hall, so high that the red rafters which interlaced overhead and supported the roof made me think of the branches of my native Forest, when the sunset reddens them.

An old elephant was walking slowly about the Hall. As soon as he saw me he advanced towards me, flapping his ears in welcome. His tusks were ornamented with rings and golden bells, and he wore on his head a diadem like that which the King had just placed on mine. But all this did not improve his appearance. His skin was mottled with dingy patches, like dried earth, and cracked in spots; his eyes and ears were encircled with redness; his tusks were yellow and broken, and he walked with difficulty. But he seemed amiable, and I returned his courtesies.

My conductor descended from my neck, while officers and servants prostrated themselves before me as they had done before the King himself.

Then they led me to a huge table of marble, where in great bowls and vessels of silver and gold were bananas, sugar-canes, all sorts of delicious fruits, and choice grasses—and cakes—and rice—and melted butter—*What a feast!*

Ah! how I wished that those of my Herd who had made a mock of me could see how I was treated by *Men!*

My heart swelled with pride, here I was to dwell, and I no longer regretted my liberty and my native Forest.

THE ADVENTURES OF GENERAL TOM THUMB
A TRUE STORY
Told by the World-Renowned Show-Man
⊱PHINEAS T. BARNUM⊰
who, as proprietor of the American Museum in New York, discovered in the year 1842 a veritable
⊰ TOM THUMB ⊱
the most famous little man ever known to the world.   He visited the Courts of
KINGS AND QUEENS
captivated the hearts of the multitude, and proved ever so merry,
quick-witted and bright that he furnished to all the same innocent
pleasure and mirth as the fabled Tom Thumb of our stories

*IN November, 1842, I (Phineas T. Barnum) heard of a remarkably small child, and at my request, my brother brought him to my hotel.   He was not two feet high, weighed less than sixteen pounds, and was the smallest child I ever saw that could walk alone.   He was a perfectly formed, bright-eyed little fellow, with light hair and ruddy cheeks, and he enjoyed the best of health. He was exceedingly bashful, but after some coaxing, he was induced to talk with me, and he told me that he was the son of Sherwood E. Stratton and that his own name was Charles E. Stratton.   After seeing and talking with him, I at once determined to secure his services from his parents and to exhibit him in public.   He and his mother came to New York Thanksgiving Day, 1842, and I announced him at once on my Museum bills as "General Tom Thumb."

I took the greatest pains to educate and train my diminutive prodigy, devoting many hours to the task by day and night, and I was very successful, for he was an apt pupil, with a great deal of native talent, and a keen sense of the ludicrous.   He speedily became a public favorite.   Accordingly I entered into an agreement for his services for another year with the privilege of exhibiting him in Europe.

★ Arranged from *The Life of P. T. Barnum,* written by himself.

On January 18, 1844, I went on board the new and fine sailing ship, *Yorkshire*, bound for Liverpool. Our party included General Tom Thumb, his parents, and his tutor. We were accompanied by several personal friends, and the City Brass Band kindly volunteered to escort us to Sandy Hook.

On our arrival at Liverpool, quite a crowd had assembled at the dock to see Tom Thumb, for it had been previously announced that he would arrive on the *Yorkshire*, but his mother managed to smuggle him ashore unnoticed, for she carried him, as if he was an infant, in her arms.

Immediately after our arrival in London, the General came out at the Princess's Theatre, and made so decided a "hit" that it was difficult to decide who was best pleased, the spectators, the manager, or myself. I took a furnished mansion in West End in the very centre of the most fashionable locality. From this magnificent mansion I sent letters of invitation to the editors and several of the nobility to visit the General. Most of them called and were highly gratified. The word of approval was indeed so passed around in high circles, that uninvited parties drove to my door in crested carriages and were not admitted.

During our first week in London, the Hon. Edward Everett, the American minister, to whom I had letters of introduction, called and was highly pleased with his diminutive, though re-nowned countryman. We dined with him the next day, by in-vitation, and his family loaded the young American with presents. Mr. Everett kindly promised to use his influence at the palace with a view of having Tom Thumb introduced to Her Majesty Queen Victoria. I breakfasted at his house one morning in com-pany with Mr. Charles Murray, who held the office of Master of the Queen's Household. Mr. Murray kindly offered his good offices in the case, and the next day one of the Queen's Life Guards, a tall, noble-looking fellow, bedecked as became his station, brought me a note, conveying the Queen's invitation to General Tom Thumb and his guardian, Mr. Barnum, to appear at Buckingham Palace on an evening specified. Special in-structions were the same day given me by Mr. Murray, by Her Majesty's command, to suffer the General to appear before her as he would appear anywhere else, without any training in the use of the titles of royalty, as the Queen desired to see him act naturally and without restraint.

On arriving at the Palace, the Lord in Waiting put me under drill as to the manner and form in which I should conduct myself in the presence of royalty. I was to answer all questions by her Majesty through him, and, in no event, to speak directly to the

Queen. In leaving the royal presence, I was to "back out," keeping my face always towards Her Majesty, and the illustrious lord kindly gave me a specimen of that sort of backward locomotion. How far I profited by his instruction and example will presently appear.

We were conducted through a long corridor to a broad flight of marble steps, which led to the Queen's magnificent picture gallery, where Her Majesty and Prince Albert, the Duchess of Kent, the Duke of Wellington and others were awaiting our arrival. They were standing at the farther end of the room when the door was thrown open, and the General walked in, looking like a wax doll, gifted with the power of locomotion. Surprise and pleasure were depicted on the countenances of the royal circle at beholding this remarkable specimen of humanity so much smaller than they had evidently expected to find him.

The General advanced with a firm step, and, as he came within hailing distance, made a very graceful bow, and exclaimed: "Good evening, ladies and gentlemen!"

A burst of laughter followed this salutation. The Queen then took him by the hand, led him about the gallery, and asked him many questions, the answers to which kept the party in an uninterrupted strain of merriment. The General familiarly informed the Queen that her picture gallery was "first rate," and told her he should like to see the Prince of Wales. The Queen replied that the Prince had retired to rest, but that he should see him on some future occasion. The General then gave his songs, dances and imitations, and, after a conversation with Prince Albert and all present, which continued for more than an hour, we were permitted to depart.

Before describing the process and incidents of "backing out," I must acknowledge how sadly I broke through the counsel of the Lord in Waiting. While Prince Albert and others were engaged with the General, the Queen was gathering information from me in regard to his history, etc. Two or three questions were put and answered through the process indicated in my drill. It was a round about way of doing business, not at all to my liking, and I suppose the Lord in Waiting was seriously shocked, if not outraged, when I entered directly into conversation with Her Majesty. She, however, seemed not disposed to check my boldness, for she immediately spoke directly to me in obtaining the information which she sought. I felt entirely at ease in her presence, and could not avoid contrasting her sensible and amiable manners with the stiffness and formality of upstart gentility at home or abroad. The Queen was modestly attired in plain black, and wore no ornaments. Indeed, surrounded as she was by ladies arrayed in the highest style of magnificence, their dresses sparkling with diamonds, she was the last person whom a stranger would have pointed out in that circle as the Queen of England.

The Lord in Waiting was perhaps mollified towards me when he saw me following his illustrious example in "backing out" from the royal presence. He was accustomed to the process, and therefore was able to keep somewhat ahead (or rather aback) of me, but even *I* stepped rather fast for the General. We had a considerable distance to travel in that long gallery before reaching the door, and whenever the General found he was losing ground, he turned around and ran a few steps, then resumed the position of "backing out," then turned around and ran, and so continued to alternate his methods of getting to the door, until the gallery fairly rang with the merriment of the royal spectators. It was really one of the richest scenes I ever saw. Running, under the circumstances, was an offence sufficiently heinous to excite the indignation of the Queen's favorite poodle dog, and he vented his displeasure by barking so sharply as to startle the General from his propriety. He, however, recovered

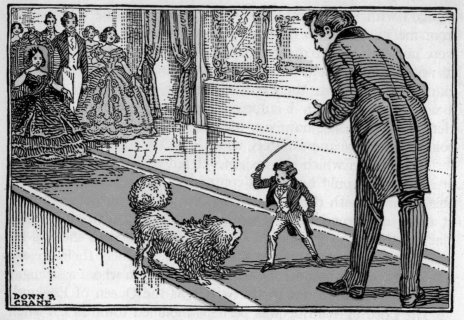

immediately, and, with his little cane, commenced an attack on the poodle, and a funny fight ensued, which renewed and increased the merriment of the royal party.

This was near the door of exit. We had scarcely passed into the ante-room, when one of the Queen's attendants came to us with the expressed hope of Her Majesty that the General had sustained no damage; to which the Lord in Waiting playfully added, that in case of injury to so renowned a personage, he should fear a declaration of war by the United States!

On our second visit to the Queen, we were received in what is called the "Yellow Drawing-Room," a magnificent apartment, surpassing in splendor and gorgeousness anything of the kind I had ever seen. It was hung with drapery of rich yellow satin damask, the couches, sofas and chairs being covered with the same material. The vases, urns and ornaments were all of modern patterns, and the most exquisite workmanship. The room was panelled in gold, and the heavy cornices beautifully carved and gilt. The tables, pianos, etc., were mounted with gold inlaid with pearl of various hues, and of the most elegant designs.

We were ushered into this gorgeous drawing-room before the Queen and royal circle had left the dining-room, and, as they approached, the General bowed respectfully. The Queen smilingly took him by the hand, and said she hoped he was very well.

"General," continued the Queen, "this is the Prince of Wales."

"How are you, Prince," said the General, shaking him by the hand; and then standing beside the Prince, he remarked, "The Prince is taller than I am, but I *feel* as big as anybody," upon which he strutted up and down the room as proud as a peacock, amid shouts of laughter from all present.

The Queen then introduced the Princess Royal, and the General immediately led her to his elegant little sofa, which we took with us, and with much politeness sat himself down beside her. Then rising from his seat, he went through his various performances, and the Queen handed him an elegant and costly souvenir, which had been expressly made for him by her order, for which he told her he was very much obliged and he would keep it as long as he lived.

On our third visit to Buckingham Palace, Leopold, King of the Belgians, was also present. He was highly pleased and asked

a multitude of questions. Queen Victoria desired the General to sing a song, and asked him what song he preferred to sing.

"Yankee Doodle," was the prompt reply.

This answer was as unexpected to me as it was to the royal party. When the merriment it occasioned had somewhat subsided, the Queen good-humoredly remarked, "That is a very pretty song, General; sing it if you please." The General complied and soon afterward we retired.

The British public was now fairly excited. Not to have seen General Tom Thumb was decidedly unfashionable, and from March 20th to July 20th, the levees of the little General at Egyptian Hall were continually crowded. At the fashionable hour, sixty carriages of the nobility have been counted at one time standing in front of our exhibition rooms in Piccadilly. Pictures of the little General were published in all the pictorial papers of the time. Polkas and quadrilles were named after him and songs were sung in his praise.

The Queen Dowager Adelaide requested the General's attendance at Marlborough House one afternoon. He went in his court dress, consisting of a richly embroidered brown silk-velvet coat and shortbreeches, white satin vest with fancy colored embroidery, white silk stockings and pumps, wig, bagwig, cocked hat and a dress sword.

"Why, General," said the Queen Dowager, "I think you look very smart today."

"I guess I do," said the General.

A large party of the nobility was present. The old Duke of Cambridge offered the little General a pinch of snuff, which he declined. The General sang his songs, performed his dances and cracked his jokes, to the great amusement and delight of the distinguished circle of visitors.

"Dear little General," said the kind-hearted Queen, taking him upon her lap, "I see you have no watch. Will you permit me to present you with a watch and chain?"

"I would like them very much," replied the General, his eyes glistening.

"I will have them made expressly for you," responded the Queen Dowager, and at the same moment she called a friend and desired him to see that the proper order was executed. A few weeks thereafter we were called again to Marlborough House. A number of the children of the nobility were present as well as some of their parents. After passing a few compliments with the General, Queen Adelaide presented him with a beautiful little gold watch, placing the chain around his neck with her own hands.

This elegant little watch was not only duly heralded, but was also placed upon a pedestal in the hall of exhibition, together with the presents from Queen Victoria, and covered with a glass vase. To these were soon added an elegant gold snuff box mounted with turquoise, presented by his Grace the Duke of Devonshire, and many other costly gifts of the nobility and gentry. The Duke of Wellington called frequently to see the little General at his levees (that same Duke of Wellington who defeated the Emperor Napoleon in the battle of Waterloo). The first time he called the General was personating Napoleon, marching up and down the platform, and apparently taking snuff in deep meditation. He was dressed in the well-known uniform of the Emperor. I introduced him to the "Iron Duke," who inquired the subject of his meditations. "I was thinking of the loss of the Battle of Waterloo," was the little General's immediate reply. This display of wit was chronicled throughout the country.

Scarcely a nobleman in England failed to see General Tom Thumb at his own house, at the house of a friend, or at the public levees in Egyptian Hall. Our visit in London and tour through the provinces were enormously successful, and after a brilliant season in Great Britain, I made preparations to take the General to Paris. On the very day after my arrival, I received a special command to appear before King Louis Philippe at the Tuileries on the following Sunday evening.

At the appointed hour, the General and I, arrayed in the conventional court costume, were ushered into a grand saloon of the palace, where we were introduced to the King, the Queen, Princess Adelaide, the Duchess d'Orleans, her son, the Count de Paris, and a dozen or more distinguished persons. General Tom Thumb went through his various performances to the manifest pleasure of all who were present, and at the close the King presented to him a large emerald brooch set with diamonds.

King Louis Philippe was so condescending and courteous, that I felt quite at home in the royal presence, and ventured upon a bit of diplomacy. The Longchamps celebration was coming, a day now conspicuous for the display of court and fashionable equipages in the Champs Elysées and the Bois de Boulogne, and, as the King was familiarly conversing with me, I ventured to say that I had hurried over to Paris to take part in the Longchamps display, and I asked him if the General's carriage could not be permitted to appear in the avenue reserved for the court and the diplomatic corps, representing that the General's small but elegant establishment, with its tiny ponies and little coachman and footman, would be in danger of damage in the general throng unless the privilege I asked was accorded. The King

smilingly turned to one of the officers of his household, and, after conversing with him for a few moments, he said to me: "Call on the Prefect of Police tomorrow afternoon, and you will find a permit ready for you."

Longchamps day arrived, and among the many splendid equipages on the grand avenue, none attracted more attention than the superb little carriage with four ponies and liveried and powdered coachman and footman, belonging to the General. It

stood out conspicuous in the line of carriages containing the Ambassadors to the Court of France. Thousands upon thousands rent the air with cheers for "General Tom Pouce."

Thus before I opened the exhibition, all Paris knew that General Tom Thumb was in the city. The élite of the city came to the exhibitions. The season was more than a success; it was a triumph. It seemed too as if the whole city was advertising me. The papers were profuse in their praises of the General and his performances. *Figaro*, the *Punch* of Paris, gave a picture of an immense mastiff running away with the General's carriage and horses in his mouth. Statuettes of General Tom Pouce appeared in all the windows, in plaster, marble, sugar and chocolate. A fine cafe on one of the boulevards took the name of "Tom Pouce" and displayed over the door a life-size statue of the General.

We were commanded to appear twice more at the Tuileries, and we were also invited to the Palace on the King's birthday, to witness the display of fireworks in honor of the anniversary. Our fourth and last visit to the royal family was by special invitation, at St. Cloud. We remained an hour, and, at parting, each of the royal party gave the General a splendid present and almost smothered him with kisses. After bidding them adieu, we retired to another portion of the palace to make a change of the General's costume, and to partake of some refreshments which had been prepared for us. Half an hour afterwards, as we were about leaving the palace, we went through a hall leading to the front door, and in doing so, passed the sitting room, in which the royal family was spending the evening. The door was open, and some of them, happening to espy the General, called out for him to come in and shake hands with them once more. We entered the apartment and there found the ladies sitting around a square table, each provided with two candles, and every one of them, including the Queen, was engaged in working at embroidery—a sight which I am sorry to say I believe is seldom seen in families of the aristocracy on either side of the water.

From France we crossed the border into Belgium. Brussels is Paris in miniature and one of the most charming cities I ever visited. We found elegant quarters, and the day after our arrival, by command we visited King Leopold and the Queen at their palace. The King and Queen had already seen the General in London, but they wished to present him to their children and the distinguished persons whom we found assembled. After a most agreeable hour we came away, the General as usual receiving many fine presents.

The following day I opened the exhibition in a beautiful hall, which on that day and on every other day while we remained there, was crowded. On the second or third day, in the midst of the exhibition, I suddenly missed the case containing the valuable presents which the General had received from Kings, Queens, noblemen and gentlemen, and instantly gave the alarm. Some thief had intruded for the express purpose of stealing these jewels, and, in the crowd, had been entirely successful in his object.

The police were notified, and I offered 2000 francs reward for the recovery of the property. A day or two afterward, a man went into a jeweler's shop and offered for sale, among other things, a gold snuff-box, mounted with turquoises, and presented by the Duke of Devonshire to the General. The jeweller, seeing the General's initials on the box, sharply questioned the man, who became alarmed and ran out of the shop. An alarm was raised and the man was caught. He made a clean breast of it, and in the course of a few hours, the entire property was returned, to the great delight of the General and myself. Wherever we exhibited afterwards, the case of presents was always carefully watched.

From Belgium we returned for a provincial tour through Great Britain. We traveled by post most of the time—that is I had a suitable carriage made for our party, and a van which conveyed the General's carriage, ponies, and such other property as we needed. We also used the railway lines freely, leaving our carriages at any station, and taking them up again when we returned. I remember once making an extraordinary effort to reach a branch line station where I meant to leave my teams and take the rail for Rugby. I had a time table and knew at what time exactly I could hit the train, but unfortunately the axle to my carriage broke and I was an hour late in reaching the station. The train had long been gone, but I *must* be in Rugby where we had advertised a performance. I found the superintendent and told him, "I must instantly have an extra train to Rugby."

"Extra train," said he with surprise and a half sneer, "why you can't have an extra train for less than sixty pounds."

"Is that all?" I asked. "Well, get up your train immediately. Here are your sixty pounds. What are sixty pounds to me, when I must be in Rugby in a hurry?"

The astonished superintendent bustled about and the train was soon ready. He was greatly puzzled to know what distinguished person—he thought he must be dealing with some prince, or at least a duke,—was willing to give so much money to save a few hours' time, and he hesitatingly asked whom he had the honor of serving.

"General Tom Thumb!"

When we were in Oxford, a dozen or more of the university students decided to play a joke on us. As the General was a little fellow, they concluded the admission fee to his entertainments should be paid in the smallest kind of money. They accordingly provided themselves with farthings, and as each man entered, instead of handing in a shilling, for his ticket, he laid down forty-eight farthings, the counting of which tiny coins, with a crowd of ladies and gentlemen about, waiting clamorously to buy their tickets, was no small joke to Mr. Stratton, the General's father, who was acting as ticket seller.

I had now spent three years with General Tom Thumb in Great Britain and on the continent. The entire period had been a season of unbroken pleasure and profit. Thus closing a truly triumphant tour, we set sail for New York, arriving in February, 1847. The General immediately appeared in the American Museum, drawing such crowds as had never been seen before. It was then determined that the General and his parents should travel through the United States. We proceeded to Washington, visiting President Polk and lady at the White House, thence toured the east, the southern states and made a journey to Havana, where we were introduced to the Captain-General and the Spanish nobility. On our return it was agreed that I should go home and travel no more with the little general. I had competent agents who could exhibit him, and I preferred to relinquish a portion of the profits rather than remain longer from home.

In 1849 I had projected a great traveling museum and menagerie, and, as I had neither time nor inclination to manage such a concern, I induced Mr. Seth B. Howes to take the charge. Mr. Sherwood E. Stratton, father of General Tom Thumb, was also admitted to partnership. We chartered the ship *Regatta*, and despatched her to Ceylon to procure, either by capture or purchase, twelve or more living elephants, besides such other wild animals as they could secure. The ship left New York in May ,1850, and was absent one year. They arrived in New York in 1851 with ten elephants, and these, harnessed in pairs to a chariot, paraded up Broadway. We added a caravan of wild animals and many museum curiosities and commenced operations under the patronage of General Tom Thumb, who traveled nearly four years as one of the attractions of "Barnum's Great Asiatic Caravan, Museum and Menagerie."

In 1861 I was visited at the Museum by a most remarkable dwarf, who was a sharp intelligent little fellow perfectly formed with a deal of drollery and wit. His name he told me was George Washington Morrison Nutt. As soon as I engaged him, placards proclaimed the presence of Commodore Nutt at the Museum. I also procured for the Commodore a pair of Shetland ponies, miniature coachman and footman in livery, gold-mounted harness and an elegant little carriage which when closed represented a gigantic English walnut. Commodore Nutt and the giantess, Anna Swan, show how extremes occasionally met at my Museum. He was the smallest of men and she was the tallest of women.

In 1862 I heard of an extraordinary dwarf girl, named Lavinia Warren, a most intelligent and refined young lady, well educated, accomplished and beautiful. I succeeded in making an engagement with her and purchased for her a very splendid wardrobe, costly jewels, and in fact everything that could add to the charms of her naturally charming little person. Commodore Nutt was on exhibition with her, and although he was several years her junior he evidently took a great fancy to her. Tom Thumb had no business engagement at that time with me, but he one day called upon me quite unexpectedly while Lavinia was holding one of her levees. Here he now saw her for the first time. He had a short interview with her, after which he came directly to my private office and desired to see me alone.

"Mr. Barnum," he said, "that is the most charming little lady I ever saw and I believe she was created on purpose to be my wife."

His visits to the museum were now very frequent and it was noticeable that the Commodore, though not exactly jealous, yet strutted around like a bantam rooster whenever the General approached Lavinia.

Tom Thumb finally returned to his home in Bridgeport and privately begged that on the following Saturday I would take Lavinia up to my home in the same town. I could do no less than accede to his proposal, but when the Commodore heard of the matter, he immediately pricked up his ears, and said, "Mr. Barnum, *I* should like to go to Bridgeport to-morrow."

"What for?" I asked.

"I want to see my little ponies. I have not seen them for several months," he replied.

I whispered in his ear, "You little rogue, that is the pony you want to see," pointing to Lavinia.

The General met us at the depot in Bridgeport, on Saturday morning, and drove us to my house in his own carriage—his coachman being tidily dressed with a broad velvet ribbon and silver buckle placed upon his hat expressly for the purpose. After resting half an hour at my home, he took Lavinia out to ride.

He stopped a few moments at his mother's house, where she met his mother and saw the apartments which his father had built expressly for him, and filled with the most gorgeous tiny furniture—all corresponding to his own diminutive size.

Tom Thumb was with us for dinner and as nine o'clock approached, I remarked that it was about time to retire, but somebody would have to sit up until eleven, in order to let in the Commodore, who was coming up on the late train. The General replied "I will sit up with pleasure, if Miss Warren will remain also."

Lavinia carelessly replied that she was used to late hours and she would wait and see the Commodore, so the family retired.

Soon after the little Commodore arrived, he came to my room.

"Mr. Barnum, does Tom Thumb *board* here?" asked the little bantam in a petulant tone of voice.

"No," said I, "Tom Thumb does not board here. I invited him to stop over night, so don't be foolish but go to bed."

"Oh, it's no affair of mine! I don't care anything about it," replied the Commodore and off he went evidently in a bad humor.

Ten minutes afterward Tom Thumb came rushing into my room. Closing the door he caught hold of my hand in a high state of excitement and whispered:

"We are engaged, Mr. Barnum! We are engaged! We are engaged," and he jumped up and down in the greatest glee.

When the Commodore heard the news he choked a little as if he was trying to swallow something. Then, turning on his heel, he said in a broken voice: "I hope you may be happy."

"Never mind, Commodore," I said to him, "Minnie Warren is a better match for you; she is a charming little creature and two years younger than you, while Lavinia is several years older."

A few weeks subsequently when time had reconciled the Commodore, he told me that Tom Thumb had asked him to stand as groomsman with Minnie as bridesmaid at the wedding.

THE TREASURE CHEST

The approaching wedding was announced. It created an immense excitement. Lavinia's levees at the museum were crowded. I had promised to give the couple a genteel and graceful wedding and I kept my word.

The day arrived, February 10, 1863. The ceremony took place in Grace Church, New York. I know not what better I could have done had the wedding of a prince been in contemplation. The church was filled by a highly select audience of ladies and gentlemen. Among them were governors of several of the states; members of congress were present, also generals of the army and many other prominent public men. After this Mr. and Mrs. Tom Thumb started on a wedding tour, taking Washington in on their way where they visited President Lincoln at the White House.

After a few months' retirement they again resumed their public career, and have since traveled around the world, Commodore Nutt and Minnie Warren accompanying them. And the union of Mr. and Mrs. Tom Thumb has proved in an eminent degree a happy marriage.

THE PLAINS' CALL
Arthur Chapman

I must ride out on the plains again,
  With a horse 'twixt knee and knee,
Where the wolves howl and the winds growl,
  And the clouds drift fast o'er me;
I must ride out on the plains once more,
On the Westland's broad and level floor.

I must ride forth on the plains at morn,
  Where the cactus flowers are,
And the lark calls, and the white walls
  Of the mountain loom afar;
I must ride out, when breaks the day—
Ride where the gods of outdoors play.

I must ride out on the plains at night,
  And smell the dew wet sage,
When the moon glows, and the late snows
  Gleam like a book's white page;
I must ride out on the plains again,
And quit this haunt of pygmy men.

A NIGHT RIDE IN A PRAIRIE SCHOONER*
Hamlin Garland

One afternoon in the autum of 1868 Duncan Stewart, leading his little fleet of "prairie schooners," entered upon "The Big Prairie" of northern Iowa, and pushed resolutely on into the west. His four-horse canvas-covered wagon was followed by two other lighter vehicles, one of which was driven by his wife, and the other by a hired freighter. At the rear of all the wagons, and urging forward a dozen or sixteen cattle, trotted a gaunt youth and a small boy.

The boy had tears upon his face, and was limping with a stone-bruise. He could hardly look over the wild oats, which tossed their gleaming bayonets in the wind, and when he dashed out into the blue joint and wild sunflowers, to bring the cattle into the road, he could be traced only by the ripple he made, like a trout in a pool. He was a small edition of his father. He wore the same color and check in his hickory shirt, and his long pantaloons of blue denim, had suspenders precisely like those of the men. Indeed, he considered himself a man, notwithstanding the tear-stains on his brown cheeks.

It seemed a long time since leaving his native Wisconsin coolly

* From *Boy Life on the Prairie*.   Used by special permission of the author and the publishers, Harper & Brothers.

behind, with only a momentary sadness, but now, after nearly a week of travel, it seemed his father must be leading them all to the edge of the world, and Lincoln was very sad and weary.

"Company, halt!" called the Captain.

One by one the teams stopped, and the cattle began to feed (they were always ready to eat), and Mr. Stewart, coming back where his wife sat, said cheerily:

"Well, Kate, here's the big prairie I told you of, and beyond that blue line of timber you see is Sun Prairie, and home."

Mrs. Stewart did not smile. She was too weary, and the wailing of little Mary in her arms was dispiriting.

"Come here, Lincoln," said Mr. Stewart. "Here we are, out of sight of the works of man. Not a house in sight—climb up here and see."

Lincoln rustled along through the tall grass, and, clambering up the wagon wheel, stood silently beside his mother. Tired as he was, the scene made an indelible impression on him. It was as though he had suddenly been transported into another world, a world where time did not exist, where snow never fell, and the grass waved forever under a cloudless sky. A great awe fell upon him as he looked, and he could not utter a word.

At last Mr. Stewart cheerily called: "Attention, battalion! We must reach Sun Prairie to-night. *Forward, march!*"

Again the little wagon train took up its slow way through the tall ranks of the wild oats, and the drooping, flaming sunflowers. Slowly the sun sank. The crickets began to cry, the night-hawks whizzed and boomed, and long before the prairie was crossed the night had come.

Being too tired to foot it any longer behind the cracking heels of the cows, Lincoln climbed into the wagon beside his little brother, who was already asleep, and, resting his head against his mother's knee, lay for a long time, listening to the *chuck-chuckle*

of the wheels, watching the light go out of the sky, and counting the stars as they appeared.

At last they entered the wood, which seemed a very threatening place indeed, and his alert ears caught every sound,—the hoot of owls, the quavering cry of coons, the twitter of night birds. But at last his weariness overcame him, and he dozed off, hearing the clank of the whipple trees, the creak of the horses' harness, the vibrant voice of his father, and the occasional cry of the hired hand, urging the cattle forward through the dark.

He was roused once by the ripple of a stream, wherein the horses thrust their hot nozzles, he heard the grind of wheels on the pebbly bottom, and the wild shouts of the resolute men as they scrambled up the opposite bank, to thread once more the dark aisles of the forest. Here the road was smoother, and to the soft rumble of the wheels the boy slept.

At last, deep in the night, so it seemed to Lincoln, his father shouted: "Wake up, everybody. We're almost home." Then, facing the darkness, he cried, in western fashion, "Hello! the house!"

Dazed and stupid, Lincoln stepped down the wheel to the ground, his legs numb with sleep. Owen followed, querulous as a sick puppy, and together they stood in the darkness, waiting further command.

From a small frame house, near by, a man with a lantern appeared.

"Hello!" he said, yawning with sleep. "Is that you, Stewart? I'd jest about give you up."

While the men unhitched the teams, Stewart helped his wife and children to the house, where Mrs. Hutchinson, a tall, thin woman, with a pleasant smile, made them welcome. She helped Mrs. Stewart remove her things, and then set out some bread and milk for the boys, which they ate in silence, their heavy eyelids drooping.

When Mr. Stewart came in, he said: "Now, Lincoln, you and Will are to sleep in the other shack. Run right along, before you go to sleep. Owen will stay here."

Without in the least knowing the why or wherefore, Lincoln set forth beside the hired man, out into the unknown. They walked rapidly for a long time, and, as his blood began to stir again, Lincoln awoke to the wonder and mystery of the hour. The strange grasses under his feet, the unknown stars over his head, the dim objects on the horizon, were all the fashioning of a mind in the world of dreams.

At last they came to a small cabin on the banks of a deep ravine. Opening the door, the men lit a candle, and spread their burden of blankets on the floor. Lincoln crept between them like a sleepy puppy, and in a few minutes this unknown actual world merged itself in the mystery of dreams.

When he woke, the sun was shining, hot and red, through the

open windows, and the men were smoking their pipes by the rough fence before the door. Lincoln hurried out to see what kind of a world this was to which his night's journey had hurried him. It was, for the most part a level land, covered with short grass intermixed with tall weeds, and with many purple and yellow flowers. A little way off, to the right, stood a small house, and about as far to the right was another, before which stood the wagons belonging to his father. Directly in front was a wide expanse of rolling prairie, cut by a deep ravine, while to the north, beyond the small farm which was fenced, a still wider region rolled away into unexplored and marvellous distance. Altogether it was a land to exalt a boy who had lived all his life in a thickly settled Wisconsin coolly, where the horizon line was high and small of circuit.

In less than two hours the wagons were unloaded, the stove was set up in the kitchen, the family clock was ticking on its shelf, and the bureau set against the wall. It was amazing to see how these familiar things and the mother's bustling presence changed the looks of the cabin. Little Mary was quite happy crawling about the floor, and Owen, who had explored the barn and found a lizard to play with, was entirely at home. Lincoln had climbed to the roof of the house, and was still trying to comprehend this mighty stretch of grasses. Sitting astride the roof board, he gazed away into the northwest, where no house broke the horizon line, wondering what lay beyond the high ridge.

While seated thus, he heard a distant roar and trample, and saw a cloud of dust rising along the fence which bounded the farm to the west. It was like the rush of a whirlwind, and, before he could call to his father, out on the smooth sod to the south burst a platoon of wild horses led by a beautiful roan mare. The boy's heart leaped with excitement as the shaggy colts swept round to the east, racing like wolves at play. Their long tails and abundant manes streamed in the wind like banners, and their imperious bugling voiced their contempt for man.

Lincoln clapped his hands with joy, and all of the family ran to the fence to enjoy the sight.   A boy, splendidly mounted on a fleet roan, the mate of the leader, was riding at a slashing pace, with intent to turn the troop to the south.   He was a superb rider, and the little Morgan strove gallantly without need of whip or spur.   He laid out like a hare.   He seemed to float like a hawk, skimming the weeds, and his rider sat him like one born to the saddle, erect and supple, and of little hindrance to the beast.

On swept the herd, circling to the left, heading for the wild lands to the east.   Gallantly strove the roan with his resolute rider, disdaining to be beaten by his own mate, his breath roaring like a furnace, his nostrils blown like trumpets, his hoofs pounding the resounding sod.

All in vain, even with the inside track he was no match for his wild, free mate.   The herd drew ahead, and plunging through a short lane, vanished over a big swell to the east, and their drumming rush died rapidly away into silence.

This was a glorious introduction to the life of the prairies, and Lincoln's heart filled with boundless joy, and longing to know it— all of it, east, west, north, and south.   He had no further wish to return to his coolly home.   The horseman had become his ideal, the prairie his domain.

THE TREASURE CHEST

THE STORY OF A SPIDER (NARBONNE LYCOSA)*
J. Henri Fabre

For three weeks and more the Lycosa trails a bag of eggs hanging to her spinnerets.

Whether she come up from her shaft to lean upon the kerb and bask in the sun, whether she suddenly retire underground in the face of danger, or whether she is roaming the country before settling down, never does she let go her precious bag, that very cumbrous burden in walking, climbing or leaping. If, by some accident, it become detached from the fastening to which it is hung, she flings herself madly on her treasure and lovingly embraces it, ready to bite whoso would take it from her.

In the early days of September, the young ones, who have been some time hatched, are ready to come out. The pill rips open along the middle fold.

The whole family emerges from the bag straightway. Then and there, the youngsters climb to the mother's back. As for the empty bag, now a worthless shred, it is flung out of the burrow; the Lycosa does not give it a further thought. Huddled together, sometimes in two or three layers, according to their number, the little ones cover the whole back of the mother, who, for seven or eight months to come, will carry her family night and day. Nowhere can we hope to see a more edifying domestic picture than that of the Lycosa clothed in her young.

From time to time, I meet a little band of gipsies passing along the high-road on their way to some neighboring fair. The new-born babe mewls on the mother's breast in a hammock formed out of a kerchief. The last-weaned is carried pick-a-back; a third toddles, clinging to its mother's skirts; others follow closely, the biggest in the rear, ferreting in the black-

*Taken from *The Life of the Spider*. Copyright, 1912, by Dodd, Mead & Company.

189

berry-laden hedgerows. They go their way, penniless and rejoicing. The sun is hot and the earth is fertile.

But how this picture pales before that of the Lycosa, that incomparable gipsy whose brats are numbered by the hundred! And one and all of them, from September to April, without a moment's respite, find room upon the patient creature's back, where they are content to lead a tranquil life and to be carted about.

The little ones are very good, none moves, none seeks a quarrel with his neighbors. Clinging together, they form a continuous drapery, a shaggy ulster under which the mother becomes unrecognizable. Is it an animal, a fluff of wool, a cluster of small seeds fastened to one another? 'Tis impossible to tell at the first glance.

The equilibrium of this living blanket is not so firm but that falls often occur, especially when the mother climbs from indoors and comes to the threshold to let the little ones take the sun. The least brush against the gallery unseats a part of the family. The mishap is not serious. The Hen, fidgeting about her Chicks, looks for the strays, calls them, gathers them together. The Lycosa knows not these maternal alarms. Impassively, she leaves those who drop off to manage their own difficulty, which they do with wonderful quickness. Commend me to those youngsters for getting up without whining, dusting themselves and resuming their seat in the saddle! The unhorsed ones promptly find a leg of the mother, the usual climbing-pole, they swarm up it as fast as they can and recover their places on the bearer's back. The living bark of animals is reconstructed in the twinkling of an eye.

I take a hair-pencil and sweep the living burden from one of my Spiders, making it fall close to another covered with her little ones. The evicted youngsters scamper about, find the new mother's legs outspread, nimbly clamber up these and mount on the back of the obliging creature, who quietly lets them have their way. They slip in among the others, or, when the layer is too thick, push to the front and pass from the abdomen to the thorax and even to the head, though leaving the region of the eyes uncovered. It does not do to blind the bearer; the common safety demands that. They know this and respect the lenses of the eyes, however populous the assembly be. The whole animal is now covered with a swarming carpet of young, all except the legs, which must preserve their freedom of action, and the under part of the body, where contact with the ground is to be feared.

My pencil forces a third family upon the already overburdened Spider, and this, too, is peacefully accepted. The youngsters huddle up closer, lie one on top of the other in layers and room is found for all. The Lycosa has lost the last semblance of an animal, has become a nameless bristling thing that walks about. Falls are frequent and are followed by continual climbings.

I perceive that I have reached the limits not of the bearer's good-will, but of equilibrium. The Spider would adopt an indefinite further number of foundlings, if the dimensions of her back afforded them a firm hold. Let us be content with this. Let us restore each family to its mother, drawing at random from the lot. There must necessarily be interchanges, but that is of no importance, real children and adopted children are the same thing in the Lycosa's eyes.

The month of March comes to an end, and the departure of the youngsters begins, in glorious weather, during the hottest hours of the morning. Laden with her swarming burden, the mother Lycosa is outside her burrow, squatting on the parapet at the entrance. She lets them do as they please, as though indifferent to what is happening, she exhibits neither encouragement nor regret. Whoso will goes, whoso will remains behind.

First these, then those, according as they feel themselves duly soaked with sunshine, the little ones leave the mother in batches, run about for a moment on the ground, and then quickly reach the trellis-work of the cage where they are kept, which they climb with surprising alacrity. They pass through the meshes, they clamber right to the top of the citadel. All, with not one exception, make for the heights, instead of roaming on the ground, as might reasonably be expected from the eminently earthly habits of the Lycosa, all ascend the dome, a strange procedure whereof I do not yet guess the object. I receive a hint from the upright ring that finishes the top of the cage. The youngsters hurry to it. It represents the porch of their gymnasium. They hang out threads across the opening, they stretch others from the ring to the nearest points of the trellis-work. On these foot-bridges they perform slack-rope exercises amid endless comings and goings. The tiny legs open out from time to time and straddle as though to reach the most distant points. I begin to realize that they are acrobats aiming at loftier heights than those of the dome.

I top the trellis with a branch that doubles the attainable height. The bustling crowd hastily scrambles up it, reaches the tip of the topmost twigs and thence sends out threads that attach themselves to every surrounding object. These form so many suspension bridges, and my beasties nimbly run along them, incessantly passing to and fro. One would say that they wished to climb higher still. I will endeavor to satisfy their desires.

I take a nine-foot reed, with tiny branches spreading right up to the top, and place it above the cage. The little Lycosa clamber to the very summit. Here, longer threads are produced from the rope-yard, and are now left to float, anon converted into bridges by the mere contact of the free end with the neighboring supports. The rope-dancers embark upon them and form garlands which the least breath of air swings daintily. The thread is invisible when it does not come between the eyes and the sun, and the whole suggests rows of Gnats dancing an aerial ballet.

Then, suddenly, teased by the air-currents, the delicate mooring breaks and flies through space. Behold the emigrants off and away, clinging to their thread. If the wind be favorable, they can land at great distances. Their departure is thus continued for a week or two, in bands more or less numerous, according to the temperature and the brightness of the day. If the sky be overcast, none dreams of leaving. The travellers need the kisses of the sun, which give energy and vigor.

At last, the whole family has disappeared, carried afar by its flying-ropes. The mother remains alone. The loss of her offspring hardly seems to distress her. She retains her usual color and plumpness, which is a sign that the maternal exertions have not been too much for her.

THE GOSSAMER SPIDER
Charlotte M. Yonge

Creature no bigger than a pin,
Most wonderful of all that spin,
   An acrobatic fairy.
Nay, what rope dancer from himself
Can draw his lines, like this small elf,
   Marking his progress airy.

O'er breezy downs, from bent to bent,
That slender, viewless pathway went,
   Traced in some moment's shimmer;
But far too fine for common sight
Until the sunset's sinking light
   Makes the whole network glimmer.

Now here, now there, a rainbow gleam
Floats o'er the turf in silvery stream
   Of strange mysterious lightness.
Then early autumn's frosts will strew
Each thread with glancing beads of dew,
   Jewels of flashing brightness.

DONN P. CRANE

WHERE LOVE IS, THERE GOD IS ALSO*
Lyof N. Tolstoy

IN a certain city of Russia dwelt Martin Avdyeeich, the cobbler. He lived in a cellar, a wretched little hole with a single window. The window looked up towards the street, and through it Martin could just see the passers-by. It is true that he could see little more than their boots, but few indeed were the boots in that neighborhood which had not passed through his hands at some time or other. While Martin was still a journeyman his wife had died, but she left him a little boy. No sooner had the little one begun to grow up and be a joy to his father's heart than he too died. Then Martin grew so despairing that he began to murmur against God.

Lo! one day there came to him an aged peasant pilgrim. Martin fell a-talking with him and began to complain of his great sorrow. "As for living any longer, thou man of God," said he, "I desire it not." But the old man said to him, "Thy speech, Martin, is not good. It is because thou wouldst fain have lived for thy own delight that thou dost now despair."

"But what then *is* a man to live for?" asked Martin.

The old man answered, "For God, Martin! He gave thee

*Used by permission of the publishers, Thomas Y. Crowell Company.

194

life, and for Him therefore must thou live. When thou dost begin to live for Him, thou wilt grieve about nothing more, and all things will come easy to thee."

Martin was silent for a moment, and then he said, "And how must one live for God?"

"Christ hath shown us the way. Buy the Gospels and read. There thou wilt find out how to live for God. There everything is explained."

These words made the heart of Martin burn within him, and he went the same day and bought for himself a New Testament, printed in very large type, and began to read. He set out thinking to read it only on holidays; but as he read, it did his heart so much good that he took to reading it every day. The more he read, the more clearly he understood what God wanted of him, and how it was that he must live for God; and his heart grew lighter and lighter continually.

Henceforth the whole life of Martin was changed. Formerly, whenever he had a holiday, he would go to the tavern to drink tea nor would he say no to a drop of brandy now and again. He had done with all that now. His life became quiet and joyful. With the morning light he sat down to his work, worked all day, then took down his lamp from the hook, placed it on the table, took down his Book from the shelf and sat him down to read.

It happened once that Martin was up reading till very late. He was reading St. Luke's Gospel and so he came to that place where the rich Pharisee invites our Lord to be his guest. He read all about how the woman who was a sinner anointed his feet and washed them with her tears. And Jesus said to Simon, "Seest thou this woman? I entered into thine house; thou gavest me no water for my feet; but she has washed my feet with tears and wiped them with the hairs of her head. Thou gavest me no kiss, but this woman, since the time that I came in, hath not ceased to kiss my feet." Martin took off his glasses, laid them on the book and fell a-thinking.

"Am I not always thinking of myself like Simon? Am I not always thinking of drinking tea, and keeping myself as warm and cosy as possible, without thinking at all about the guest? Simon thought about himself, but did not give the slightest thought to his guest. But who was his guest? The Lord Himself. Suppose He were to come to me, should I receive Him as Simon did?"

Martin leaned both his elbows on the table and, without perceiving it, fell a-dozing.

"Martin!"—it was as though the voice of some one spoke close to his ear.

Martin started up from his nap. "Who's there?"

He turned around, he looked at the door, but there was no one. Again he dozed off. Suddenly he heard quite plainly, "Martin, Martin, I say! Look tomorrow into the street. I am coming."

Martin awoke, rose from his chair and began to rub his eyes. He did not know himself whether he had heard these words asleep or awake.

At dawn next day, he arose, prayed to God, lit his stove, got ready his gruel and cabbage soup, filled his samovar, put on his apron and sat him down by his window to work. There he sat and thought of nothing but the things of yesternight. He thought at one time that he must have gone off dozing and then again he thought he really must have heard that voice. He looked as much out his window as at his work, and whenever a strange pair of boots passed by, he bent forward and looked out of the window, so as to see the face as well as the feet of the passer-by. There passed close to the window an old soldier, one of Nicholas's veterans, in tattered old boots with a shovel in his hands. The old fellow was called Stepanuich, and lived with the neighboring shop keeper who gave him a home out of charity. Stepanuich stopped before Martin's window to sweep away the snow.

"I'm not growing wiser as I grow older," thought Martin, "I make up my mind that Christ is coming to me, and lo! 'tis only Stepanuich clearing away the snow." He looked through the window again, and there he saw that Stepanuich had placed the shovel against the wall, and was warming himself and taking breath a bit.

"It is quite plain that the old fellow has scarcely strength enough to scrape away the snow," thought Martin to himself, "Suppose I make him drink a little tea! The samovar is just on the boil." He put down his awl, got up, placed the samovar on the table, put some tea in it, and tapped on the window with his fingers. Stepanuich turned round and came to the window. Martin beckoned to him, and then went and opened the door.

"Come in and warm yourself," cried he. "You're a bit chilled, eh?"

"Christ reward you! Yes!" said Stepanuich. He came in, shook off the snow, and began to wipe his feet so as not to soil the floor.

"Come in and sit down," said Martin. "Here, take a cup of tea." He filled two cups and gave one to his guest, but as he drank, he could not help glancing at the window from time to time.

"Dost thou expect anyone?" asked his guest.

"Do I expect anyone? Well, honestly, I hardly know. I am expecting and I am not expecting. Whether it was a vision or no, I know not. I was reading yesterday about our little Father, Christ, how He came down upon earth, how He went to Simon the Pharisee, and Simon did not receive Him at all. But suppose,

I thought, if He came to one like me, would I receive Him? So thinking, I fell asleep. Then, little brother mine, I heard my name called. I started up. A voice was whispering at my very ear. 'Look out tomorrow,' it said, 'I am coming.' And so it befell twice. Now look! wouldst thou believe it? the idea stuck to me—I scold myself for my folly, and yet I look for Him, our little Father, Christ!"

Stepanuich shook his head and said nothing, but he drank his cup dry and put it aside. Then Martin took up the cup and filled it again. "Drink some more," he said, "'Twill do thee good. Now it seems to me that when our little Father went about on earth, He despised no one, but sought unto the simple folk most of all. Those disciples of His too, He chose most of them from amongst our brother laborers, sinners like unto us. 'He who would become the first among you,' he says, 'let him be the servant of all.'"

Stepanuich forgot his tea. He was an old man, soft-hearted and tearful. He sat and listened and the tears rolled down his cheeks. "I thank thee, Martin Avdyeeich," said he. "I fared well at thy hands, and thou hast refreshed me both in body and soul."

"Thou wilt show me a kindness by coming again," said Martin. Stepanuich departed, and Martin sat down again by the window to work. He had some back-stitching to do, but he was looking for Christ and could think of nothing but Him and His work. Two soldiers passed by, one in boots of Martin's own making. A baker with a basket also passed. Then there came alongside the window a woman in worsted stockings and roughly made shoes. Martin saw that she was a stranger, poorly clad, and that she had a little child with her. She was leaning up against the wall with her back to the wind, trying to wrap the child up, but she had nothing to wrap it in, for she wore thin, summer clothes, and thin enough they were. From his corner, Martin heard the child crying and the woman trying to comfort it, but she could not. Then he got up, went out of the door onto the steps and cried, "My good woman! My good woman!"

The woman heard him and turned round.

"Why dost thou stand out in the cold there with the child? Come inside! In the warm room thou wilt be better able to tend him. This way!"

The woman was amazed to see an old fellow in an apron, with glasses on his nose calling to her. She came towards him. They went down the steps into the room together.

"There," said Martin, "Sit down, friend, nearer to the stove, and warm and feed thy little one."

He spread the cloth on the table, got a dish, put some cabbage soup into the dish, and placed it on the table.

"Seat thyself and have something to eat," said he, "and I will sit down a little with the youngster. I have had children of my own and know how to manage them."

The woman sat down at the table and began to eat, and Martin sat down on the bed with the child. He smacked his lips at him again and again. And all the time the child never left off shrieking. Then Martin hit upon the idea of shaking his fingers at him, so he snapped his fingers up and down, backwards and forwards, and the child stared at the fingers and was silent and presently it began to laugh. Martin was delighted. The woman went on eating and told him who she was and whence she came. "I am a soldier's wife," she said. "My husband they drove away from me to the army and nothing has been heard of him since. I took a cook's place but they could not keep me and the child. It is now three months since I have been drifting about without any fixed resting place. I have eaten away my all. I am chilled to death and he is quite tired out."

"Have you no warm clothes?" asked Martin.

"Ah, kind friend, this is indeed warm-clothes time, but yesterday I sold my last shawl for a few cents."

Martin went to the wall cupboard, rummaged about a bit, and then brought back with him an old jacket.

"Look," said he, " 'tis a shabby thing, 'tis true, but it will do to wrap up in."

The woman looked at the old jacket, then she gazed at the old man, and taking the jacket, fell a-weeping. "Christ requite thee, dear little father," said she. "It is plain that it was He who sent me by thy window, and He who made thee look out of the window and have compassion on me."

Martin smiled slightly and said, "Yes, He must have done it." Then he told his dream to the soldier's wife also, and how he had heard a voice promising that Christ should come to him that day.

"All things are possible," said the woman. Then she rose up, put on the jacket, and wrapped it round her little one, and began to curtsy and thank Martin once more.

"Take this and buy back your shawl," said Martin, giving her a two grivenka piece. So the woman thanked him again and went away.

Martin sat down and worked on and on, but he did not forget the window, and whenever it was darkened, he immediately looked up to see who was passing. Soon he saw how an old woman, a huckster, had taken her stand there. She carried a basket of apples, and across one shoulder bore a sack full of shavings. She must have picked them up near some new building, and was taking them home with her. It was plain that the shavings were very heavy, so she placed the apple basket on a small post and started to shift the sack from one shoulder to the other. As she did so, an urchin in a ragged cap suddenly turned up, goodness knows from whence, grabbed at one of the apples in the basket and would have made off with it, but the wary old woman turned quickly around and gripped him by the sleeve. The lad fought and tried to tear himself loose, but the old woman seized him with both hands, knocked his hat off and tugged hard at his hair. The lad howled and the woman reviled him. Martin did not stop to put away his awl; he pitched it on the floor and rushed into the street.

"I didn't take it!" said the boy. "What are you whacking me for?"

Martin tried to part the two. He seized the lad by the arm and said: "Let him go, little mother! Forgive him for Christ's sake."

"I'll forgive him so that he shan't forget the taste of fresh birch-rods. I mean to take the rascal to the police station."

Martin began to entreat with the old woman.

"Let him go, little mother; he will not do so any more."

The old woman let him go. The lad would have bolted, but Martin held him fast.

"Beg the little mother's pardon," said he, "and don't do such

things any more. I saw thee take the apple."

Then the lad began to cry and beg pardon.

"Well, that's all right if thou art sorry! Now there's an apple for thee." Martin took one out of the basket and gave it to the boy. "I'll pay thee for it, little mother," he said to the old woman.

"Thou wilt ruin boys that way, the black-guards," grumbled the woman. "If I had the rewarding of him, he should not be able to set down for a week!"

"Oh, little mother, little mother," cried Martin, "that is one way of looking at things but it is not God's way. God bade us forgive if we would be forgiven."

The old woman shook her head and sighed. "Boys will be boys, I suppose. Well, God be with him," she said.

But just as she was about to hoist the sack again on to her shoulder, the lad rushed forward and said:

"Give it here, and I'll carry it for thee, granny! It's all in my way."

The old woman shook her head, but she did put the sack on the lad's shoulder. And so they trudged down the street together, side by side. Martin followed them with his eyes till they were out of sight, then he went in and sat down to work again. Soon it grew dark; he was scarcely able to see the stitches, and the lamp-lighter came by to light the street lamps. So Martin put away his tools, swept up the cuttings, placed the lamp on the table, and took down the Gospels from the shelf. He wanted to find the passage where he had last evening placed a strip of morocco leather by way of a marker. But just as he opened the book, he recollected his dream of yesterday evening.

No sooner did he call it to mind than it seemed to him as if some persons were moving about and shuffling with their feet behind him. He looked round and saw—yes someone was really there, but who he could not exactly make out. Then a voice whispered in his ear, "Martin, Martin, does thou not know me?"

"Who are thou?" cried Martin.

"'Tis I," cried the voice, "lo, 'tis I!" And forth from the dark corner stepped Stepanuich. He smiled; it was as though a little cloud was breaking and he was gone.

 "It is I!" cried the voice again, and forth from the corner stepped a woman with a little child. The woman smiled, the child laughed, and they also disappeared.

"And it is I!" cried the voice. The old woman and the lad with the apple stepped forth. Both of them smiled and they also disappeared.

The heart of Martin was glad; he began to read the Gospels at the place where he had opened them. And at the top of the page he read these words:

"I was an-hungered and thirsty and ye gave Me to drink. I was a stranger and ye took Me in." At the bottom of the page he read further.

"Inasmuch as ye have done it to the least of these, My brethren, ye have done it unto Me."

And Martin understood that his dream had not deceived him, and that the Saviour had really come to him that day and he had really received Him.

THE KNIGHTS OF THE SILVER SHIELD*
Raymond MacDonald Alden

THERE was once a splendid castle in a forest, with great stone walls and a high gateway, and turrets that rose away above the tallest trees. The forest was dark and dangerous, and many cruel giants lived in it; but in the castle was a company of knights, who were kept there by the king of the country, to help travelers who might be in the forest, and to fight with the giants.

Each of these knights wore a beautiful suit of armor and carried a long spear, while over his helmet there floated a great red plume that could be seen a long way off by any one in distress. But the most wonderful thing about the knights' armor was their shields. They were not like those of other knights, but had been made by a great magician who had lived in the castle many years before. They were made of silver, and sometimes shone in the sunlight with dazzling brightness; but at other times the surface of the shields would be clouded as though by a mist, and one could not see his face reflected there.

Now, when each young knight received his spurs and his armor, a new shield was also given him from among those that the magician had made; and when the shield was new its surface was always cloudy and dull. But as the knight began to do service against the giants, or went on expeditions to help poor travelers in the forest, his shield grew brighter and brighter, so that he could see his face clearly reflected in it. But if he proved to be a lazy or cowardly knight, and let the giants get the better of him, or did not care what became of the travelers, then the shield grew more and more cloudy, until the knight became ashamed to carry it.

But this was not all. When any one of the knights fought a particularly hard battle, and won the victory, or when he went on some hard errand for the lord of the castle, and was successful, not only did his silver shield grow brighter, but when one looked into the center of it he could see something like a golden star shining in its very heart. This was the greatest honor that a knight could achieve, and the other knights always spoke of such a one as having "won his star." It was usually not till he was pretty old and tried as a soldier that he could win it. At the time when this story begins, the lord of the castle himself was the only one of the knights whose shield bore the golden star.

There came a time when the worst of the giants in the forest gathered themselves together to have a battle against the knights. They made a camp in a dark hollow not far from the castle, and gathered all their best warriors together, and all the knights made ready to fight them. The windows of the castle were closed and barred; the air was full of the noise of armor; and the knights were so excited that they could scarcely rest or eat.

Now there was a young knight in the castle, named Sir Roland, who was among those most eager for the battle. He was a splendid warrior, with eyes that shone like stars whenever there was anything to do in the way of knightly deeds. And although he was still quite young, his shield had begun to shine enough to show plainly that he had done bravely in some of his errands through the forest. This battle, he thought, would be the great opportunity of his life. And on the morning of the day when they were to go forth to it, and all the knights assembled in the great hall of the castle to receive the commands of their leaders, Sir Roland hoped that he would be put in the most dangerous place of all, so that he could show what knightly stuff he was made of. But when the lord of the castle came to him as he went about in full armor giving his commands, he said: "One brave knight must stay behind and guard the gateway of the castle, and it is you, Sir Roland, being one of the youngest, whom I have chosen for this."

At these words Sir Roland was so disappointed that he bit his lip, and closed his helmet over his face so that the other knights might not see it. For a moment he felt as if he must reply angrily to the commander, and tell him that it was not right to leave so sturdy a knight behind, when he was eager to fight. But he struggled against this feeling, and went quietly to look after his duties at the gate. The gateway was high and narrow, and was reached from outside by a high, narrow bridge that crossed the moat, which surrounded the castle on every side. When an enemy approached, the knight on guard rang a great bell just inside the gate, and the bridge was drawn up against the castle wall, so that no one could come across the moat. So the giants had long ago given up trying to attack the castle itself.

Today the battle was to be in the dark hollow in the forest, and it was not likely that there would be anything to do at the castle gate, except to watch it like a common doorkeeper. It was not strange that Sir Roland thought some one else might have done this.

Presently all the other knights marched out in their flashing armor, their red plumes waving over their heads, and their spears in their hands. The lord of the castle stopped only to tell Sir Roland to keep guard over the gate until they had all returned, and to let no one enter. Then they went into the shadows of the forest, and were soon lost to sight.

Sir Roland stood looking after them long after they had gone, thinking how happy he would be if he were on the way to the battle like them. But after a little he put this out of his mind, and tried to think of pleasanter things. It was a long time before anything happened, or any word came from the battle.

THE TREASURE CHEST

At last Sir Roland saw one of the knights come limping down the path to the castle, and he went out on the bridge to meet him. Now this knight was not a brave one, and he had been frightened away as soon as he was wounded.

"I have been hurt," he said, "so that I can not fight any more. But I could watch the gate for you, if you would like to go back in my place."

At first Sir Roland's heart leaped with joy, but then he remembered what the commander had told him, and he said:

"I should like to go, but a knight belongs where his commander has put him. My place is here at the gate, and I can not open it even for you. Your place is at the battle."

The knight was ashamed when he heard this, and he presently turned about and went into the forest again.

So Sir Roland kept guard silently for another hour. Then there came an old beggar woman down the path to the castle, and asked Sir Roland if she might come in and have some food. He told her that no one could enter the castle that day, but that he would send a servant out to her with food, and that she might sit and rest as long as she would.

"I have been past the hollow in the forest where the battle is going on," said the old woman, while she was waiting.

"And how do you think it is going?" asked Sir Roland.

"Badly for the knights, I am afraid," said the old woman. "The giants are fighting as they have never fought before. I should think you had better go and help your friends."

"I should like to, indeed," said Sir Roland. "But I am set to guard the gateway of the castle, and can not leave."

"One fresh knight would make a great difference when they are all weary with fighting," said the old woman. "I should think that, while there are no enemies about, you would be much more useful there."

"You may well think so," said Sir Roland, "and so may I; but it is neither you nor I that is commander here."

"I suppose," said the old woman then, "that you are one of the kind of knights who like to keep out of fighting. You are lucky to have so good an excuse for staying at home." And she laughed a thin and taunting laugh.

Then Sir Roland was very angry, and thought that if it were only a man instead of a woman, he would show him whether he liked fighting or no. But as it was a woman, he shut his lips and set his teeth hard together, and as the servant came just then with the food he had sent for, he gave it to the old woman quickly, and shut the gate that she might not talk to him any more.

It was not very long before he heard some one calling outside. Sir Roland opened the gate, and saw standing at the other end of the drawbridge a little old man in a long cloak. "Why are you knocking here?" he said. "The castle is closed today?"

"Are you Sir Roland?" said the little old man.

"Yes," said Sir Roland.

"Then you ought not to be staying here when your commander and his knights are having so hard a struggle with the giants, and when you have the chance to make yourself the greatest knight in this kingdom. Listen to me! I have brought you a magic sword."

As he said this, the old man drew from under his coat a wonderful sword that flashed in the sunlight as if it were covered with diamonds. "This is the sword of all swords," he said, "and it is for you, if you will leave your idling here by the castle gate, and carry it to the battle. Nothing can stand before it. When you lift it the giants will fall back, your master will be saved, and you will be crowned the victorious knight—the one who will soon take his commander's place as lord of the castle."

Now Sir Roland believed that it was a magician who was speaking to him, for it certainly appeared to be a magic sword. It seemed so wonderful that the sword should be brought to him, that he reached out his hand as though he would take it, and the little old man came forward, as though he would cross the drawbridge into the castle. But as he did so, it came to Sir Roland's mind again that that bridge and the gateway had been intrusted to him, and he called out "No!" to the old man,

so that he stopped where he was standing. But he waved the shining sword in the air again, and said: "It is for you! Take it, and win the victory!"

Sir Roland was really afraid that if he looked any longer at the sword, or listened to any more words of the old man, he would not be able to hold himself within the castle. For this reason he struck the great bell at the gateway, which was the signal for the servants inside to pull in the chains of the drawbridge, and instantly they began to pull, and the drawbridge came up, so that the old man could not cross it to enter the castle, nor Sir Roland to go out.

Then, as he looked across the moat, Sir Roland saw a wonderful thing. The little old man threw off his black cloak, and as he did so he began to grow bigger and bigger, until in a minute more he was a giant as tall as any in the forest. At first Sir Roland could scarcely believe his eyes. Then he realized that this must be one of their giant enemies, who had changed himself to a little old man through some magic power, that he might make his way into the castle while all the knights were away. Sir Roland shuddered to think what might have happened if he had taken the sword and left the gate unguarded. The giant shook his fist across the moat that lay between them, and then, knowing that he could do nothing more, he went angrily back into the forest.

Sir Roland now resolved not to open the gate again, and to pay no attention to any other visitor. But it was not long before he heard a sound that made him spring forward in joy. It was the bugle of the lord of the castle, and there came sounding after it the bugles of many of the knights that were with him, pealing so joyfully that Sir Roland was sure they were safe and happy. As they came nearer, he could hear their shouts of victory. So he gave the signal to let down the drawbridge again, and went out to meet them. They were dusty and bloodstained and weary, but they had won the battle with the giants; and it had been such a great victory that there had never been a happier home-coming.

Sir Roland greeted them all as they passed in over the bridge and then, when he had closed the gate and fastened it, he followed them into the great hall of the castle. The lord of the castle took his place on the highest seat, with the other knights about him, and Sir Roland came forward with the key of the gate, to give his account of what he had done in the place to

THE TREASURE CHEST

which the commander had appointed him. The lord of the castle bowed to him as a sign for him to begin, and just as he opened his mouth to speak, one of the knights cried out:

"The shield! the shield! Sir Roland's shield!"

Every one turned and looked at the shield which Sir Roland carried on his left arm. He himself could see only the top of it, and did not know what they could mean. But what they saw was the golden star of knighthood, shining brightly from the center of Sir Roland's shield. There had never been such amazement in the castle before.

Sir Roland knelt before the lord of the castle to receive his commands. He still did not know why every one was looking at him so excitedly.

"Speak, Sir Knight," said the commander, as soon as he could find his voice after his surprise, "and tell us all that has happened today at the castle. Have you been attacked? Have any giants come hither? Did you fight them alone?"

"No, my Lord," said Sir Roland. "Only one giant has been here, and he went away silently when he found he could not enter."

Then he told all that had happened through the day.

When he had finished, the knights all looked at one another, but no one spoke a word. Then they looked again at Sir Roland's shield, to make sure that their eyes had not deceived them, and there the golden star was still shining.

After a little silence the lord of the castle spoke.

"Men make mistakes," he said, "but our silver shields are never mistaken. Sir Roland has fought and won the hardest battle of all today."

Then the others all rose and saluted Sir Roland, who was the youngest knight that ever carried the golden star.

MEG MERRILIES
John Keats

Old Meg she was a gipsy,
   And lived upon the moors;
Her bed it was the brown heath turf,
   And her house was out of doors.

Her apples were swart blackberries,
   Her currants pods o' broom;
Her wine was dew of the wild white rose,
   Her book a churchyard tomb.

Her brothers were the craggy hills,
   Her sisters larchen-trees;
Alone with her great family
   She lived as she did please.

No breakfast had she many a morn,
   No dinner many a noon,
And 'stead of supper she would stare
   Full hard against the moon.

And with her fingers old and brown
   She plaited mats of rushes,
And gave them to the cottagers
   She met among the bushes.

Old Meg was brave as Margaret Queen,
   And tall as Amazon;
An old red blanket cloak she wore,
   A ship-hat had she on;
God rest her aged bones somewhere!
   She died full long agone!

MAGGIE TULLIVER GOES TO LIVE
WITH THE GYPSIES*
George Eliot

A WIDE plain where the broadening Floss hurries on between its green banks to the sea, and the loving tide rushing to meet it, checks its passage with an impetuous embrace. On this mighty tide the black ships are borne along to the town of St. Ogg's which shows its aged, fluted red roofs and the broad gables of its wharves between the low wooded hill and the river brink. Far away on each hand stretch the rich pastures and the patches of dark earth made ready for the seed. Just by the red-roofed town the tributary Ripple flows with a lively current into the Floss. And here is Dorlcote Mill with its trimly kept, comfortable dwelling house, as old as the elms and chestnuts that shelter it from the northern blast. The rush of the water and the booming of the mill bring a dreamy deafness which seems to heighten the peacefulness of the scene. And now there is the thunder of the huge covered wagon coming home with sacks of grain. That little girl who has stood so long on just the same spot at the edge of the stream is watching the unresting wheel sending out its diamond jets of water. And that queer white cur with the brown ear seems to be leaping and barking at the wheel; perhaps he is jealous because his playfellow is so rapt in its movement. It is time the little playfellow went in and there is a very bright fire to tempt her; the red light shines out from the left hand parlor where Mr. and Mrs. Tulliver are talking.

*Arranged from *The Mill on the Floss.*

213

"It seems a bit of a pity," said Mr. Tulliver, "as the lad should take after the mother's side i'stead o' the little wench. The little un's twice as cute as Tom."

"Yes," said Mrs. Tulliver, "but her cuteness all runs to naughtiness. How to keep her in a clean pinafore two hours together passes my cunning. An' now you put me in mind," she continued, rising and going to the window, "I don't know where she is now, an' it's pretty nigh tea time. Ah, I thought so,—wanderin' up an' down by the water like a wild thing; she'll tumble in some day."

Mrs. Tulliver rapped the window sharply, beckoned, and shook her head,—a process which she repeated more than once before she returned to her chair.

"You talk o' cuteness, Mr. Tulliver," she observed as she sat down, "but I'm sure the child's half an idiot i' some things; for if I send her upstairs to fetch anything, she forgets what she's gone for, an' perhaps 'ull sit down on the floor i' the sunshine an' plait her hair an' sing to herself like a bedlam creatur' all the while I'm waiting for her down stairs. That niver run i' my family, thank God! no more nor a brown skin as makes her look like a mulatter!"

"Pooh, nonsense!" said Mr. Tulliver, "she's a straight, black-eyed wench as anybody need wish to see. I don't know i' what she's behind other folks's children; and she can read almost as well as the parson."

"But her hair won't curl all I can do with it, and she's so franzy about having it put i' paper, and I've such work as never was to make her stand and have it pinched with th' irons."

"Cut it off—cut if off short," said the father rashly.

"How can you talk so, Mr. Tulliver? She's too big a gell—gone nine and tall of her age—to have her hair cut short; an' there's her cousin Lucy's got a row o' curls round her head, an' not

a hair out o' place. It seems hard as my sister Deane should have
that pretty child. I'm sure Lucy takes more after me nor my own
child does. Maggie, Maggie," continued the mother in a tone of
half coaxing fretfulness, as Maggie entered the room, "where's the
use o' my telling you to keep away from the water? You'll
tumble in and be drownded some day an' then you'll be sorry
you didn't do as mother told you."

Maggie's hair, as she threw off her bonnet, painfully confirmed
her mother's accusation. Mrs. Tulliver, desiring her daughter
to have a curled crop, "like other folks's children," had had it
cut too short in front to be pushed behind the ears; and as it was
usually straight an hour after it had been taken out of paper,
Maggie was incessantly tossing her head to keep the dark heavy
locks out of her gleaming black eyes,—an action which gave her
very much the air of a small Shetland pony.

"Oh dear, oh dear, Maggie, what are you thinkin' of, to
throw your bonnet down there? Take it upstairs, there's a good
gell, an' let your hair be brushed, an' put your other pinafore on,
an' change your shoes, do, for shame, an' come an' go on with your
patchwork like a little lady."

"Oh, mother," said Maggie in a vehemently cross tone, "I
don't *want* to do my patchwork."

"What! not your pretty patchwork, to make a counterpane
for your aunt Glegg?"

"It's foolish work," said Maggie with a toss of her mane—
"tearing things to pieces to sew 'em together again. And I don't,
want to do anything for my aunt Glegg. I don't like her."

And Maggie went out, dragging her bonnet by the string,
while Mr. Tulliver laughed audibly.

"I wonder at you, as you'll laugh at her, Mr. Tulliver," said
the mother with feeble fretfulness in her tone. "You encourage
her i' naughtiness. An' her aunts will have it as it's me spoils her."

Few wives were more submissive than Mrs. Tulliver on all points unconnected with her family relations; but she had been a Miss Dodson, and the Dodsons were a very respectable family indeed,—as much looked up to as any in their own parish or the next to it. The Miss Dodsons had always been taught to hold up their heads very high. There were particular ways of doing everything in that family; particular ways of bleaching the linen, of making the cowslip wine, curing the hams and keeping the bottled gooseberries; so that no daughter of that house could be indifferent to the privilege of having been born a Dodson, rather than a Gibson or a Watson. And it is remarkable that while each individual Dodson was forever finding fault with every other individual Dodson, each was satisfied, not only with him or her self, but with the Dodsons as a whole. Mrs. Tulliver was a thorough Dodson. True, she had groaned a little in her youth under the yoke of her elder sisters, and still shed occasional tears at the disagreeable truths they never shrank from telling her, but she had no mind to let her husband or children fail in full respect to Aunt Glegg or any other member of the Dodson family. Now Tom was thought to be somewhat like the Dodsons,—he had light brown hair, cheeks of cream and roses, full lips and a nose and eyebrows expressing nothing in particular, a face as different as possible from poor Maggie's, which Nature seemed to have moulded and colored with the most decided intention. Mrs. Tulliver was thankful to have one child who took after her own family, at least in his features and complexion, but Tom was as far from appreciating his kin on his mother's side as Maggie herself, generally running away for the day with a large supply of the most portable food, when he received timely warning that his aunts and uncles were coming,—a moral symptom from which Aunt Glegg argued the gloomiest views for his future.

"My children are so awkward wi' their aunts and uncles,"

Mrs. Tulliver would sigh, "Maggie's ten times naughtier when they come than she is other days, and Tom doesn't like 'em. And there's Lucy Deane's such a good child,—you may set her on a stool and there she'll sit for an hour together, and never offer to get off."

It was Easter week and Mrs. Tulliver found it advisable to invite sister Glegg, sister Pullet and sister Deane to dinner to consult with them on important matters. On Wednesday, the day before the aunts and uncles were coming, there were such various and suggestive  scents as of plum cake in the oven and jellies in the hot state, mingled with the aroma of gravy, that it was impossible to feel altogether gloomy. Tom and Maggie made several inroads into the kitchen, and like other marauders, were induced to keep aloof for a time only by being allowed to carry away a sufficient load of booty.

"Tom," said Maggie, as they sat on the boughs of the elder-tree, eating their jam-puffs, "shall you run away tomorrow?"

"No," said Tom, slowly, when he had finished his puff, and was eyeing the third which was to be divided between them,—"no, I sha'n't."

"Why, Tom? Because Lucy's coming?"

"No," said Tom, opening his pocket-knife and holding it over the puff with his head on one side in an uncertain manner. (It was a difficult problem to divide that very irregular polygon into two equal parts.) "What do I care about Lucy? She's only a girl,—she can't play at bandy."

"Is it the tipsy cake, then?" said Maggie, while she leaned forward towards Tom with her eye fixed on the hovering knife.

"No, you silly, that'll be good the day after. It's the pudden. I know what the pudden's to be,—apricot roll-up. O my buttons!"

With this interjection the knife descended on the puff and it was in two, but the result was not satisfactory to Tom, for he still eyed the halves doubtfully—one was decidedly better than the other.

"Shut your eyes, Maggie."

"What for?"

"You never mind what for. Shut 'em when I tell you."

Maggie obeyed.

"Now which'll you have, Maggie,—right or left?"

"I'll have that with the jam run out," said Maggie, keeping her eyes shut to please Tom.

"Why, you don't like that, you silly. You may have it if it comes to you fair, but I shan't give it you without. Right or left,—choose now. Ha!" said Tom in a tone of exasperation as Maggie peeped. "You keep your eyes shut else you sha'n't have any."

Maggie would gladly have given up the best piece to Tom, but her power of sacrifice did not extend so far as to go without any, so she shut her eyes quite close till Tom told her to "say which," and then she said, "Left hand."

"You've got it," said Tom in rather a bitter tone.

"What! the bit with the jam run out?"

"No; here take it," said Tom, firmly handing the best piece to Maggie.

"Oh, please, Tom, have it; I don't mind—I like the other; please take this."

"No, I shan't," said Tom crossly, beginning on his own piece.

Maggie, thinking it was no use to contend further, began too, and ate up her half puff with considerable relish as well as rapidity. But Tom had finished first and had to look on while Maggie ate her last morsel or two, feeling in himself a capacity for more.

"Oh, you greedy thing," said Tom when she had finished the last morsel. He was conscious of having acted very fairly, and thought she ought to have considered this and made up to him for it. He would have refused a bit of hers beforehand, but one has naturally a different point of view before and after one's own share of puff is swallowed.

Maggie turned quite pale. She loved Tom with all the strength of her warm, impetuous nature and could not bear to have him think ill of her. "Oh, Tom," she cried, "why didn't you ask me?"

"I wasn't going to ask you, you greedy. You might have thought of it without, when I gave you the best bit."

"But I wanted you to have it; you know I did," said Maggie.

"Yes, but I wasn't going to do what wasn't fair. If I go halves, I'll go 'em fair; only I wouldn't be a greedy."

With this cutting remark, Tom jumped down from his bough and walked off, throwing a stone with a "hoigh!" as a friendly attention to Yap, the dog, who had also been looking on while the eatables vanished with an agitation of the ears and feelings which could hardly have been without bitterness. Yet the excellent dog accepted Tom's attention with as much alacrity as if he had been treated quite generously.

But Maggie sat still on her bough and gave herself up to the keen sense of unmerited reproach. She would have given the world not to have eaten all her puff, and to have saved some of it for Tom. She would have gone without it many times over, sooner than Tom should call her greedy and be cross with her. And he had said he wouldn't have it, and she ate it without thinking; how could she help it? The tears flowed so plentifully that Maggie saw nothing around her for the next ten minutes; but by that time resentment began to give way to the desire for reconciliation, and she jumped from her bough to look for Tom.

The next day the Dodsons arrived, one and all, at Dorlcote Mill. Aunt and Uncle Glegg came first, Aunt Glegg in her severe bonnet and slate colored gown with a mouldy odor about it suggestive of a damp clothes chest. Then came Aunt and Uncle Pullet in a one-horse chaise. Mr. Pullet was a small man with a high nose, small twinkling eyes and thin lips, who bore about the same relation to his tall good-looking wife with her balloon sleeves, abundant mantle, and large be-feathered and be-ribboned bonnet as a small fishing smack bears to a brig with all its sails spread. Lastly, appeared Mr. and Mrs. Deane with little Lucy, and Mrs. Tulliver had to look on with a silent pang while Lucy's blond curls were adjusted. Maggie always looked twice as dark as usual when she was by the side of Lucy.

She did today when she and Tom came in from the garden with their father and their uncle Glegg. Maggie had thrown her bonnet off very carelessly, and, coming in with her hair rough as well as out of curl, rushed at once to Lucy who was standing by her mother's knee. Certainly the contrast between the cousins was conspicuous; it was like the contrast between a rough, dark, over-grown puppy and a white kitten. Lucy put up the neatest little rosebud mouth to be kissed; everything about her was neat—her little round neck with the row of coral beads; her little straight nose, not at all snubby; her little clear eyebrows rather darker than her curls to match her hazel eyes which looked up with shy pleasure at Maggie, taller by the head, though scarcely more than a year older. Maggie always looked at Lucy with delight. She was fond of fancying a world where the people never grew any larger than children of their own age, and she made the queen of it just like Lucy, with a little crown on her head and a little sceptre in her hand—only the queen was Maggie herself in Lucy's form.

"Oh, Lucy," she burst out, after kissing her, "you'll stay with Tom and me, won't you? Oh, kiss her, Tom."

Tom, too, had come up to Lucy, but he was not going to kiss her—no; he came up to her with Maggie because it seemed easier on the whole than saying, "How do you do?" to all those aunts and uncles. He stood looking at nothing in particular with the blushing, awkward air and semi-smile which are common to shy boys when in company.

"Heyday!" said Aunt Glegg with loud emphasis. "Do little boys and gells come into a room without taking notice o'their uncles and aunts? That wasn't the way when I was a little gell."

"Go and speak to your aunts and uncles, my dears," said Mrs. Tulliver looking anxious. She wanted to whisper a command to Maggie to go and have her hair brushed.

"Well, and how do you do? And I hope you're good children, are you?" said Aunt Glegg, in the same loud emphatic way as she shook their hands, hurting them with her large rings, and kissing their cheeks much against their desire. "Look up, Tom, look up. Boys as go to boarding schools should hold their heads up. Look at me now." Tom declined the pleasure apparently, for he tried to draw his hand away. "Put your hair behind your ears, Maggie, and keep your frock on your shoulder."

Aunt Glegg always spoke to them in this loud, emphatic way, as if she considered them deaf, or perhaps rather idiotic; it was a means, she thought, of making them feel that they were accountable creatures, and might be a salutary check on naughty tendencies. Bessy's children were so spoiled—they'd need have somebody to make them feel their duty.

"Well, my dear," said aunt Pullet in a compassionate voice, "you grow wonderful fast. I think the gell has too much hair. I'd have it thinned and cut shorter if I was you; it isn't good for her health. It's that as makes her skin so brown, I shouldn't wonder. Don't you think so, sister Deane?"

"I can't say, I'm sure, sister," said Mrs. Deane, shutting her lips close again and looking at Maggie with a critical eye.

"No, no!" said Mr. Tulliver, "the child's healthy enough; there's nothing ails her. But it 'ud be as well if Bessy 'ud have her hair cut so as it 'ud lie smooth."

A dreadful resolve was gathering in Maggie's breast, but it was arrested by the desire to know from her aunt Deane whether she would leave Lucy behind. Aunt Deane would hardly ever let Lucy come to see them. After various reasons for refusal, Mrs. Deane appealed to Lucy herself.

"You wouldn't like to stay without mother, should you, Lucy?"

"Yes, please, mother," said Lucy timidly, blushing very pink all over her little neck.

"Well done, Lucy! Let her stay, Mrs. Deane, let her stay," said Mr. Deane.

"Maggie," said Mrs. Tulliver, beckoning Maggie to her and whispering in her ear as soon as this point of Lucy's staying was settled, "go and get your hair brushed, do, for shame. I told you not to come in without going to Martha first; you know I did."

"Tom, come out with me," whispered Maggie, pulling his sleeve as she pushed him, and Tom followed willingly enough.

"Come upstairs with me, Tom," she whispered when they were outside the door. "There's something I want to do before dinner."

"There's no time to play at anything before dinner," said Tom.

"Oh, yes, there is time for this; come, Tom."

Tom followed Maggie upstairs and saw her go at once to

a drawer, from which she took out a large pair of scissors.

"What are they for, Maggie?" said Tom, feeling his curiosity awakened.

Maggie answered by seizing her front locks and cutting them straight across the middle of her forehead.

"Oh, my buttons! Maggie, you'll catch it!" exclaimed Tom; "you'd better not cut any more off."

Snip! went the great scissors again while Tom was speaking, and he couldn't help feeling it was rather good fun; Maggie would look so queer.

"Here, Tom, cut it behind for me," said Maggie, excited by her own daring and anxious to finish the deed.

"You'll catch it, you know," said Tom, nodding his head in an admonitory manner, and hesitating a little as he took the scissors.

"Never mind, make haste!" said Maggie, giving a little stamp with her foot. Her cheeks were quite flushed.

The black locks were so thick, nothing could be more tempting to a lad who had already tasted the forbidden pleasure of cutting the pony's mane. One delicious grinding snip and then another and another, and the hinder-locks fell heavily on the floor, and Maggie stood cropped in a jagged uneven manner but with a sense of clearness and freedom as if she had emerged from a wood into the open plain.

"Oh, Maggie," said Tom, jumping around her, and slapping his knees as he laughed, "Oh, my buttons! what a queer thing you look! Look at yourself in the glass; you look like the idiot we throw out nut-shells to at school."

Maggie felt an unexpected pang. She had thought beforehand chiefly of her own deliverance from her teasing hair and teasing remarks about it, and something also of the triumph she would have over her mother and her aunts by this very de-

cided course of action. But now, when Tom began to laugh at her and say she was like the idiot, the affair had quite a new aspect. She looked in the glass and still Tom laughed and clapped his hands, and Maggie's flushed cheeks began to pale and her lips to tremble a little.

"Oh, Maggie, you'll have to go down to dinner directly," said Tom. "Oh, my!"

"Don't laugh at me, Tom," said Maggie with an outburst of angry tears, stamping and giving him a push.

"Now, then, spitfire," said Tom. "What did you cut it off for then? I shall go down. I can smell the dinner going in."

He hurried down stairs and left poor Maggie to bitterness. She could see clearly enough now the thing was done, that it was very foolish, and that she should have to hear and think more about her hair than ever, for Maggie rushed to her deeds with passionate impulse and then saw their consequences afterward. Tom never did the same sort of foolish things as Maggie, having a wonderful instinctive discernment beforehand of what would turn to his advantage or disadvantage; and so it happened that, though he was much more wilful and inflexible than Maggie, his mother hardly ever called him naughty. But if Tom ever did make a mistake of that sort he stood by it. If he broke the lash of his father's gig-whip by lashing the gate, he couldn't help it,—the whip shouldn't have got caught in the hinge. He was convinced, not that the whipping of gates by all boys was a justifiable act, but that he, Tom Tulliver, was justifiable in whipping that particular gate, whereas Maggie was always being sorry and wishing she had done something different.

As she stood crying before the glass, Maggie felt it impossible that she should go down to dinner and endure the severe eyes and severe words of her aunts; and if she had only let her hair alone, she could have sat with Tom and Lucy, and had the apricot pudding and the custard! What could she do but sob?

"Maggie," said Tom, peeping into the room ten minutes after, "why don't you come and have your dinner? There's lots o' goodies and mother says you're to come. What are you crying for, you little spooney?"

Oh, it was dreadful! Tom was so hard and unconcerned; If *he* had been crying on the floor, Maggie would have cried too. And there was the dinner, so nice; and she was *so* hungry. It was very bitter. But Tom was not altogether hard; he was not inclined to cry and did not feel that Maggie's grief spoiled his prospect of the sweets; but he went and put his head near her and said in a lower comforting tone,—

"Won't you come then Maggie? Shall I bring you a bit o' pudding when I've had mine, and a custard and things?"

"Ye-e-es," said Maggie, beginning to feel life a little more tolerable.

"Very well," said Tom, going away. But he turned again at the door and said, "But you'd better come, you know. There's the dessert,—nuts, you know, and cowslip wine."

Maggie's tears had ceased and she looked reflective as Tom left her. His good-nature had taken off the keenest edge of her suffering and nuts with cowslip wine began to assert their legitimate influence.

Slowly she rose from her scattered locks, and slowly she made her way down-stairs. Then she stood with one shoulder against the frame of the dining parlor door, peeping in when it was ajar. She saw Tom and Lucy with an empty chair between them, and there were the custards on a side table; it was too much. She slipped in and went towards the empty chair. But she had no sooner sat down than she repented and wished herself back again.

Mrs. Tulliver gave a little scream as she saw her and dropped the large gravy spoon into the dish with the most serious results to the table-cloth. Mrs. Tulliver's scream made all eyes turn towards the same point as her own, and Maggie's cheeks and ears began to burn, while uncle Glegg, a kind-looking, white-haired old gentleman, said:

"Heyday! what little gell's this? Why I don't know her. Is it some little gell you've picked up in the road?"

"Why, she's gone and cut her hair herself," laughed Mr. Tulliver in an undertone to Mr. Deane.

"Why, little miss, you've made yourself look very funny," said Uncle Pullet and perhaps he never in his life made a remark which was felt to be more cutting.

"Fie, for shame!" said Aunt Glegg in her loudest, severest tone of reproof. "Little gells as cut their own hair should be whipped and fed on bread and water,—not come and sit down with their aunts and uncles."

"Ay, ay," said Uncle Glegg, meaning to give a playful turn to this denunciation, "she must be sent to jail I think, and they'll cut the rest of her hair off there, and make it all even."

"She's more like a gipsy nor ever," said Aunt Pullet in a pitying tone.

"She's a naughty child, as 'll break her mother's heart," said Mrs. Tulliver with the tears in her eyes.

Maggie seemed to be listening to a chorus of reproach and derision. Her first flush came from anger, which gave her a

momentary power of defiance. "Oh, my! Maggie, I told you you'd catch it," whispered Tom. He meant to be friendly, but Maggie felt convinced that Tom was rejoicing in her shame. Her feeble power of defiance left her in an instant, her heart swelled, and getting up from her chair, she ran to her father, hid her face on his shoulder, and burst out into loud sobbing.

"Come, come, my wench," said her father soothingly putting his arm round her, "never mind; you was i' the right to cut it off if it plagued you; give over crying; father'll take your part."

Delicious words of tenderness! Maggie never forgot any of these moments when her father "took her part."

"How your husband does spoil that child, Bessy!" said Mrs. Glegg in a loud "aside" to Mrs. Tulliver. "It'll be the ruin of her if you don't take care. *My* father never brought his children up so, else we should ha' been a different family to what we are."

Mrs. Tulliver's sorrows seemed at this moment to have reached the point where she could feel no more. She took no notice of her sister's remark, but threw back her cap-strings and carved the pudding in mute resignation.

With the dessert, there came entire deliverance for Maggie, for the children were told they might have their nuts and wine in the summer house, since the day was so mild; and they scampered out among the budding bushes of the garden with the alacrity of small animals getting from under a burning-glass.

That night all the uncles and aunts departed, leaving Lucy Deane behind, but the next day, Mrs. Tulliver was to take the children to sister Pullet's at Garum Firs for tea. The day began ill with Maggie. The pleasure of having Lucy to look at, and the prospect of the afternoon visit at Garum Firs, where she would hear Uncle Pullet's musical box, had been marred as early as eleven o'clock by the advent of the hair dresser from St. Ogg's, who had spoken in the severest terms of the condition in which he had found her hair, holding up one jagged lock after another and saying, "See here! tut, tut, tut," in a tone of mingled disgust and pity, which to Maggie's imagination was equal to the strongest expression of public opinion.

Already at twelve o'clock Mrs. Tulliver had on her visiting costume, with a protective covering of brown holland; Maggie was frowning and twisting her shoulders, that she might if possible shrink away from the prickliest of tuckers, while her mother was remonstrating, "Don't, Maggie, my dear; don't make yourself so ugly!" and Tom's cheeks were looking particularly brilliant as a relief to his best blue suit which he wore with becoming calmness.

As for Lucy, she was just as pretty and neat as she had been yesterday; no accidents ever happened to her clothes, and she was never uncomfortable in them, so that she looked with wondering pity at Maggie, pouting and writhing under the exasperating tucker. Maggie would certainly have torn it off, if she had not been checked by the memory of her recent humiliation about her hair; as it was she confined herself to fretting and twisting and behaving peevishly about the card-houses which they were allowed to build till dinner as a suitable amusement for boys and girls in their best clothes. Tom could build perfect pyramids of houses, but Maggie's would never bear the laying on of the roof. It was always so with the things that Maggie made, and Tom had concluded that no girls could ever make anything. But it happened that Lucy proved wonderfully clever at building; she handled the cards so lightly and moved so gently that Tom condescended to admire her houses as well as his own, the more readily because she had asked him to teach her. Maggie, too, would have admired Lucy's houses and would have given up her own unsuccessful building to contemplate them without ill-temper if her tucker had not made her peevish, and if Tom had not inconsiderately laughed when her houses fell and told her she was "a stupid."

"Don't laugh at me, Tom," she burst out angrily; "I'm not a stupid. I know a great many things you don't."

"Oh, I daresay, Miss Spitfire! I'd never be such a cross thing as you, making faces like that. Lucy doesn't do so. I like Lucy better than you. I wish Lucy was *my* sister."

"Then it is very wicked and cruel of you to wish so," said Maggie, starting up hurriedly from her place on the floor and up-setting Tom's wonderful pagoda. She really did not mean to do it, but the evidence was against her, and Tom turned white with anger but said nothing; he would have struck her, only he knew it was cowardly to strike a girl and Tom Tulliver was quite de-termined he would never do anything cowardly.

Maggie stood in dismay and terror while Tom got up from the floor and walked away, pale, from the scattered ruins of his pagoda, and Lucy looked on mutely like a kitten pausing from its lapping.

"Oh, Tom," said Maggie at last, going half way towards him, "I didn't mean to knock it down, indeed, indeed I didn't."

Tom took no notice of her, but took, instead, two or three hard peas out of his pocket, and shot them with his thumb-nail against the window, vaguely at first, but presently with the distinct aim of hitting an aged fly which was buzzing about in the sunshine.

Thus the morning had been made heavy to Maggie, and Tom's persistent coldness to her all through their walk to Garum Firs spoiled the fresh air and sunshine for her. Tom, you perceive, was rather a severe personage. He was particularly clear and positive on one point, namely that he would punish everybody who deserved it, and he was troubled with no doubts as to the exact amount of their deserts. Why, he wouldn't have minded being punished himself if he deserved it, but then he never did deserve it. He called Lucy to look at the half-built bird's nest, without caring to show it to Maggie, and peeled a willow switch for Lucy and himself, without offering one to Maggie. Lucy had said, "Maggie, shouldn't *you* like one?" But Tom was deaf.

Still, the sight of the peacock spreading his tail on the stack-yard wall, just as they reached Garum Firs, was enough to divert the mind for a time from grievances. And this was only the beginning of beautiful sights at Garum Firs. All the farmyard life was wonderful there,—bantams speckled and top-knotted; Friesland hens with their feathers all turned the wrong way; Guinea fowls that flew and screamed and dropped their pretty spotted feathers; pouter pigeons and a tame magpie; nay, a goat and a wonderful brindled dog, half mastiff, half bull-dog, as large as a lion. Then there were white railings and white gates all about and glittering weathercocks of various design, and garden-walks paved with pebbles in beautiful patterns,—nothing was quite common at Garum Firs.

Uncle Pullet had seen the expected party approaching from the window, and made haste to unbar and unchain the front door, kept always in this fortified condition from fear of tramps who might be supposed to know of the glass case of stuffed birds in the hall and to contemplate rushing in and carrying it away on their heads. Aunt Pullet, too, appeared at the doorway, and, as soon as her sister was within hearing, said, "Stop the children, for God's sake, Bessy! don't let 'em come up the door-step; Sally's bringing the old mat and the duster to rub their shoes!"

THE TREASURE CHEST

When the ceremony of shoe-wiping was over, Aunt Pullet conducted Mrs. Tulliver and the girls in solemn procession upstairs along the bright and slippery corridor into the darkened best room where the outer light, entering feebly, showed what looked like the ghosts of furniture in white shrouds. Meanwhile Tom was seated in irksome constraint on the edge of a sofa below, directly opposite his Uncle Pullet.

"Well, young sir, what do you learn at school?" was a standing question with Uncle Pullet; whereupon Tom always looked sheepish, rubbed his hands across his face and answered, "I don't know."

The appearance of the little girls suggested to Uncle Pullet that he offer them certain small sweet cakes, of which he kept a stock under lock and key for his own private eating on wet days; but the children had no sooner got the tempting delicacy between their fingers, then Aunt Pullet desired them to abstain from eating it till the tea-tray and the plates came, since with these crisp cakes they would make the floor "all over" crumbs. Lucy didn't mind that much, for the cake was so pretty she thought it rather a pity to eat it; but Tom, watching his opportunity while the elders were talking, hastily stowed his in his mouth at two bites and chewed it furtively. As for Maggie, becoming fascinated as usual by a colored print on the wall, she presently let fall her cake, and in an unlucky movement crushed it beneath her foot,—a source of so much agitation to Aunt Pullet and disgrace to Maggie that she began to despair of hearing the musical snuff box today, till it occurred to her that Lucy was in high favor enough to venture on asking for a tune. So she whispered to Lucy; and Lucy, who always did what she was desired to do, went up quietly to her uncle's knee, and blushing all over her neck while she fingered her necklace, said, "Will you please play us a tune, Uncle?"

When the fairy tune began, Maggie quite forgot that she had a load on her mind, that Tom was angry with her; and by the time that "Hush, ye pretty warbling choir," had been played, her face wore that bright look of happiness while she sat immovable with her hands clasped, which sometimes comforted her mother with the sense that Maggie could look pretty now and then, in spite of her brown skin. But when the magic music ceased, she jumped up, and running towards Tom, put her arm round his neck and said, "Oh, Tom, isn't it pretty?"

Now this caress was to Tom quite uncalled for. Moreover he had his glass of cowslip wine in his hand, and Maggie jerked him so that she made him spill half of it.

"Look there now!" he cried angrily.

"Why don't you sit still?" her mother said peevishly.

232

"Little gells mustn't come to see me if they act like that," said Aunt Pullet.

"Why, you're too rough, little miss," said Uncle Pullet.

Poor Maggie sat down again with the music all chased out of her soul and the seven small demons all in again. Mrs. Tulliver, foreseeing nothing but misbehavior while the children remained indoors, took an early opportunity of suggesting that, now they were rested after their walk, they might go and play out of doors; and Aunt Pullet gave permission, only bidding them not to go off the paved walks in the garden, and if they wanted to see the poultry fed, to view them from a distance on the horse-block, a restriction which had been imposed upon the children ever since Tom had been found guilty of running after the peacock, with a vague idea that fright would make one of its feathers drop off.

All the disagreeable recollections of the morning were thick upon Maggie when Tom, whose displeasure towards her had been considerably refreshed by her foolish trick of causing him to up-set his cowslip wine, said, "Here, Lucy, you come along with me," and walked off to the area where the toads were, as if there were no Maggie in existence. Seeing this, Maggie lingered at a distance, looking like a small Medusa with her snakes cropped. Lucy was naturally pleased that cousin Tom was so good to her, and it was very amusing to see him tickling a fat toad with a piece of string when the toad was safe down the area with an iron grating over him. Still Lucy wished Maggie to enjoy the spectacle also, especially as she would doubtless find a name for the toad, and say what had been his past history; for Lucy had a delighted semi-belief in Maggie's stories about the live things they came upon by accident,—how Mrs. Earwig had a wash at home, and one of her children had fallen into the hot copper for which reason she was running so fast to fetch the doctor. Tom had a profound contempt for this nonsense of Maggie's, smashing the earwig at

once as a superfluous yet easy means of proving the entire un-
reality of such a story; but Lucy, for the life of her, could not
help fancying there was something in it, and at all events thought
it was very pretty make-believe. So now the desire to know the
history of a very portly toad, added to her habitual affectionate-
ness, made her run back to Maggie and say, "Oh, there is such a
big funny toad, Maggie! Do come and see!"

Maggie said nothing but turned away from her with a deeper
frown. As long as Tom seemed to prefer Lucy to her, Lucy made
part of his unkindness.

Tickling a fat toad is an amusement that it is possible to ex-
haust and Tom by and by began to look around for some other
mode of passing the time. But in so prim a garden where they
were not to go off the paved walks, there was not a great choice
of sport. The only great pleasure such a restriction suggested
was the pleasure of breaking it, and Tom began to meditate a visit
to the pond, about a field's length from the garden.

"I say, Lucy," he began, as he coiled up his string again,
"what do you think I mean to do?"

"What Tom?" said Lucy with curiosity.

"I mean to go to the pond and look at the pike. You may go
with me if you like," said the young sultan.

"Oh, Tom, *dare* you?" said Lucy. "Aunt said we mustn't go
out of the garden."

"Nobody 'ull see us," said Tom. "Besides I don't care if
they do,—I'll run off home."

"But I couldn't run," said Lucy who had never before been
exposed to such severe temptation.

"Oh, never mind; they won't be cross with *you*," said Tom.
"You say I took you."

Tom walked along and Lucy trotted by his side, timidly enjoying the rare treat of doing something naughty,—excited also

by the mention of that celebrity the pike, about which she was quite uncertain whether it was a fish or a fowl. Maggie saw them leaving the garden and could not resist the impulse to follow. That Tom and Lucy should do or see anything of which she was ignorant would have been an intolerable idea to Maggie. So she kept a few yards behind them unobserved by Tom, who was presently absorbed in watching for the pike,—a highly interesting monster. The pike, like other celebrities, did not show when he was watched for, but Tom caught sight of something which attracted him to another spot on the brink of the pond.

"Here, Lucy," he said in a loud whisper, "come here! take care! keep on the grass!—don't step where the cows have been!" he added, pointing to a peninsula of dry grass with trodden mud on each side of it.

Lucy came carefully as she was bidden, and bent down to look  at what seemed a golden arrow-head darting through the water. It was a water-snake, Tom told her; and Lucy at last could see the serpentine wave of its body. Maggie had drawn nearer and nearer; she *must* see it too, though it was bitter to her like everything else since Tom did not care about her seeing it. At last she was close by Lucy; and Tom, who had been aware of her approach, but would not notice it till he was obliged, turned round and said,—

"Now get away, Maggie; there's no room for you on the grass here. Nobody asked *you* to come."

There were passions at war in Maggie at that moment to have made a tragedy, but the utmost she could do, with a fierce thrust of her small brown arm, was to push poor little pink-and-white Lucy into the cow-trodden mud.

Then Tom could not restrain himself, and gave Maggie two smart slaps on the arm as he ran to pick up Lucy who lay crying helplessly. Maggie retreated to the roots of a tree a few yards off and looked on impenitently. Usually her repentance came quickly after one rash deed, but now Tom and Lucy had made her so miserable, she was glad to spoil their happiness,—glad to make everybody uncomfortable. Why should she be sorry? Tom was slow to forgive her, however sorry she might have been.

"I shall tell mother, you know, Miss Mag," said Tom loudly and emphatically as soon as Lucy was up and ready to walk away, crying piteously. It was not Tom's practice to "tell," but here justice clearly demanded that Maggie should be visited with the utmost punishment.

"Sally," said Tom when they reached the kitchen door, and Sally looked at them in speechless amaze, with a piece of bread-and-butter in her mouth and a toasting-fork in her hand,—"Sally, tell mother it was Maggie pushed Lucy into the mud."

"But Lors ha' massy, how did you get near such mud as that?" said Sally making a wry face.

Tom's imagination had not been rapid enough to include this question among the foreseen consequences, but it was no sooner put than he foresaw that Maggie would not be considered the only culprit in the case. He walked quietly away from the kitchen door, leaving Sally to the pleasure of guessing. Sally lost no time in presenting Lucy at the parlor door.

"Goodness gracious!' Aunt Pullet exclaimed, "Keep her at the door, Sally! Don't bring her off the oil-cloth, whatever you do!"

"Why she's tumbled into some nasty mud," said Mrs. Tulliver, going up to Lucy to examine into the amount of damage.

"If you please, 'um, it was Miss Maggie as pushed her in," said

Sally. "Master Tom's been and said so, and they must ha' been to the pond for it's only there they could ha' got into such dirt."

Mrs. Tulliver was mute, feeling herself a truly wretched mother, while Mrs. Pullet began to give elaborate directions to Sally how to guard the premises from serious injury in the course of removing the dirt. Mrs. Tulliver went out to speak to her naughty children, supposing them to be close at hand; but it was not until after some search that she found Tom leaning with rather a hardened, careless air against the white paling of the poultry yard, and lowering his piece of string as a means of exasperating the turkey-cock

"Tom, you naughty boy, where's your sister?" said Mrs. Tulliver in a distressed voice.

"I don't know," said Tom; his eagerness for justice on Maggie had diminished since he had seen that it could hardly be brought about without the injustice of some blame on his own conduct.

"Why, where did you leave her?" said his mother, looking round.

"Sitting under the tree against the pond," said Tom, apparently indifferent to everything but the string and the turkey-cock.

"Then go and fetch her in this minute, you naughty boy."

You may conceive the terrified search for Maggie and the difficulty of convincing her mother that she was not in the pond,— tea deferred, and the poultry alarmed by the unusual running to and fro, till Mr. Pullet, confused and overwhelmed, reached down a key to unlock the goose-pen as a likely place for Maggie to lie concealed in. Tom, after a while, started the idea that Maggie was gone home (without thinking it necessary to state that it was what he should have done himself under the circumstances), and the suggestion was seized as a comfort by his mother.

"Sister, for goodness' sake let 'em put the horse in the carriage and take me home. Lucy can't walk in her dirty clothes," she said, looking at that innocent victim who was wrapped up in a shawl, and sitting with naked feet on the sofa. Aunt Pullet was

quite willing to take the shortest means of restoring her premises to order and quiet, and it was not long before Mrs. Tulliver was in the chaise, looking anxiously at the most distant point before her.

Maggie's intentions, as usual, were on a larger scale than Tom had imagined. The resolution that gathered in her mind, after Tom and Lucy had walked away, was not so simple as that of going home. No! she would run away and go to the gypsies, and Tom should never see her any more. That was by no means a new idea to Maggie; she had been so often told she was like a gypsy, and "half wild," that when she was miserable it seemed to her the only way of escaping blame, and being entirely in harmony with circumstances, would be to live in a little brown tent on the commons; the gypsies, she considered, would gladly receive her, and pay her much respect on account of her superior knowledge. She had once mentioned her views on this point to Tom, and suggested that he should stain his face brown and they should run away together; but Tom rejected the scheme with contempt, observing that gypsies were thieves, and hardly got anything to eat, and had nothing to drive but a donkey. Today, however, Maggie thought her misery had reached a pitch at which gypsydom was her only refuge, and she rose from her seat on the roots of the tree with the sense that this was a great crisis in her life; she would run straight away till she came to Dunlow Common, where there would certainly be gypsies; and cruel Tom, and the rest of her relations who found fault with her, should never see her any more. She thought of her father as she ran along, but she reconciled herself to the idea of parting with him, by determining that she would secretly send him a letter by a small gypsy, who would run away without telling where she was and just let him know that she was well and happy and always loved him very much.

Maggie soon got out of breath with running. She presently passed through the gate into the lane, not knowing where it would lead her. But she was soon aware, not without trembling, that there were two men coming along the lane in front of her. The formidable strangers were two shabby looking men with flushed faces, one of them carrying a bundle on a stick over his shoulder. The man with a bundle stopped, and in a half-whining, half coaxing tone asked her if she had a copper to give a poor man. Maggie had a sixpence in her pocket,—her Uncle Glegg's present,—which she immediately drew out and gave this poor man with a polite smile, hoping he would feel very kindly towards her as a generous person.

"That's the only money I've got," she said apologetically.

"Thank you, little miss," said the man in a less respectful and grateful tone than Maggie anticipated, and she even observed that he smiled and winked at his companion. She walked on hurriedly but was aware that the two men were standing still, probably to look after her, and she presently heard them laughing loudly. It was clear that she was not likely to make a favorable impression on passengers, and she thought she would turn into the fields again, but not on the same side of the lane as before, lest they should be Uncle Pullet's fields. She turned through the first gate that was not locked, and felt a delightful sense of privacy in creeping along by the hedge rows. Sometimes she had to climb over high gates, but that was a small evil; she was getting out of reach very fast, and she should probably soon come within sight of Dunlow Common, or at least of some other common. She hoped so, for she was getting rather tired and hungry, and until she reached the gypsies, there was no definite prospect of bread-and-butter. At last, however, the green fields came to an end, and Maggie found herself looking through the bars of a gate into a lane with a wide margin of grass on each side of it, where she saw a donkey with a log tied to his foot feeding on the grassy margin. She crept through the bars of the gate and walked on with new spirit, though not without haunting images of Appolyon, and a highwayman with a pistol, and a blinking dwarf in yellow with a mouth from ear to ear, and other miscellaneous dangers. She hardly dared look on one side of her, lest she should see the diabolical blacksmith of her picture book, in his leathern apron, grinning at her with arms akimbo. It was not without a leaping of the heart that she caught sight of a small pair of bare legs sticking up, feet uppermost, by the side of a hillock; they seemed something hideously preternatural,—a diabolical kind of fungus; for she was too much agitated at the first glance to see the ragged clothes and the dark shaggy head attached to them. It was a boy asleep, and Maggie trotted along faster and more lightly lest she should wake him; it did not occur to her that he was one of her friends, the gypsies, who in all probability would have very genial manners. But the fact was so, for at the next bend in the lane Maggie actually saw the little semi-circular black tent with the blue smoke rising before it, which was to be her refuge. She even saw a tall female figure by the column of smoke, doubtless the gypsy-mother who provided the tea and other groceries; it was astonishing to herself that she did not feel more delighted. She went on, however, and it was plain she had attracted attention; for the tall woman, who proved to be a young woman with a baby on her arm, walked slowly to meet her. Maggie looked up in the

THE TREASURE CHEST

new face rather tremblingly as it approached, and was reassured by the thought that her Aunt Pullet and the rest were right when they called her a gypsy; for this face with the bright dark eyes and the long hair, was really something like what she used to see in the glass before she cut her hair off.

"My little lady, where are you going to?" the gypsy said in a tone of coaxing deference.

It was delightful and just what Maggie expected; the gypsies saw at once that she was a little lady, and were prepared to treat her accordingly.

"Not any farther," said Maggie, feeling as if she were saying what she had rehearsed in a dream. "I'm come to stay with *you*, please."

"That's pretty; come then. Why, what a nice little lady you are to be sure!" said the gypsy, taking her by the hand. Maggie thought her very agreeable, but wished she had not been so dirty.

There was quite a group round the fire when they reached it. An old gypsy woman was seated on the ground nursing her knees, and occasionally poking a skewer into the round kettle that sent forth an odorous steam; two small shock-headed children were lying prone and resting on their elbows, something like small sphinxes; and a placid donkey was bending his head over a tall girl, who, lying on her back, was scratching his nose and indulging him with a bit of excellent stolen hay. The slanting sunlight fell kindly upon them, and the scene was really very pretty and comfortable, Maggie thought, only she hoped they would soon set out the teacups. Everything would be quite charming when she had taught the gypsies to use a washing basin and to feel an interest in books. It was a little confusing, though, that the young woman began to speak to the old one in a language which Maggie did not understand, while the tall girl, who was feeding the donkey, sat up and stared at her without offering any salutation. At last the old woman said,—

"What! my pretty lady, are you come to stay with us? Sit ye down and tell us where you come from."

It was just like a story; Maggie liked to be called pretty lady

242

and treated in this way. She sat down and said, "I'm come from home because I'm unhappy and I mean to be a gypsy. I'll live with you if you like, and I can teach you a great many things."

"Such a clever little lady," said the woman with the baby, sitting down by Maggie, and allowing baby to crawl; "and such a pretty bonnet and frock," she added, taking off Maggie's bonnet and looking at it while she made an observation to the old woman in the unknown language. The tall girl snatched the bonnet and put it on her own head hind-foremost with a grin; but Maggie was determined not to show any weakness on this subject.

"I don't want to wear a bonnet," she said; "I'd rather wear a red handkerchief, like yours (looking at her friend by her side).

"Oh, what a nice little lady!—and rich, I'm sure," said the old woman. "Didn't you live in a beautiful house at home?"

"Yes, my home is pretty, and I'm very fond of the river where we go fishing, but I'm often very unhappy. I should have liked to bring my books with me, but I came away in a hurry you know. But I can tell you almost everything there is in my books, I've read them so many times, and that will amuse you. And I can tell you something about Geography too,—that's about the world we live in. Did you ever hear about Columbus?"

Maggie's eyes had begun to sparkle and her cheeks to flush,— she was really beginning to instruct the gypsies, and gaining great influence over them. The gypsies themselves were not without amazement at this talk, though their attention was divided by the contents of Maggie's pocket, which the friend at her right hand had by this time emptied without attracting her notice.

"Is that where you live, my little lady?" said the old woman at the mention of Columbus.

"Oh, no!" said Maggie with some pity; "Columbus was a very wonderful man who found out half the world, and they put

chains on him and treated him very badly, you know, but perhaps it's rather too long to tell before tea—*I want my tea so.*"

The last words burst from Maggie in spite of herself, with a sudden drop from patronising instruction to simple peevishness.

"Why, she's hungry, poor little lady," said the younger woman. "Give her some o' the cold victual. You've been walking a good way, I'll be bound, my dear. Where's your home?"

"It's Dorlcote Mill, a good way off," said Maggie. "My father is Mr. Tulliver, but we mustn't let him know where I am, else he'll fetch me home again. Where does the queen of the gypsies live?"

"What! do you want to go to her, my little lady?" said the younger woman. The tall girl meanwhile was constantly staring at Maggie and grinning. Her manners certainly were not agreeable.

"No," said Maggie, "I'm only thinking that if she isn't a very good queen, you might choose another. If I was a queen, I'd be a very good queen and kind to everybody."

"Here's a bit o' nice victual, then" said the old woman, handing to Maggie a lump of dry bread, which she had taken from a bag of scraps, and a piece of cold bacon.

"Thank you," said Maggie, looking at the food without taking it, "but will you give me some bread-and-butter and tea instead? I don't like bacon.

"We've got no tea nor butter," said the old woman, with something like a scowl, as if she were getting tired of coaxing.

"Oh, a little bread and treacle would do," said Maggie. "We ha'n't got no treacle," said the old woman crossly, whereupon there followed a sharp dialogue between the two women in their unknown tongue and one of the small sphinxes snatched at the bread-and-bacon and began to eat it. At this moment the tall girl who had gone a few yards off, came back, and said something which produced a strong effect. The old woman, seeming to forget Maggie's hunger, poked the skewer into the pot with new vigor, and the younger crept under the tent, and reached out some platters and spoons. Maggie trembled a little and was afraid the tears would come into her eyes. Meanwhile the tall girl gave a shrill cry and presently came running up the boy whom Maggie had passed as he was sleeping,—a rough urchin about the age of Tom. He stared at Maggie and there ensued much incomprehensible chattering. She felt very lonely, and was quite sure she should begin to cry before long; the gypsies didn't seem to mind her at all, and she felt quite weak among them. But the springing tears were checked by a new terror when two men came up whose approach had been the cause of the sudden excitement. The elder of the two carried a bag which he flung down, addressing the women in a loud and scolding tone, which they answered by a shower of treble sauciness; while a huge cur ran barking up to Maggie, and threw her into a tremor that only found a new cause in the curses with which the younger man called the dog off, and gave him a rap with a great stick he held in his hand.

Maggie felt that it would be impossible she should ever be queen of these people, or ever communicate to them amusing and useful knowledge. Both of the men now seemed to be inquiring about Maggie for they looked at her. At last the younger woman said in her previous deferential, coaxing tone,—

"This nice little lady's come to live with us; aren't you glad?"

"Ay, very glad," said the younger man, who was looking at Maggie's silver thimble and other small matters that had been taken from her pocket. He returned them all except the thimble to the younger woman with some observation, and she immediately restored them to Maggie's pocket, while the men seated themselves and began to attack the contents of the kettle—a stew of meat and potatoes,— which had been taken off the fire and turned out into a yellow platter. Maggie began to think that Tom must be right about the gypsies; they certainly must be thieves unless the man meant to return her thimble by-and-by. She would willingly have given it to him, for she was not at all attached to her thimble; but the feeling that she was among thieves prevented her from feeling any revival of deference and attention towards her; all thieves except Robin Hood were wicked people. The women saw she was frightened.

"We've got nothing nice for a lady to eat," said the old woman in her coaxing tone. "And she's so hungry, sweet little lady."

"Here, my dear, try if you can eat a bit o' this," said the younger woman, handing some of the stew on a brown dish with an iron spoon to Maggie, who, remembering that the old woman had seemed angry with her for not liking the bread-and-bacon, dared not refuse the stew, though fear had chased away her appetite. If her father would but come by in the gig and pick her up! Or even if Jack the Giantkiller, or Mr. Greatheart, or St. George who slew the dragon would happen to pass that way! But Maggie thought with a sinking heart that these heroes were never seen in the neighborhood of St. Ogg's; nothing very wonderful ever came there.

THE TREASURE CHEST

Maggie's ideas about gypsies had undergone a rapid modification in the last five minutes. From having considered them very respectable companions, amenable to instruction, she had begun to think that they meant perhaps to kill her as soon as it was dark, and cut up her body for gradual cooking; the suspicion crossed her that the fierce-eyed old man was perhaps the devil, who might drop that disguise at any moment and turn into the grinning blacksmith, or else a fiery-eyed monster with dragon's wings. It was no use trying to eat the stew and yet the thing she most dreaded was to offend the gypsies by betraying her extremely unfavorable opinion of them.

"What! you don't like the smell of it, my dear?" said the young woman, observing that Maggie did not even take a spoonful of the stew. "Try a bit, come?"

"No, thank you," said Maggie, summoning all her force for a desperate effort, and trying to smile in a friendly way. "I haven't time I think; it seems getting darker. I think I must go home now, and come again another day, and then I can bring you a basket with some jam tarts and things."

Maggie rose from her seat, devoutly hoping her hint about the tarts would tempt Apollyon to let her go, but her hope sank when the old gypsy woman said, "Stop a bit, little lady; we'll take you home all safe, when we've done supper. You shall ride home like a lady."

Maggie sat down again with little faith in this promise, though she presently saw the tall girl putting a bridle on the donkey, and throwing a couple of bags on his back.

"Now then, little missis," said the younger man, rising and leading the donkey forward, "tell us where you live."

"Dorlcote Mill is my home," said Maggie eagerly. "My father is Mr. Tulliver. He lives there."

"What! a big mill a little way this side o' St. Ogg's?"

"Yes," said Maggie. "Is it far off? I think I should like to walk there, if you please."

"No, no, it'll be getting dark; we must make haste. And the donkey'll carry you as nice as can be; you'll see."

He lifted Maggie as he spoke, and set her on the donkey. She felt relieved that it was not the old man who seemed to be going with her, but she had only a trembling hope that she was really going home.

"Here's your pretty bonnet," said the younger woman, putting that recently despised but now welcome article of costume on Maggie's head; "and you'll say we've been very good to you, won't you, and what a nice little lady we said you was."

"Oh, yes, thank you," said Maggie, "I'm very much obliged to you, but I wish you'd go with me, too." She thought anything was better than going with one of the dreadful men alone.

"Ah, you're fondest o' me, aren't you?" said the woman. "But I can't go. You'll go too fast for me."

It now appeared that the man also was to be seated on the donkey holding Maggie before him, and she was as incapable of remonstrating against this arrangement as the donkey himself, though no nightmare had ever seemed to her more horrible. When the woman had patted her on the back and said, "Good-bye," the donkey at a strong hint from the man's stick set off at a rapid walk along the lane towards the point Maggie had come from an hour ago, while the tall girl and the rough urchin, also furnished with sticks, obligingly escorted them for the first hundred yards with much screaming and thwacking.

Not Leonore, in that preternatural midnight excursion with her phantom lover, was more terrified than poor Maggie in this entirely natural ride on a short-paced donkey, with a gypsy behind her who considered he was earning half-a-crown. The red light of the setting sun seemed to have a portentous meaning, with which the alarming bray of the second donkey with the log on its foot must surely have some connection. Two low, thatched cottages—the only houses they passed in this lane—seemed to add to its dreariness; they had no windows to speak of, and the doors were closed; it was probable that they were inhabited by witches, and it was a relief to find that the donkey did not stop there.

At last—oh, sight of joy!—this lane, the longest in the world, was coming to an end, was opening on a broad highroad where there was actually a coach passing! And there was a finger-post at the corner,—she had surely seen that finger-post before,—"To St. Ogg's 2 miles." The gypsy really meant to take her home then; he was probably a good man after all, and might have been rather hurt at the thought that she didn't like coming with him alone. This idea became stronger as she felt more and more certain that she knew the road quite well, and she was considering how she might open a conversation with the injured gypsy, and not only gratify his feelings but efface the impression of her cowardice, when, as they reached a cross-road, Maggie caught sight of someone coming on a white-faced horse.

"Oh, stop, stop!" she cried out. "There's my father! Oh, father, father!"

The sudden joy was almost painful, and before her father reached her, she was sobbing. Great was Mr. Tulliver's wonder,

for he had made a round from Basset, and had not yet been home.

"Why, what's the meaning o'this?" he said, checking his horse, while Maggie slipped from the donkey and ran to his stirrup.

"The little miss lost herself, I reckon," said the gypsy. "She'd come to our tent at the far end o' Dunlow Lane, and I was bringing her where she said her home was. It's a good way to come arter being on the tramp all day."

"Oh, yes, father, he's been very good to bring me home," said Maggie,—"a very kind, good man!"

"Here, then, my man," said Mr. Tulliver, taking out five shillings. "It's the best day's work you ever did. I couldn't afford to lose the little wench; here lift her up before me."

"Why Maggie, how's this, how's this?" he said as they rode along, while she laid her head against her father and sobbed. "How came you to be rambling about and lose yourself?"

"Oh, father," sobbed Maggie, "I ran away because I was so unhappy; Tom was so angry with me. I couldn't bear it."

"Pooh, pooh," said Mr. Tulliver, soothingly, "you mustn't think o' running away from Father. What 'ud Father do without his little wench?"

"Oh no, I never will again, father—never."

Mr. Tulliver spoke his mind very strongly when he reached home that evening; and the effect was seen in the remarkable fact that Maggie never heard one reproach from her mother, or one taunt from Tom, about this foolish business of her running away to the gypsies. Maggie was rather awe-stricken by this unusual treatment, and sometimes thought that her conduct had been too wicked to be alluded to.

THE TREASURE CHEST

THE CLOCKS OF RONDAINE*
Frank R. Stockton

CENTURIES ago, there stood on the banks of a river a little town called Rondaine. The river was a long and winding stream which ran through different countries, and was sometimes narrow and swift, and sometimes broad and placid; sometimes hurrying through mountain passes, and again meandering quietly through fertile plains; in some places of a blue color and almost transparent, and in others of a dark and sombre hue; and so it changed until it threw itself into a warm, far-spreading sea.

But it was quite otherwise with the little town. As far back as anybody could remember, it had always been the same that it was at the time of our story; and the people who lived there could see no reason to suppose that it would ever be different from what it was then. It was a pleasant little town, its citizens were very happy; and why there should be any change in it, the most astute old man in all Rondaine could not have told you.

If Rondaine had been famed for anything at all, it would have been for the number of its clocks. It had many churches, some little ones in dark side streets, and some larger ones in wider avenues; and in the steeple of each of these churches there was a clock. There were town buildings, very old ones, which stood upon the great central square. Each of these had a tower, and in each tower was a clock. Then there were clocks at street corners, and two clocks in the market-place, and clocks over shop-doors, a clock at each end of the bridge, and several large clocks a little way out of town. Many of these clocks were fashioned in some quaint and curious way. In one of the largest a stone man came out and struck the hours with a stone hammer, while a stone woman struck the half hours with a stone broom; and in another an iron donkey kicked the hours on a bell behind him.

251

It would be impossible to tell all the odd ways in which the clocks of Rondaine struck; but in one respect they were alike; they all did strike. The good people of the town would not have tolerated a clock which did not strike.

It was very interesting to lie awake in the night and hear the clocks of Rondaine strike. First would come a faint striking from one of the churches in the by-streets, a modest sound, as if the clock was not sure whether it was too early or not; then from another quarter would be heard a more confident clock striking the hour clearly and distinctly.

When they were quite ready, but not a moment before, the seven bells of the large church on the square would chime the hour; after which, at a respectful interval of time, the other church clocks of the town would strike. After the lapse of three or four minutes, the sound of all these bells seemed to wake up the stone man in the tower of the town building, and he struck the hour with his hammer. When this had been done, the other town-clocks felt at liberty to strike, and they did so. And when every sound had died away, so that he would be certain to be heard if there was any one awake to hear, it would be very likely that the iron donkey would kick out the hour on his bell. But there were times when he kicked before any of the clocks began to strike.

One by one the clocks on the street corners struck, the up-town ones first, and afterward those near the river. These were followed by the two clocks on the bridge, the one at the country end waiting until it was quite sure that the one at the town end had finished. Somewhat later would be heard the clock of Vougereau, an old country-house in the suburbs.

The very last clock to strike in Rondaine was one belonging to a little old lady with white hair, who lived in a little white house in one of the prettiest and cleanest streets in the town.

THE TREASURE CHEST

Her clock was in a little white tower at the corner of her house, and was the only strictly private clock which was in the habit of making itself publicly heard. Long after every other clock had struck, and when there was every reason to believe that for some time nothing but half-hours would be heard in Rondaine, the old lady's clock would strike quickly and. with a tone that said, "I know I am right, and I wish other people to know it."

In a small house which stood at a corner of two streets in the town there lived a young girl named Arla. For a year or more this young girl had been in the habit of waking up very early in the morning, sometimes long before daylight, and it had become a habit with her to lie and listen to the clocks. Her room was at the top of the house, and one of its windows opened to the west and another to the south, so that sounds entered from different quarters. Arla liked to leave these windows open so that the sounds of the clocks might come in.

Arla knew every clock by its tone, and she always made it a point to lie awake until she was positively sure that the last stroke of the clock at Vougereau had sounded; but it often happened that sleep overcame her before she heard the clock of the little old lady with white hair. It was so very long to wait for that!

It was not because she wanted to know the hour that Arla used to lie and listen to the clocks. She could tell this from her own little clock in her room. This little clock, which had been given to her when she was a small girl, not only struck the hours and half-hours and quarter-hours, but there was attached to it a very pretty contrivance which also told the time. On the front of the clock, just below the dial, was a sprig of a rosebush beautifully made of metal, and on this, just after the hour had sounded, there was a large green bud; at a quarter past the hour this bud opened a little, so that the red petals could be seen; fifteen minutes later it was a half-blown rose, and at a quarter of an hour more it was nearly full blown; just before the hour the rose opened to its fullest extent, and so remained until the clock had finished striking, when it immediately shut up into a great green bud. This clock was a great delight to Arla; for not only was it a very pleasant thing to watch the unfolding of the rose, but it was a continual satisfaction to her to think that her little clock always told her exactly what time it was, no matter what the other clocks of Rondaine might say.

Arla's father and mother were thrifty, industrious people, who were very fond of their daughter, and wished her to grow up a thoughtful, useful woman. In the very early morning, listening to the clocks of Rondaine or waiting for them, Arla did a great deal of thinking; and it so happened, on the morning of the day before Christmas, when the stars were bright and the air frosty, and every outside sound very clear and distinct, that Arla began to think of something which had never entered her mind before.

"How in the world," she said to herself, "do the people of Rondaine know when it is really Christmas. Christmas begins as soon as it is twelve o'clock on Christmas Eve; but as some of the people depend for the time upon one clock and some upon others, a great many of them cannot truly know when Christmas Day has really begun. Even some of the church clocks make people think that Christmas has come, when in reality it is yet the day before. And not one of them strikes at the right time. As for the iron donkey, I believe he kicks whenever he feels like it. And yet there are people who go by him! I know this, for they have told me so. But the little old lady with white hair is worse off than anybody else. Christmas must always come ever so long before she knows it."

With these thoughts on her mind, Arla could not go to sleep again. She heard all the clocks strike, and lay awake until her own little clock told her that she ought to get up. During this time she had made up her mind what she should do. There was yet one day before Christmas; and if the people of the town could be made to see in what a deplorable condition they were on account of the difference in their clocks, they might have time to set the matter right so that all the clocks should strike the correct hour, and everybody should know exactly when Christmas Day began. She was sure that the citizens had never given this matter proper thought; and it was quite natural that such should be the case, for it was not every one who was in the habit of lying awake in the very early morning; and in the daytime, with all the out-door noises, one could not hear all the clocks strike in Rondaine. Arla therefore thought that a great deal depended upon her, who knew exactly how this matter stood.

When she went down to breakfast she asked permission of her mother to take a day's holiday. As she was a good girl, and never neglected either her lessons or her tasks, her mother was quite willing to give her the day before Christmas in which she could do as she pleased.

DONN P. CRANE

The day was cool, but the sun shone brightly and the air was pleasant. In the country around about Rondaine Christmas-time was not a very cold season. Arla put on a warm jacket and a pretty blue hood, and started out gayly to attend to the business in hand. Everybody in Rondaine knew her father and mother, and a great many of them knew her, so there was no reason why she should be afraid to go where she chose. In one hand she carried a small covered basket in which she had placed her rose clock.

THE TREASURE CHEST

The works of this little clock were regulated by a balance-wheel, like those of a watch, and therefore it could be carried about without stopping it.

The first place she visited was the church at which she and her parents always attended service. It was a small building in a little square at the bottom of a hill, and, to reach it, one had to go down a long flight of stone steps. When she entered the dimly lighted church, Arla soon saw the sacristan, a pleasant-faced little old man whom she knew very well.

"Good-morning, sir," said she. "Do you take care of the church clock?"

The sacristan was sweeping the stone pavements of the church, just inside the door. He stopped and leaned upon his broom. "Yes, my little friend," he said, "I take care of everything here except the souls of the people."

"Well, then," said Arla, "I think you ought to know that your clock is eleven minutes too fast. I came here to tell you that, so that you might change it, and make it strike properly."

The sacristan's eyes began to twinkle. He was a man of merry mood. "That is very good of you, little Arla; very good indeed. And, now that we are about it, isn't there something else you would like to change? What do you say to having these stone pillars put to one side, so that they may be out of the way of the people when they come in? Or those great beams in the roof—they might be turned over, and perhaps we might find that the upper side would look fresher than this lower part, which is somewhat time-stained, as you see? Or, for the matter of that, what do you say to having our clock-tower taken down and set out there in the square before the church door?

Then short-sighted people could see the time much better, don't you think? Now tell me, shall we do all these things together, wise little friend?"

A tear or two came into Arla's eyes, but she made no answer.

"Good-morning, sir," she said, and went away.

"I suppose," she said to herself as she ran up the stone steps, "that he thought it would be too much trouble to climb to the top of the tower to set the clock right. But that was no reason why he should make fun of me. I don't like him as much as I used to."

The next church to which Arla went was a large one, and it was some time before she could find the sacristan. At last she saw him in a side chapel at the upper end of the church, engaged in dusting some old books. He was a large man, with a red face, and he turned around quickly, with a stern expression, as she entered.

"Please, sir," said Arla, "I came to tell you that your church clock is wrong. It strikes from four to six minutes before it ought to. It should be changed so that it will be sure to strike at the right time."

The face of the sacristan grew redder and twitched visibly at her remark.

"Do you know what I wish?" he almost shouted in reply.

"No, sir," answered Arla.

"I wish," he said, "that you were a boy, so that I might take you by the collar and soundly cuff your ears, for coming here to insult an officer of the church in the midst of his duties! But, as you are a girl, I can only tell you to go away from here as rapidly and as quietly as you can, or I shall have to put you in the hands of the church authorities!"

258

Arla was truly frightened, and although she did not run—for she knew that would not be proper in a church—she walked as fast as she could into the outer air.

"What a bad man," she then said to herself, "to be employed in a church! It surely is not known what sort of a person he is, or he would not be allowed to stay there a day!"

Arla thought she would not go to any more churches at present, for she did not know what sort of sacristans she might find in them.

"When the other clocks in the town all strike properly," she thought, "it is most likely they will see for themselves that their clocks are wrong, and they will have them changed."

She now made her way to the great square of the town, and entered the building at the top of which stood the stone man with his hammer. She found the doorkeeper in a little room by the side of the entrance. She knew where to go, for she had been there with her mother to ask permission to go up and see the stone man strike the hour with his hammer, and the stone woman strike the half-hour with her broom.

The doorkeeper was a grave, middle-aged man with spectacles; and, remembering what had just happened, Arla thought she would be careful how she spoke to him.

"If you please, sir," she said, with a courtesy, "I should like to say something to you. And I hope you will not be offended when I tell you that your clock is not quite right. Your stone man and your stone woman are both too slow; they sometimes strike as much as seven minutes after they ought to strike."

The man looked steadily at her through his spectacles.

"I thought," continued Arla, "that if this should be known to you, you would have the works of the stone man and the stone woman altered so that they might strike at the right time. They can be heard so far, you know, that it is very necessary they should not make mistakes."

"Child," said the man, with his spectacles still steadily fixed on her, "for one hundred and fifty-seven years the thunder and the lightning in time of storm have roared and flashed around that clock, and the sun in time of fair weather has shone upon it. In that century and a half and seven years men and women have lived and have died, and their children and their grandchildren and their great-grandchildren; kings and queens have passed, and one generation after another, many times. And yet, through all these years, that stone man and that stone woman have stood there, and in storm and in fair weather, by daylight or in the darkness of night, they have struck the hours and the half-hours. Of all things that one hundred and fifty-seven years ago were able to lift an arm to strike, they alone are left. And now you, a child of thirteen, or perhaps fourteen years, come to me and ask me to change that which has not been changed for a century and a half and seven years!"

Arla could answer nothing with those spectacles fixed upon her. They seemed to glare more and more as she looked at them. "Good-morning, sir," she said, dropping a courtesy as she moved backward toward the door. Reaching it, she turned and hurried into the street.

"If those stone people," she thought, "have not been altered in all these years, it is likely they would now be striking two or three hours out of the way! But I don't know. If they kept on going slow for more than a century they must have come around to the right hour sometimes. But they will have to strike ever and ever so much longer before they come around there again!"

Arla now walked on until she came to a street corner where a cobbler had a little shop. In the angle of the wall of the house, at the height of the second story, was a clock. This cobbler did not like the confined air and poor light of his shop, and whenever the weather allowed he always worked outside on the side-walk. To-day, although it was winter, the sun shone brightly on this side of the street, and he had put his bench outside, close to his door, and was sitting there, hard at work. When Arla stopped before him he looked up and said, cheerfully:

"Good-morning, Mistress Arla. Do you want them half-soled, or heeled, or a patch put on the toes?"

"My shoes do not need mending," said Arla. "I came to ask if you could tell me who has charge of the clock at this corner."

"I can easily do that," he said, "for I am the man. I am paid by the year, for winding it up and keeping it in order. The pay is not great; but if it were larger, more people might want it, and I might lose it; and if it were less how could I afford to do it at all? So I am satisfied."

"But you ought not to be entirely satisfied," said Arla, "for the clock does not keep good time. I know when it is striking, for it has a very jangling sound, and it is the most irregular clock in Rondaine. Sometimes it strikes as much as twenty-five minutes after the hour, and very often it does not strike at all."

The cobbler looked up at her with a smile. "I am sorry," he said, "that it has a jangling stroke, but the fashioning of clocks is not my trade, and I could not mend its sound with awl, hammer, or waxed-end. But it seems to me, my good maiden, that you never mended a pair of shoes."

"No, indeed!" said Arla; "I should do that even worse than you would make clocks."

"Never having mended shoes, then," said the cobbler, "you do not know what a grievous thing it is to have twelve o'clock, or six o'clock, or any other hour, in fact, come before you are ready for it. Now, I don't mind telling you, because I know you are too good to spoil the trade of a hard-working cobbler— and shoemaker too, whenever he gets the chance to be one— that when I have promised a customer that he shall have his shoes or his boots at a certain time of day, and that time is drawing near, and the end of the job is still somewhat distant, then do I skip up the stairway and set back the hands of the clock according to the work that has to be done. And when my customer comes I look up to the clock-face and I say to him, 'Glad to see you!' and then he will look up at the clock and will say, 'Yes, I am a little too soon;' and then, as likely as not, he will sit down on the door-step here by me and talk entertainingly; and it may happen that he will sit there without grumbling for many minutes after the clock has pointed out the hour at which the shoes were promised.

"Sometimes, when I have been much belated in beginning a job, I stop the clock altogether, for you can well see for yourself that it would not do to have it strike eleven when it is truly twelve. And so, if my man be willing to sit down, and our talk be very entertaining, the clock being above him where he cannot see it without stepping outward from the house, he may not notice that it is stopped. This once served me very well, for an old gentleman, over-testy and over-punctual, once came to me for his shoes, and looking up at the clock, which I had prepared for him, exclaimed, 'Bless me! I am much too early!' And he sat down by me for three-quarters of an hour, in which time I persuaded him that his shoes were far too much worn to be worth mending any more, and that he should have a new pair, which, afterward, I made."

"I do not believe it is right for you to do that," said Arla; "but even if you think so, there is no reason why your clock should go wrong at night, when so many people can hear it because of the stillness."

"Ah, no!" said the cobbler, "I do not object to the clock being as right as you please in the night; but when my day's work is done, I am in such a hurry to go home to my supper that I often forget to put the clock right, or to set it going if it is stopped.

But so many things stop at night—such as the day itself—and so many things then go wrong such as the ways of evil-minded people—that I think you truly ought to pardon my poor clock."

"Then you will not consent," said Arla, "to make it go right?"

"I will do that with all cheerfulness," answered the cobbler, pulling out a pair of waxed-ends with a great jerk, "as soon as I can make myself go right. The most important thing should always be done first; and, surely, I am more important than a clock!" And he smiled with great good-humor.

Arla knew that it would be of no use to stand there any longer and talk with this cobbler. Turning to go, she said:

"When I bring you shoes to mend, you shall finish them by my clock, and not by yours."

"That will I, my good little Arla," said the cobbler, heartily. "They shall be finished by any clock in town, and five minutes before the hour, or no payment."

Arla now walked on until she came to the bridge over the river. It was a long, covered bridge, and by the entrance sat the bridgekeeper.

"Do you know, sir," said she, "that the clock at this end of your bridge does not keep the same time as the one at the other end? They are not so very different, but I have noticed this one is always done striking at least two minutes before the other begins."

The bridge-keeper looked at her with one eye, which was all he had.

DONN P. CRANE

MY BOOK HOUSE

"You are as wrong as anybody can be," said he. "I do not say anything about the striking, because my ears are not now good enough to hear the clock at the other end when I am near this one; but I know they both keep the same time. I have often looked at this clock and have then walked to the other end of the bridge, and have found that the clock there was exactly like it."

Arla looked at the poor old man, whose legs were warmly swaddled on account of rheumatism, and said:

"But it must take you a good while to walk to the other end of the bridge."

"Out upon you!" cried the bridge-keeper. "I am not so old as that yet! I can walk there in no time!"

Arla now crossed the bridge and went a short distance along a country road until she came to the great stone house known as Vougereau. This belonged to a rich family who seldom came there, and the place was in charge of an elderly man who was the brother of Arla's mother. When his niece was shown into a room on the ground floor, which served for his parlor and his office, he was very glad to see her; and while Arla was having something to eat and drink after her walk, the two had a pleasant chat.

"I came this time, Uncle Anton," she said, "not only to see you, but to tell you that the great clock in your tower does not keep good time."

Uncle Anton looked at her a little surprised.

"How do you know that, my dear?" he said.

Then Arla told him how she had lain awake in the early morning, and had heard the striking of the different clocks. "If you wish to make it right," said she, "I can give you the proper time, for I have brought my own little clock with me."

She was about to take her rose-clock out of her basket, when her uncle motioned to her not to do so.

"Let me tell you something," said he. "The altering of the

264

time of day, which you speak of so lightly, is a very serious matter, which should be considered with all gravity. If you set back a clock, even as little as ten minutes, you add that much to the time that has passed. The hour which has just gone by has been made seventy minutes long. Now, no human being has the right to add anything to the past, nor to make hours longer than they were originally made. And, on the other hand, if you set a clock forward even so little as ten minutes, you take away that much from the future, and you make the coming hour only fifty minutes long. Now, no human being has a right to take anything away from the future, or to make the hours shorter than they were intended to be. I desire, my dear niece, that you will earnestly think over what I have said, and I am sure that you will then see for yourself how unwise it would be to trifle with the length of the hours which make up our day. And now, Arla, let us talk of other things."

And so they talked of other things until Arla thought it was time to go. She saw there was something wrong in her uncle's reasoning, although she could not tell exactly what it was, and thinking about it, she slowly returned to the town. As she approached the house of the little old lady with white hair, she concluded to stop and speak to her about her clock. "She will surely be willing to alter that," said Arla, "for it is so very much out of the way."

The old lady knew who Arla was, and received her very kindly; but when she heard why the young girl had come to her, she flew into a passion.

"Never, since I was born," she said, "have I been spoken to like this! My great-grandfather lived in this house before me; that clock was good enough for him! My grandfather lived in this house before me; that clock was good enough for him! My father and mother lived in this home before me; that clock was good enough for them! I was born in this house, have always lived in it, and expect to die in it; that clock is good enough for me! And sooner than raise my hand against the clock of my ancestors, and the clock of my whole life, I would cut off that hand!"

Some tears came into Arla's eyes; she was a little frightened. "I hope you will pardon me, good madame," she said, "for, truly, I did not wish to offend you. Nor did I think that your clock is not a good one. I only meant that you should make it better; it is nearly an hour out of the way."

The sight of Arla's tears cooled the anger of the little old lady with white hair. "Child," she said, "you do not know what you are talking about, and I forgive you. But remember this: never ask persons as old as I am to alter the principles which have always made clear to them what they should do, or the clocks which have always told them when they should do it."

The poor girl now felt a good deal discouraged.

"The people don't seem to care whether their clocks are right or not," she said to herself, "and if they don't care, I am sure it is of no use for me to tell them about it. If even one clock could be made to go properly, it might help to make the people of Rondaine care to know exactly what time it is. Now, there is that iron donkey. If he would but kick at the right hour it would be an excellent thing, for he kicks so hard that he is heard all over the town."

Determined to make this one more effort, Arla walked quickly to the town-building, at the top of which was the clock with the iron donkey. This building was a sort of museum; it had a great many curious things in it, and it was in charge of a very ingenious man, who was learned and skilful in various ways.

THE TREASURE CHEST

When Arla had informed the superintendent of the museum why she had come to him, he did not laugh at her nor did he get angry. He was accustomed to giving earnest consideration to matters of this sort, and he listened attentively to all that Arla had to say.

"You must know," he said, "that our iron donkey is a very complicated piece of mechanism. Not only must he kick out the hours, but five minutes before doing so he must turn his head around and look at the bell behind him; and then, when he has done kicking, he must put his head back into its former position. All this action requires a great many wheels and cogs and springs and levers, and these cannot be made to move with absolute regularity. When it is cold, some of the works contract; and when it is warm, they expand; and there are other reasons why he is very likely to lose or gain time. At noon, on every bright day, I set him right, being able to get the correct time from a sun-dial which stands in the court-yard. But his works—which I am sorry to say are not well made—are sure to get a great deal out of the way before I set him again."

"Then, if there are several cloudy or rainy days together, he goes very wrong indeed," said Arla.

"Yes, he truly does," replied the superintendent, "and I am sorry for it. But there is no way to help it except to make him all over again at my own expense, and that is something I cannot afford to do. The clock belongs to the town, and I am sure the citizens will not be willing to spend the money necessary for a new donkey-clock; for, so far as I know, every person but your-self is perfectly satisfied with this one."

"I suppose so," said Arla, with a sigh; "but it really is a great pity that every striking-clock in Rondaine should be wrong!"

"But how do you know they are all wrong?" asked the super-intendent.

"Oh, that is easy enough," said Arla. "When I lie awake in the early morning, when all else is very still, I listen to their striking, and then I look at my own rose-clock to see what time it really is."

"Your rose-clock?" said the superintendent.

"This is it," said Arla, opening her basket and taking out her little clock.

The superintendent took it into his hands and looked at it attentively, both outside and inside. And then, still holding it, he stepped out into the court-yard. When in a few moments he returned, he said:

"I have compared your clock with my sun-dial, and find that it is ten minutes slow. I also see that, like the donkey, its works are not adjusted in such a way as to be unaffected by heat and cold."

"*My—clock—ten—minutes—slow!*" exclaimed Arla, with wide-open eyes.

"Yes," said the superintendent, "that is the case today, and on some days it is, probably, a great deal too fast. Such a clock as this—which is a very ingenious and beautiful one—ought frequently to be compared with a sun-dial or other correct time-keeper, and set to the proper hour. I see it requires a peculiar key with which to set it. Have you brought this with you?"

"No sir," said Arla; "I did not suppose it would be needed."

"Well, then," said the superintendent, "you can set it forward ten minutes when you reach home; and if tomorrow morning you compare the other clocks with it, I think you will find that not all of them are wrong."

Arla sat quiet for a moment, and then she said: "I think I shall not care any more to compare the clocks of Rondaine with my little rose-clock. If the people are satisfied with their own clocks, whether they are fast or slow, and do not care to know exactly when Christmas Day begins, I can do nobody any good by listening to the different strikings and then looking at my own little clock, with a night-lamp by it."

"Especially," said the superintendent, with a smile, "when you are not sure that your rose-clock is right. But if you bring here your little clock and your key on any day when the sun is shining, I will set it to the time shadowed on the sun-dial, and show you how to do it yourself."

"Thank you very much," said Arla, and she took her leave.

As she walked home, she lifted the lid of her basket and looked at her little rose-clock. "To think of it!" she said. "That you should be sometimes too fast and sometimes too slow! And, worse than that, to think that some of the other clocks have been right and you have been wrong! But I do not feel like altering you today. If you go fast sometimes, and slow sometimes, you must be right sometimes, and one of these days, when I take you to be compared with the sun-dial, perhaps you will not have to be altered so much."

Arla went to bed that night quite tired with her long walks, and when she woke it was broad daylight. "I do not know," she said to herself, "exactly when Christmas began, but I am very sure that the happy day is here."

"Do you lie awake in the morning as much as you used to?" asked Arla's mother, a few weeks after the Christmas holidays.

"No, mother dear," said Arla; "I now sleep with one of my windows shut, and I am no longer awakened by that chilly feeling which used to come to me in the early morning, when I could draw the bed-covers close about me and think how wrong were the clocks of Rondaine."

And the little rose-clock never went to be compared with the sun-dial. "Perhaps you are right now," Arla would say to her clock each day when the sun shone, "and I will not take you until some time when I feel very sure that you are wrong."

THE SWINEHERD
Hans Christian Andersen

THERE was once a poor Prince; he had only quite a tiny kingdom, but it was big enough to allow him to marry, and he was bent upon marrying.

Now it certainly was rather bold of him to say to the Emperor's daughter, "Will you have me?" He did, however, venture to say so, for his name was known far and wide; and there were hundreds of Princesses who would have said "Yes," and "Thank you, kindly," but see if *she* would!

Just let us hear about it.

A rose tree grew on the grave of the Prince's father,—such a beautiful rose tree; it only bloomed every fifth year, and then only bore one blossom; but what a rose that was! By merely smelling it one forgot all one's cares and sorrows.

Then he had a nightingale which sang as if every lovely melody in the world dwelt in her little throat. This rose and this nightingale were to be given to the Princess, so they were put into great silver caskets and sent to her.

The Emperor had them carried before him into the great Hall where the Princess was playing at "visiting" with her ladies-in-waiting; they had nothing else to do. When she saw the caskets with the gifts she clapped her hands with delight.

"If only it were a little pussy cat!" said she,—but there was the lovely rose.

"Oh, how wonderfully it is made!" said all the ladies-in-waiting.

"It is more than beautiful," said the Emperor; "it is neat."

But the Princess touched it, and then she was ready to cry.

"Fie, papa!" she said; "it is not *made* at all, it is nothing but a *real* rose!"

"Fie," said all the ladies-in-waiting; "it is nothing but a *real* rose!"

"Well, let us see what there is in the other casket, before we get angry," said the Emperor, and out came the nightingale. It sang so beautifully that at first no one could find anything to say against it.

"*Superbe! charmant!*" said the ladies-in-waiting, for they all chattered French, each one worse than the other.

"How that bird reminds me of our late Empress's musical box," said an old courtier. "Ah yes, they are the same tunes, and the same beautiful expression."

"So they are," said the Emperor, and he cried like a child.

"I should hardly think it could be a *real* bird," said the Princess.

"Yes, it is a real one," said those who had brought it.

"Then let it fly away," said the Princess, and she positively refused to see the Prince. But he was not to be discouraged; he stained his face brown and black, and, pulling his cap over his eyes, he knocked at the door.

"Good morning, Emperor," said he, "can I be taken into service in the palace?"

"Well, there are so many wishing to do that," said the Emperor, "but let me see!—yes, I need somebody to look after the pigs, for we have so many of them."

So the Prince was made imperial swineherd. A horrid little room was given him near the pig-sties, and here he had to live. The whole day long he sat busily at work, and by evening, he had made a beautiful little pot with bells all round it. When the pot boiled the bells rang out merrily and played the old tune:—

> "*Alas, my darling Augustine!*
> *All is lost, lost, lost!*"

But the most peculiar thing about it was, that by holding one's finger in the steam one could immediately smell what kind of meals were being cooked at every stove in the town. Now this was a very different matter from the rose.

The Princess came walking along with all her ladies-in-waiting, and when she heard the tune she stopped at once and looked greatly pleased for she, too, could play "Alas, my darling Augustine!" It was the only tune that she could play on the piano, and she played it with only one finger.

"Why, that is my tune," she said; "this must be a well educated swineherd. Listen, you must go in and ask him what the price of that instrument is."

So one of the ladies-in-waiting had to go in, but she put wooden shoes on first, so as not to soil her slippers.

"How much do you want for the pot?" she asked.

"I must have ten kisses from the Princess," said the swineherd.

"Mercy on us!" said the lady.

"I won't take less," said the swineherd.

"Well, what does he say?" asked the Princess.

"I really cannot tell you," said the lady-in-waiting, "it is too shocking."

"Then you must whisper it." And she whispered it.

"He is a wretch!" said the Princess, and went away at once.

But she had only gone a little way when she heard the bells tinkling beautifully:

"Alas! my darling Augustine!
All is lost, lost, lost!"

"Go and ask him if he will take ten kisses from my ladies-in-waiting."

"No, thank you," said the swineherd; "ten kisses from the Princess, or I keep my pot."

"How tiresome it is," said the Princess. "Then you will have to stand round me, so that no one may see."

So the ladies-in-waiting stood round her and spread out their skirts while the swineherd took his ten kisses, and then the Princess got the pot.

What a delight it was to them. The pot was kept on the boil day and night. They knew what was cooking on every stove in the town, from the chamberlain's to the shoemaker's. The ladies-in-waiting danced about and clapped their hands.

"We know who has sweet soup and pancakes for dinner, and who has cutlets; how amusing it is."

"Highly interesting," said the mistress of the robes.

"Yes, but you must keep the secret of how I got it, for I am the Emperor's daughter," said the Princess.

"Mercy on us! Quite so," they all answered.

The swineherd—that is to say, the Prince, only nobody knew that he was not a real swineherd—did not let the day pass in idleness, and he now constructed a rattle. When it was swung round it played all the waltzes, gallops and jig tunes which have ever been heard since the creation of the world.

"But this is *superbe!*" said the Princess, as she walked by. "I have never heard finer compositions. Go and ask him what the instrument costs, but let us have no more kissing."

"He wants a hundred kisses from the Princess!" said the lady-in-waiting.

"I think he is mad!" said the Princess, and she went away, but she had not gone far when she stopped.

"One must encourage art," she said; "I am the Emperor's daughter. Tell him he can have ten kisses, the same as yesterday, and he can take the others from the ladies-in-waiting."

"But we don't like that at all," said the ladies.

"Oh nonsense! If I can kiss him you can do the same. Remember that I pay your wages as well as give you board and lodging." So the lady-in-waiting had to go to the swineherd again.

"A hundred kisses from the Princess," said he, "or let each keep his own."

"Stand in front of me then," said the Princess, and all the

ladies-in-waiting stood round, while the swineherd kissed her.

"Whatever is the meaning of that crowd round the pig-sties?" said the Emperor, who had stepped out on to the balcony. He rubbed his eyes and put on his spectacles. "Why it is the ladies-in-waiting! What game are they up to? I must go and see!" So he pulled up the heels of his slippers for they were shoes which he had trodden down.

Bless us, what a hurry he was in! When he got into the yard, he walked very softly and the ladies were so busy counting the kisses, so that there should be fair play, and neither too few nor too many kisses, that they never heard the Emperor. He stood on tiptoe.

"What is all this?" he said, when he saw that the swineherd and the Princess were kissing each other, and he thumped them on the head with his slipper just as the swineherd was taking the eighty-sixth kiss.

"Be off with you!" cried the Emperor, for he was furious, and on the spot he expelled both the Princess and the swineherd from his empire. There stood the Princess crying, and the rain poured down in torrents.

"Oh, miserable creature that I am!" cried the Princess, "if only I had accepted the handsome Prince who sent me the rose and the nightingale. Oh, how unhappy I am!"

But the swineherd went behind a tree, wiped the black and brown stain from his face, and threw away his ugly clothes. Then he came forward in princely attire, so handsome that the Princess could not help curtseying to him.

"Thou hast taught me to despise thee," he said. "Thou wouldst not have an honourable prince; thou couldst not value the *real* rose or the nightingale, but thou wouldst kiss a swineherd for the sake of a silly toy, a trumpery *made* musical box! As thou hast chosen, so must thou abide!"

Then he went back into his own little kingdom and shut and locked the door. So she had to stand outside and sing in earnest:

"Alas! my darling Augustine!
All is lost, lost, lost!"

DEAR SENSIBILITY
Dear Sensibility, O la!
I heard a little lamb cry baa!
Says I, "So you have lost mama?"
　　　　　　"Ah!"
The little lamb, as I said so,
Frisking about the fields did go,
And frisking, trod upon my toe,
　　　　　　"Oh!"
　　　　—Old Rhyme.

THE BOY OF CADORE*
Katherine Dunlap Cather

THE boy's eyes were dark, and they gazed wistfully after the horseman who was dashing along the white highway.

"Think of it, Catarina!" he exclaimed. "He rides to the wonderful city."

Catarina looked at her brother as if she did not understand. There were many towns along the road that ribboned away to the south, each of which seemed large indeed to the mountain girl, yet she had never thought of them as wonderful.

"The wonderful city?" she repeated. "Where is that, Tiziano?"

"Why, don't you know?" he asked in surprise. "As if it could be other than Venice, the great city of St. Mark!"

But the name did not thrill black-eyed Catarina. Older than her brother, and far less of a dreamer, she had heard that dreadful things happened in the city, and that sometimes people went hungry there. In the mountains there was food enough and to spare, and though no one was rich and lived in a palace with tapestried walls and gorgeous furnishings, neither were there any very poor. So she shrugged her shoulders and replied: "Oh, Venice! I don't know why you call that wonderful. There are no mountains there, nor meadows where wild flowers grow. Are you tired of the Dolomites, Tiziano?"

"Ah, no!" came the earnest reply. "But the artists live in the city, and if I could go there, I might study with Bellini, and paint some of the things that are in my heart."

Catarina was just a practical village girl, who thought that if one had enough to eat and wear, he ought to be satisfied. So her voice was chiding and a bit impatient as she answered.

"You talk so much about painting, and seeing things no one else sees, that the villagers say unless you get over your dreaming ways, you will grow up to be of no account. That is why Father

*From *Boyhood Stories of Famous Men*. Reprinted by the courteous permission of the publishers, The Century Co.

thinks of apprenticing you to Luigi, the cobbler. For he can teach you his trade, which would be far better than always thinking about Venice. For, Tiziano, there are other things in the world beside painting."

Tiziano shook his head, but did not reply. Nothing else mattered half so much to him, and many a night, when the rest of the family were sleeping, he lay in his bed wondering how he could persuade his father to let him go away to study. It was well known that he spent many hours drawing on boards, stones, and anything he could find, and that the village priest, the good padrone, had praised his work. But little was thought of that. Other youths of Cadore had sketched as well and amounted to nothing. So why should he be sent to the city just because he could copy a mountain or a bit of woodland? For he could not make them understand that color was what seemed to burn in his soul, because that he could not express with charcoal.

A whistle came from down the road, and Catarina saw her brother Francesco beckoning them to hurry.

"They must be ready to begin weaving the garlands!" she exclaimed.

So they broke into a run toward the village inn.

It was the glowing, fragrant June time of the Italian highlands, when the hillsides and meadows of the fertile Dolomite valleys were masses of many colored bloom, and next day the Festival of Flowers was to take place. They had spent the afternoon blossom hunting, and now, when sunset was crimsoning the peaks, were homeward bound with their spoils, to aid in preparing for the revelry.

In a few minutes, they joined the other young people at the inn, and began making garlands, and planning games and frolics as they worked. Pieve di Cadore was very far from the world in those days of little travel, and when the time of a festival was at hand, the villagers were as light-hearted as the gay Venetians at carnival time. Songs and merry jests went round.

"Have you heard that Salvator, the miller's son, is going to Venice to study the art of carving?" asked a girl whose tongue kept pace with her hands. "Since his father has become rich, he has given up the idea of having him follow his own trade, and thinks it more elegant to become a sculptor."

Sebastiano, whose uncle was a lawyer's clerk in Bergamo, and who knew more of city ways than the other village youths, remarked: "I didn't know he had the love of carving. It takes something beside a rich father to make an artist."

The talkative girl tossed her head.

"That may be!" she retorted. "But no money, no masters, and without them, pray, how can one do anything?"

"So I tell Tiziano when he talks about going to the city to study painting," Catarina broke in. "Father is not rich, and it would be better for him to think of learning cobbling with Luigi."

Peals of laughter followed the announcement, and some one called out, "Tiziano! Why, he hasn't had even a drawing-master. He builds the tower of his castle before the foundation."

Tiziano's face turned red. He had no teacher, it was true. But he believed he could prove he was worth one if given a chance.

"Oh, if I only had some paints!" he thought. "Maybe they would stop calling me a dreamer, for I am sure I could make a picture, and then perhaps I could go."

But pigments were rare and costly, and though his father was a well-to-do mountaineer, he had no gold to waste in buying colors for a lad who had never been taught to use them.

The next morning, the boy noticed stains on the stone walk made by flowers crushed there the day before. They were bright and fresh as if painted, and it put an idea into his head. He did not speak of it, however, although it was on his mind so much

that, when the gaily decked villagers danced on the green, he did not see them, but, as soon as a chance came, he crept from the revelers and went out into the meadows.

Catarina saw him go, and wondered what took him from the merriment. Her curiosity was greater than her desire for fun, so she followed, and overtook him just as he reached a hillside aglow with blossoms.

"What are you doing, Tiziano?" she called.

The boy looked up as if doubtful whether to tell or not. But he knew his sister loved him even though she did criticize his dreaming, and that she would keep his secret.

"I am going to paint a picture," he answered.

For a minute she stood and stared. Then, thinking he was teasing, she retorted: "Of course you are, without any paints!"

But his earnest face told he was not joking.

"I shall use blossoms," he continued, with a wonderful light in his eyes. "See, all the colors are here, and I have found that they will stain. I saw where they did it on the stone walk."

Catarina was not a dreamer like her brother, and never saw pictures where others found only a bit of color, but she believed that what he proposed to do was not impossible, for she too had noticed the stains on the stone. And she began to think that he must be a very bright lad, for no ordinary one would have thought of it, and that perhaps his wanting to go to Venice was not a wild idea after all. She had heard the padrone say that no undertaking that fills the heart is impossible to one who has patience and courage and persistence, and that help always comes to those who try to help themselves. So she decided to help Tiziano, even though it was only in the keeping of his secret and the gathering of materials for the work.

So into the fragrant patches they went and began collecting blossoms of every hue—reds, pinks, blues, and purples such as sunset painted on the mountains, and warm yellows and lavenders that the boy saw in the pictures of his fancy. Then they hurried to an old stone house that stood on land owned by their father. It was a vacant house, seldom visited by the family, and never by the villagers, and there, where he would be safe from molestation, he was to paint the picture that they hoped would be the means of taking him to Venice. Catarina wanted to stay and watch the work, but Tiziano objected.

"I don't want even you to see it until it is finished, because at first it will not seem like a picture."

So she went away and left him outlining with a bit of charcoal on the wall.

For many days afterward, whenever he could steal away without being noticed, he worked with his flower paints. Catarina went over the meadows on feet that seemed to be winged, always watching that none of the villagers saw her put the blossoms in at the window near which her brother worked. So, while each petal made only a tiny stain, and the boy painted with the rapidity of one inspired, he not once needed to stop for materials.

Little by little the picture grew beneath the magic of his touch, and he and Catarina kept the secret well. Only the flocks pasturing on the fragrant uplands went near the deserted house, so no one knew that a boy was at work there who was destined to win glory for Italy. Little did the villagers dream, as Catarina skipped over the meadows, that the blossoms she gathered were being put to an immortal use.

One evening, when the sun was dipping behind the peaks and the merry voices of shepherds homeward bound with their flocks sounded down from the heights, Tiziano stepped to the door of the house and called to his sister outside:

"It is finished, Catarina, and is the very best that I can do!"

She went dancing in, filled with joy that the task was done, but when she stood in front of the picture, the merriment went out of her face, and she spoke in tones of reverence:

"Oh, Tiziano, a madonna!"

"Yes," he agreed. "A madonna and child, with a boy like me offering a gift. It is what was in my heart, Catarina."

For some minutes she stood there forgetting everything else in the beauty of the fresco. Then, thinking of what it would mean to her brother when the villagers knew he had done such a wonderful thing, she started out to spread the news.

"Come and see!" she called to Luigi, the cobbler, as she hurried past the door where he was sorting his leather. "Tiziano has painted a madonna on the walls of the old stone house."

Word travels fast when it goes by the tongues of villagers, and soon a group of folk moved toward the building where the lad waited. His father, coming down from a day's hunting in the mountains, saw them go, and followed, wondering what was the matter. But by the time he reached the place, such a crowd had gathered that he could not see the fresco.

Murmurs of "How did he do it?" "Where did he get his paints?" rose on all sides, and every one was so excited that the father could not find out why they were there. Then he heard Tiziano's voice: "I did it with flowers from the hillsides. Catarina gathered them while I worked."

Exclamations of amazement followed, and the good padrone

DONN P. CRANE

spoke reverently: "With the juices of flowers! Il divino Tiziano!"

Antonio Vecelli looked about him as if dazed, for he could not believe what he heard.

"Am I mad," he asked a villager who was standing close by, "or did the padrone call my Tiziano 'the divine'?"

"No," came the answer. "You are not mad."

And when they told him the story, and the crowd stepped back that he might see, he, too, thought it a wonderful thing.

Whether or not Salvator, the miller's son, went to the city to study sculpture, no one knows. But Tiziano did go, and the boy of Cadore became the marvel of Venice. There, guided by the master hand of Bellini, he began plying the brushes that were busy for almost eighty years, painting pictures whose glorious coloring has never been equaled, and proving to the mountain folk that it isn't bad, after all, to be a dreamer, for dreams combined with work do marvelous things. And if the father who thought he had gone mad when the village priest spoke his boy's name as reverently as he would a saint's, could come again to-day to the valley of flowers in the Italian highlands, he would hear the selfsame words that were used that twilight time in speaking of his lad.

"Ecco!" the villagers say, as they point to a noble statue that looks out toward the meadows in which Catarina gathered blossoms, "Il divino Tiziano.—See, the divine Titian!"

And by that name the world knows him to this very day.

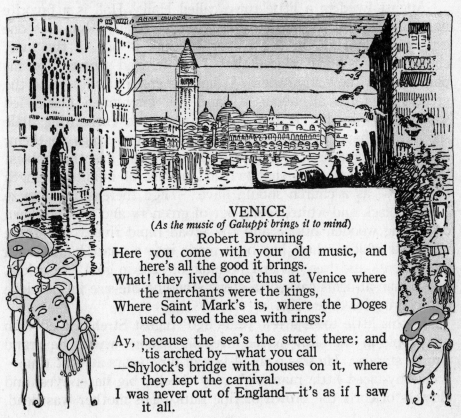

VENICE
(As the music of Galuppi brings it to mind)
Robert Browning

Here you come with your old music, and
    here's all the good it brings.
What! they lived once thus at Venice where
    the merchants were the kings,
Where Saint Mark's is, where the Doges
    used to wed the sea with rings?

Ay, because the sea's the street there; and
    'tis arched by—what you call
—Shylock's bridge with houses on it, where
    they kept the carnival.
I was never out of England—it's as if I saw
    it all.

THE NUREMBERG STOVE
Louise de la Ramée

August lived in a little town called Hall. Hall is a favorite name for several towns in Austria and Germany; but this one especial little Hall, in the Upper Innthal, is one of the most charming Old-World places that I know, and August for his part did not know any other. It has the green meadows and the great mountains all about it, and the gray-green glacier-fed water rushes by it. It has paved streets and enchanting little shops that have all latticed panes and iron gratings to them; it has a very grand old Gothic church, that has the noblest blendings of light and shadow, and a look of infinite strength and repose as a church should have. Then there is the Muntze Tower, black and white, rising out of greenery and looking down on a long wooden bridge and the broad rapid river; and there is an old schloss which has been made into a guard-house, with battlements and frescoes and heraldic devices in gold and colors, and a man-at-arms carved in stone standing life-size in his niche and bearing his date 1530.

In this little town a few years ago August Strehla lived with his people in the stone-paved irregular square where the grand church stands. He was a small boy of nine years at that time— a chubby-faced little man with rosy cheeks, big hazel eyes, and clusters of curls the brown of ripe nuts. His mother was dead, his father was poor, and there were many mouths at home to feed.

In this country the winters are long and very cold, and this night was terribly cold and dreary. The good burghers of Hall had shut their double shutters, and the few lamps there were, flickered dully behind their quaint, old-fashioned iron casings. The mountains indeed were beautiful, all snow-white under the stars. Hardly any one was astir; a few good souls wending home from vespers, a tired post-boy who blew a shrill blast from his tasselled horn as he pulled up his sledge before a hostelry, and little August, were all who were abroad, for the snow fell heavily and the good folks of Hall go early to their beds. He was half frozen and a little frightened, but he kept up his courage by saying over and over again to himself, "I shall soon be at home with dear Hirschvogel."

He went on through the streets into the place where the great church was, and where near it stood his father's house with the Pilgrimage of the Three Kings painted on its wall.

The snow outlined with white every gable and cornice of the beautiful old wooden houses; the moonlight shone on the gilded signs, the lambs, the grapes, the eagles, and all the quaint devices that hung before the doors. Here and there, where a shutter had not been closed, a ruddy fire-light lit up a homely interior, with the noisy band of children clustering round the house-mother and a big brown loaf, while the oilwicks glimmered, and the hearth-logs blazed, and the chestnuts sputtered in their iron roasting-pot. At August's knock the solid oak door of his father's home, four centuries old if one, flew open, and the boy darted in.

It was a large barren room into which he rushed with so much pleasure, and the bricks were bare and uneven. It had a walnut-wood press, handsome and very old, a broad deal table, and several wooden stools for all its furniture; but at the top of the chamber, sending out warmth and color together as the lamp shed its rays upon it, was a tower of porcelain, burnished with all the hues of a king's peacock and a queen's jewels, and surmounted with armed figures, and shields, and flowers of heraldry, and a great golden crown upon the highest summit of all.

It was a stove of 1532, and on it were the letters H. R. H., for it was the handwork of the great potter of Nuremberg, Augustin Hirschvogel, who put his mark thus, as all the world knows.

The stove no doubt had stood in palaces and been made for princes, had warmed the crimson stockings of cardinals and the gold-broidered shoes of archduchesses; no one knew what it had seen or done or been fashioned for; but it was a right royal thing. Yet perhaps it had never been more useful than it was now in this poor desolate room, sending down heat and comfort into the troop of children tumbled together on a wolf-skin at its feet, who received frozen August among them with loud shouts of joy.

"Oh, dear Hirchvogel, I am so cold, so cold!" said August, kissing its gilded lion's claws. "Is father not in, Dorothea?"

"No, dear. He is late."

Dorothea was a girl of seventeen, dark-haired and serious. She was the eldest of the Strehla family; and there were ten of them in all. Next to her there came Jan and Karl and Otho, big lads, gaining a little for their own living; and then came August, who went up in the summer to the high alps with the farmers' cattle, but in winter could do nothing; and then all the little ones, who could only open their mouths to be fed like young birds—Albrecht and Hilda, and Waldo and Christof, and last of all little three-year old Ermengilda, with eyes like forget-me-nots.

They were of that mixed race, half Austrian, half Italian, so common in the Tyrol; some of the children were white and golden as lilies, others were brown and brilliant as fresh-fallen chestnuts. The father was a good man, but weak and weary with so many to find food for and so little to do it with. He worked at the salt-furnaces, and by that gained a few florins. Dorothea was one of those maidens who almost work miracles, so far can their industry and care and intelligence make a home sweet and wholesome and a single loaf seem to swell into twenty. The children were always clean and happy, and the table was seldom without its big pot of soup once a day. Still, very poor they were, and Dorothea's heart ached with shame, for she knew that their father's debts were many for flour and meat and clothing. Of fuel to feed the big stove they had always enough without cost, for their mother's father was alive, and sold wood and fir cones and coke, and never grudged them to his grandchildren.

"Father says we are never to wait for him; we will have supper, now you have come home, dear," said Dorothea.

Supper was a huge bowl of soup, with big slices of brown bread swimming in it and some onions bobbing up and down; the bowl was soon emptied by ten wooden spoons, and then the three eldest boys slipped off to bed, being tired with their rough bodily labor in the snow all day. Dorothea drew her spinning-wheel by the stove and set it whirring, and the little ones got August down upon the old worn wolf skin and clamored to him for a picture or a story. For August was the artist of the family.

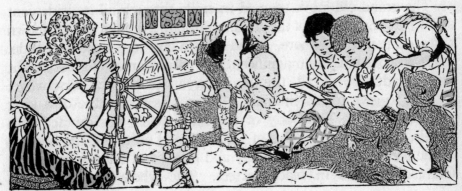

He had a piece of planed deal that his father had given him, and some sticks of charcoal, and he would draw a hundred things he had seen in the day, sweeping each out with his elbow when the children had seen enough of it and sketching another in its stead—faces and dogs' heads, and men in sledges, and old women in their furs, and pine-trees, and cocks and hens, and all sorts of animals, and now and then—very reverently—a Madonna and Child. It was all very rough, for there was no one to teach him anything. But it was all life-like, and kept the whole troop of children shrieking with laughter, or watching breathless, with wide open, wondering, awed eyes.

They were all so happy; what did they care for the snow outside? Their little bodies were warm, and their hearts merry; even Dorothea, troubled about the bread for the morrow, laughed as she spun; and August, with all his soul in his work, cried out loud, smiling, as he looked up at the stove that was shedding its heat down on them all:

"Oh, dear Hirschvogel! you are almost as great and good as the sun! No; you are greater and better, I think, because he goes away nobody knows where all these long, dark, cold hours; but you—you are always ready; just a little bit of wood to feed you, and you will make a summer for us all the winter through!"

The grand old stove seemed to smile through all its iridescent surface at the praises of the child. No doubt, though it had known three centuries and more, it had known but very little gratitude.

It was one of those magnificent stoves in enamel, of great height and breadth, with all the majolica lustre which Hirschvogel learned to give to his enamels. There was the statue of a king at each corner. The body of the stove itself was divided into panels, which had the Ages of Man painted on them; the borders of the panels had roses and holly and laurel and other foliage, and German mottoes in black letters. The whole was burnished

THE TREASURE CHEST

with gilding in many parts, and was radiant everywhere with that brilliant coloring of which the Hirschvogel family were all masters.

Nothing was known of the stove at this latter day in Hall. The grandfather Strehla, who had been a master-mason, had dug it up out of some ruins where he was building, and, finding it without a flaw, had taken it home, and only thought it worth finding because it was such a good one to burn. That was now sixty years past, and ever since then the stove had stood in the big, desolate, empty room, warming three generations of the Strehla family, and having seen nothing prettier perhaps in all its many years than the children tumbled now in a cluster, like gathered flowers, at its feet.

To the children the stove was a household god. In summer they laid a mat of fresh moss all round it, and dressed it up with green boughs and the number-less beautiful wild flowers of the Tyrol country. In winter all their joys centered in it, and scamp-ering home from school over the ice and snow, they were happy, knowing that they would soon be cracking nuts or roasting chest-nuts in the broad ardent glow of its noble tower, which rose eight feet high above them with all its spires and pinnacles and crowns.

Once a traveling peddler had told them that the letters on

it meant Augustin Hirschvogel, and that Hirschvogel had been a great German potter and painter, in the city of Nuremberg, and had made many such stoves, that were all miracles of beauty and of workmanship, putting all his heart and soul and faith into his labors, as the men of those earlier ages did, and thinking but little of gold or praise.

So the stove had got to be called Hirschvogel in the family, as if it were a living creature, and little August was very proud because he had been named after that famous old German who had had the genius to make so glorious a thing. All the children loved the stove, but with August the love of it was a passion; and in his secret heart he used to say to himself, "When I am a man, I will make just such things too, and then I will set Hirsch-vogel in a beautiful room in a house that I will build myself. That is what I will do."

For August, a salt-baker's son and a little cow-keeper when he was anything, was a dreamer of dreams, and when he was upon the high alps with his cattle, with the stillness and the sky around him, was quite certain that he would live for greater things than driving the herds up when the spring-tide came among the blue sea of gentians, or toiling down in the town with wood and with timber as his father and grandfather did every day of their lives. He was a strong and healthy little fellow, fed on the free mountain air and he was very happy, and loved his family devotedly, and was as active as a squirrel and as playful as a hare. But he was always thinking, thinking, thinking, for all that.

August lay now in the warmth of the stove and told the children stories, his own little brown face growing red with excitement as his imagination glowed to fever-heat. That human being on the panels, had always had the most intense interest for August, and he had made, not one history for him, but a thousand; he seldom told them the same tale twice.

In the midst of their chatter and laughter a blast of frozen air and a spray of driven snow struck like ice through the room, and reached them even in the warmth of the old wolf-skins and the great stove. It was the door which had opened and let in the cold; it was their father who had come home. The younger children ran joyous to meet him, Dorothea pushed the one wooden arm-chair of the room to the stove, and August flew to set the jug of beer on a little round table, and fill a long clay pipe; for their father was good to them all, and they had been trained by the mother they had loved to dutifulness and obedience and a watchful affection.

Tonight Karl Strehla responded very wearily to the young ones' welcome, and came to the wooden chair with a tired step and sat down heavily, not noticing either pipe or beer. He was a fair, tall man, gray before his time, and bowed with labor.

"Take the children to bed," he said, suddenly, and Dorothea obeyed. August stayed behind, curled before the stove.

When Dorothea came down again, the cuckoo-clock in the corner struck eight; she looked to her father and the untouched pipe, then sat down to her spinning, saying nothing.

There was a long silence; the cuckoo called the quarter twice; August dropped asleep; Dorothea's wheel hummed like a cat.

Suddenly Karl Strehla struck his hand on the table, sending the pipe on the ground.

"I have sold Hirschvogel," he said; and his voice was husky and ashamed in his throat. The spinning-wheel stopped. August sprang erect out of his sleep.

"Sold Hirschvogel!"

"I have sold Hirschvogel!" said Karl Strehla, in the same husky, dogged voice. "I have sold it to a traveling trader for two hundred florins. What would you?—I owe double that. He saw it this morning when you were all out. He will pack it and take it to Munich tomorrow."

Dorothea gave a low shrill cry: "Oh, father!—the children—in mid-winter!" She turned white as the snow without.

August stood, half blind with sleep, staring with dazed eyes. "It is not true?" he muttered. "You are jesting, father?" Strehla broke into a dreary laugh.

"It is true. Would you like to know what is true too?—that the bread you eat, and the meat you put in this pot, and the roof you have over your heads, are none of them paid for, have been none of them paid for, for months and months. If it had not been for your grandfather, I should have been in prison all summer and autumn, and he is out of patience and will do no more now. Boy, you stare at me as if I were a mad dog! You have made a god of yon china thing. Well,—it goes: goes tomorrow. Two hundred florins, that is something. It will keep me out of prison for a little, and with the spring things may turn—"

August stood like a creature paralyzed. His eyes were wide open, fastened on his father's with terror and incredulous horror; his face had grown as white as his sister's; his chest heaved with tearless sobs.

"It is not true!" he echoed, stupidly. It seemed to him that the very skies must fall, if they could take away Hirschvogel. They might as soon talk of tearing God's sun out of the heavens.

"You will find it true," said his father, doggedly, and angered because he was in his own soul bitterly ashamed to have bartered away the heirloom and treasure of his race and the comfort of his young children. "The dealer has paid me half the money tonight, and will pay me the other half tomorrow. No doubt it is worth a great deal more—but beggars cannot be choosers. The little black stove in the kitchen will warm you all just as well. Who would keep a gilded, painted thing in a poor house like this, when one can make two hundred florins by it? What is it, when all is said?—a bit of hardware much too grand-looking for such a room as this."

August gave a shrill shriek, and threw himself at his father's feet.

"Oh, father!" he cried, his hands closing on Strehla's knees. "Oh, father, dear father, you cannot mean what you say? Send *it* away—our life, our sun, our joy, our comfort? Sell *me* rather. But Hirschvogel! You must be in jest. You could not do such a thing. It is not a piece of hardware, as you say; it is a living thing, for a great man's thoughts and fancies have put life into it, and it loves us though we are only poor little children, and we love it with all our hearts and souls! Oh, listen; I will go and try and get work tomorrow! I will ask them to let me cut ice or make the paths through the snow. There must be something I could do, and I will beg the people we owe money to to wait; they are all neighbors, they will be patient. But sell Hirschvogel!—oh, never! never! never! Give the florins back to the man. Oh, father, dear father! do hear me, for pity's sake!"

Strehla was moved by the boy's anguish. He loved his children, and their pain was pain to him. But stronger than emotion, was the anger that August roused in him: he hated and despised himself for the barter of the heirloom of his race, and every word of the child stung him with a stinging sense of shame.

And he spoke in his wrath rather than in his sorrow.

"You are a little fool," he said, harshly, as they had never heard him speak. "Get up and go to bed. There is no more to be said. Children like you have nothing to do with such matters. The stove is sold, and goes to Munich tomorrow. What is it to you?

Be thankful I can get bread for you. Get on your legs, I say, and go to bed."

Then Strehla took the oil-lamp that stood at his elbow and stumbled off to his own chamber.

August laughed aloud; then all at once his laughter broke down into bitterest weeping. He threw himself forward on the stove, covering it with kisses, and sobbing as though his heart would burst from his bosom. What could he do? Nothing, nothing, nothing!

"August, dear August," whispered Dorothea, piteously, and trembling all over,—for she was a very gentle girl, and fierce feeling terrified her,—"August, do not lie there. Come to bed. In the morning you will be calmer. It is horrible indeed, but if it be father's will—"

"Let me alone," said August through his teeth, striving to still the storm of sobs that shook him from head to foot. "Let me alone. In the morning!—how can you speak of the morning?"

"Come to bed, dear," sighed his sister. "Oh, August, do not lie and look like that! you frighten me. Do come to bed."

"I shall stay here."

"Here! all night!"

"They might take it in the night. Besides, to leave it *now!*"

"But it is cold! the fire is out."

"It will never be warm any more, nor shall we."

All his childhood had gone out of him, all his gleeful, careless, sunny temper had gone with it; he spoke sullenly and wearily, choking down the great sobs in his chest. To him it was as if the end of the world had come.

His sister lingered by him while striving to persuade him to go to his place in the little crowded bed chamber with Albrecht and Waldo and Christof. But it was in vain. "I shall stay here," was all he answered her. And he stayed—all the night long.

THE TREASURE CHEST

The lamps went out; the rats came and ran across the floor; as the hours crept on through midnight and past, the cold intensified and the air of the room grew like ice. August did not move; he lay with his face downward on the golden and rainbow-hued pedestal of the household treasure, which henceforth was to be cold for evermore, an exiled thing in a far off land.

Whilst yet it was dark his three elder brothers came down the stairs and let themselves out, each bearing his lantern and going to his work in stone-yard and timber-yard and at the salt-works. They did not notice him; they did not know what had happened.

A little later his sister came down with a light in her hand to make ready the house ere morning should break.

She stole up to him and laid her hand on his shoulder timidly.

"Dear August, you must be frozen. August, do look up! do speak! It is morning, only so dark!"

August shuddered all over. "The morning!" he echoed. He slowly rose up to his feet. "I will go to grandfather," he said, very low. "He is always good: perhaps he could save it."

Loud blows with the heavy iron knocker of the house-door drowned his words. A strange voice called aloud through the keyhole: "Let me in! Quick!—there is no time to lose! More snow like this, and the roads will all be blocked. Let me in! Do you hear? I am come to take the great stove."

August sprang erect, his fists doubled, his eyes blazing.

"You shall never touch it!" he screamed; "you shall never touch it!"

"Who shall prevent us?" laughed a big man, who was a Bavarian, amused at the fierce little figure fronting him.

"I!" said August. "You shall never have it!"

"Strehla," said the big man, as August's father entered the room, "you have got a little mad dog here: muzzle him."

One way and another they did muzzle him. He fought like a little demon, and hit out right and left. But he was soon mastered by four grown men, and his father flung him with no light hand out from the door of the back entrance, and the buyers of the stately and beautiful stove set to work to pack it heedfully and carry it away.

When Dorothea stole out to look for August, he was nowhere in sight. She went back to little 'Gilda, and sobbed, whilst the others stood looking on, dimly understanding that with Hirschvogel was going all the warmth of their bodies, all the light of their hearth. In another moment Hirschvogel was gone—gone forever and aye.

August had stood still for a time, leaning against the back wall of the house. The wall looked on a court where a well was. Into the court an old neighbor hobbled for water, and, seeing the boy, said; "Child, is it true your father is selling the big stove?"

August nodded his head, then burst into a passion of tears.

"Well, for sure he is a fool," said the neighbor. "Heaven forgive me for calling him so before his own child! but the stove was worth a mint of money. If sell it he must, he should have taken it to good Herr Steiner over at Spruz, who would have given him honest value. But if I were you I would do better than cry. I would go after it."

Then the old man hobbled away.

August remained leaning against the wall; his head was buzzing and his heart fluttered with the new idea which had presented itself to his mind. "Go after it," had said the old man. He thought, "Why not go with it?"

He was by this time in that state of exaltation in which the impossible looks quite natural and commonplace. He ran out of the court-yard, and across to the huge Gothic porch of the church. From there he could watch unseen his father's door.

Presently his heart gave a great leap, for he saw the straw-enwrapped stove brought out and laid with infinite care on the bullock dray. Two of the Bavarian men mounted beside it, and the sleigh-wagon slowly crept over the snow of the place. The noble old minster looked its grandest and most solemn, with its dark-gray stone and its vast archways, and its strange gargoyles and lamp-irons black against the snow; but for once August had no eyes for it: he only watched for his old friend. Then he, a little unnoticeable figure enough, like a score of other boys in Hall, crept, unseen by any of his brothers or sisters, out of the porch and followed in the wake of the dray.

Its course lay towards the station of the railway. August heard the Bavarians arguing a great deal, and learned that they meant to go too and wanted to go with the great stove itself.

But this they could not do, for neither could the stove go by a passenger-train nor they themselves go in a goods-train. So at length they insured their precious burden for a large sum, and consented to send it by a luggage-train which was to pass through Hall in half an hour.

August heard, and a desperate resolve made itself up in his little mind. Where Hirschvogel went, would he go. He gave one terrible thought to Dorothea—poor, gentle Dorothea!— sitting in the cold at home, then set to work to execute his project. How he managed it he never knew very clearly himself, but certain it is that when the goods-train from the north moved out of Hall, August was hidden behind the stove in the great covered truck, and wedged, unseen and undreamt of by any human creature, amidst the cases of wood-carving, of clocks, of Vienna toys, of Turkish carpets, of Russsian skins, which shared the same abode as did his swathed and bound Hirschvogel.

It was very dark in the closed truck, which had only a little window above the door. But August was not frightened; he was close to Hirschvogel, and presently he meant to be closer still; for he meant to do nothing less than get inside Hirschvogel itself. Being a shrewd little boy, and having had by great luck two silver groschen in his breeches-pocket, which he had earned the day before by chopping wood, he had bought some bread and sausage at the station of a woman there who knew him, and who thought he was going out to his uncle Joachim's chalet above Jenbach. This he ate in the darkness.

When he had eaten, he set to work like a little mouse to make a hole in the withes of straw and hay which enveloped the stove. He gnawed, and nibbled, and pulled, and pushed, making his hole where he guessed that the opening of the stove was,—the opening through which he had so often thrust the big oak logs to feed it. No one disturbed him; the heavy train went lumbering on and on, and he saw nothing at all of the beautiful mountains, and shining waters, and great forests through which he was being carried. He was hard at work getting through the straw and hay and twisted ropes; and at last he found the door of the stove, which he knew so well, and which was quite large enough for a child of his age to slip through. Slip through he did, as he had often done at home for fun, and curled himself up there to see if he could anyhow remain during many hours. He found that he could; air came in through the brass fret-work of the stove; and with admirable caution in such a little fellow, he leaned out, drew the hay and straw together, and rearranged the ropes, so that no one could ever have dreamed a little mouse had been at them. Then he curled himself up again, this time more like a dormouse than anything else; and, being safe inside his dear Hirschvogel and intensely cold, he went fast asleep as if he were in his own bed at home with Albrecht and Christof on either side of him. The train lumbered on, and the child slept soundly for a long while. When he did awake, it was quite dark; he could not see, and for a while he was sorely frightened, and sobbed in a quiet heart-broken fashion, thinking of them all at home. But August was brave, and he had a firm belief that God and Hirschvogel would take care of him. So he got over his terror and his sobbing both.

The goods-trains are usually very slow, and are many days doing what a quick train does in a few hours. This one was quicker than most, because it was bearing goods to the King of Bavaria; still, it took all the short winter's day and the long winter's night and half another day to go over ground that the mail-trains cover in a forenoon. It passed pretty Rosenheim, that marks the border of Bavaria. And here the Nuremberg stove, with August inside it, was lifted out heedfully and set under a covered way. When it was lifted out, the boy had hard work to keep in his screams; he was tossed to and fro as the men lifted the huge thing, and the earthenware walls of his beloved fire-king were not cushions of down. However, though they swore and grumbled at the weight of it, they never suspected that a living child was inside it, and they carried it out on to the platform and set it down under the roof of the goods-shed. There it passed the rest of the night and all the next morning, and August was all the while within it.

He had still some of his loaf, and a little—a very little—of his sausage. What he did begin to suffer was thirst. It was many hours since he had last taken a drink from the wooden spout of their old pump, which brought them the sparkling, ice-cold water of the hills. But, fortunately for him, the stove, having been marked and registered as "fragile and valuable," was not treated quite like a mere bale of goods, and the Rosen-heim station-master resolved to send it on by a passenger-train that would leave there at daybreak.

Munich was reached, and August, hot and cold by turns, and shaking like a little aspen-leaf, felt himself once more carried out on the shoulders of men, rolled along on a truck, and finally set down, where he knew not, only he knew he was thirsty—so thirsty! If only he could have reached his hand out and scooped up a little snow! He thought he had been moved on this truck many miles, but in truth the stove had been only taken from the railway-station to a shop in the Marienplatz. Fortunately, the stove was always set upright on its four gilded feet, an injunction to that effect having been affixed to its written label, and on its gilded feet it stood now in the small dark curiosity-shop of one, Hans Rhilfer.

"I shall not unpack it till Anton comes," he heard a man's voice say; and then he heard a key grate in a lock, and by the unbroken stillness that ensued he concluded he was alone, and ventured to peep through the straw and hay. What he saw was a small square room filled with pots and pans, pictures, carvings, old blue jugs, old steel armor, shields, daggers, Chinese idols, Vienna china, Turkish rugs and all the rubbish of a *bric-a-brac* dealer's. It seemed a wonderful place to him; but, oh! was there one drop of water in it all? That was his single thought. There was not a drop of water, but there was a lattice window grated, and beyond the window was a wide stone ledge covered with snow. August cast one look at the locked door, darted out of his hiding-place, ran and opened the window, crammed the snow into his mouth again and again, and then flew back into the stove, drew the hay and straw over the place he entered by, and shut the brass door down on himself.

Presently the key turned in the lock, he heard heavy footsteps and the voice of the man who had said to his father, "You have a little mad dog; muzzle him!" The voice said, "Ay, ay, you have called me a fool many times. Now you shall see what I have gotten for two hundred dirty florins. *Potztausend!* never did *you* do such a stroke of work!"

Then the other voice grumbled and swore, and the steps of the two men approached more closely, and the heart of the child went pit-a-pat, pit-a-pat. They began to strip the stove of its wrappings; that he could tell by the noise they made with the hay and the straw. Soon they had stripped it wholly; that, too, he

301

knew by the oaths and exclamations of wonder and surprise
and rapture which broke from the man who had not seen it before.

"A right royal thing! A wonderful and never-to-be-rivalled
thing! Grander than the great stove of Hohen-Salzburg! Sublime! magnificent! matchless!"

After standing by the Nuremberg master's work for nigh an
hour, praising and marvelling, the men moved to a little distance
and began talking of sums of money and divided profits, of which
discourse he could make out no meaning. All he could make out
was that the name of the king—the king—the king came very
often in their arguments. He fancied at times they quarrelled,
for they swore lustily and their voices rose hoarse and high; but
after a while they seemed to agree to something, and were in great
glee. He made out that they were going to show Hirschvogel
to some great person. He kept quite still and dared not move.

Presently the door opened again sharply. He could hear the
two dealers' voices murmuring unctuous words, in which "honor,"
"gratitude," and many fine long noble titles played the chief
parts. The voice of another person, more clear and refined than
theirs, answered them curtly, and then, close by the stove and
the boy's ear, ejaculated a single *"Wunderschon!"*

The poor little boy, meanwhile, within, was hugged up into
nothing, dreading that every moment the stranger would open the
stove. And open it truly he did, and examined the brass-work
of the door; but inside it was so dark that crouching August
passed unnoticed, screwed up into a ball like a hedgehog as he
was. The gentleman shut to the door at length, without having
seen anything strange inside it; and then talked long and low
with the tradesmen. The child could distinguish little that he
said, except the name of the king and the word "gulden" again
and again. After a while he went away, one of the dealers accompanying him, one of them lingering behind to bar up the

shutters. Then this one also withdrew, double-locking the door.

He would have to pass the night here, that was certain. He and Hirschvogel were locked in, but at least they were together. If only he could have had something to eat! He thought with a pang of how at this hour at home they ate the sweet soup, sometimes with apples in it from Aunt Maila's farm orchard, and sang together, and listened to Dorothea's reading of tales, and basked in the glow that beamed on them from the great Nuremberg fire-king. After a time he dropped asleep.

Midnight was chiming from all the brazen tongues of the city when he awoke, and, all being still, ventured to put his head out the door of the stove to see why such a strange bright light was round him. What he saw was nothing less than all the *bric-a-brac* in motion.

A big jug was solemnly dancing a minuet with a plump Faenza jar; a tall dutch clock was going through a gavotte with a spindle-legged ancient chair; an old violin of Cremona was playing itself; a queer shrill plaintive music that thought itself merry came from a painted spinnet covered with faded roses, and a Japanese bronze was riding along on a griffin. A great number of little Dresden cups and saucers were all skipping and waltzing; the teapots, with their broad round faces, were spinning their own lids like tee-totums; and a little Saxe poodle, with a red ribbon at its throat, was running from one to another. August looked on at these mad freaks and felt no sensation of wonder. He only, as he heard the violin and the spinnet playing, felt an irresistible desire to dance too. No doubt his face said what he wished; for a lovely little lady, all in pink and gold and white, with powdered hair, and high-heeled shoes, and all made of the very finest and fairest Meissen china, tripped up to him, and smiled, and gave him her hand, and led him out to a minuet.

"I am the Princess of Saxe-Royale," she said with a smile.

Then he ventured to say to her: "Madame, my princess, could you tell me kindly why some of the figures dance and speak, and some lie up in a corner like lumber? Is it rude to ask?"

"My dear child," said the powdered lady, "is it possible that you do not know the reason? Why, those silent, dull things are *imitation;* lies, falsehoods, fabrications! They only *pretend* to be what we *are!* They never wake up; how can they? No imitation ever had any soul in it yet."

Then from where the great stove stood there came a solemn voice. All eyes turned upon Hirschvogel, and the heart of its little human comrade gave a great jump of joy. At last he would hear Hirschvogel speak.

"My friends," said that clear voice from the turret of Nuremberg faience. "We were made in days when men were true creatures, and so we, the work of their hands, were true too. We derive all the value in us from the fact that our makers wrought at us with zeal, with integrity, with faith—not to win fortunes, but to do nobly an honest thing and create for the honor of the Arts and God. I see amidst you a little human thing who loves me and in his own childish way loves Art. Now I want him forever to remember that we are what we are, and precious in the eyes of the world, because centuries ago those who were of single mind and of pure hand so created us, scorning sham and haste and counterfeit. Well do I recollect my master, Augustin Hirsch-vogel. He led a wise and blameless life, and wrought in loyalty and love, and made his time beautiful thereby. For many, many years I, once honored of emperors, dwelt in a humble house and warmed in successive winters three generations of little, cold, hungry children. When I warmed them they forgot that they were hungry; they laughed and told tales, and slept at last about my feet. Then I knew that, humble as had become my lot, it was one that my master would have wished for me, and I was content. That was better than to stand in a great hall of a great city, cold and empty, even though wise men came to gaze and throngs of fools gaped, passing with flattering words. Where I go now I know not; but since I go from that humble house where they loved me, I shall be sad and alone."

Then the voice sank away in silence, and a strange golden light that had shone on the great stove faded away. A soft pathetic melody stole gently through the room. It came from the old, old spinet that was covered with the faded roses.

Then that sad, sighing music of a bygone day died too; the clocks of the city struck six of the morning; day was rising over the Bayerischenwald. August awoke with a great start, and found himself lying on the bare bricks of the floor of the chamber, and all the *bric-a-brac* was lying quite still all around.

He rose slowly to his feet. Tramp, tramp, came a heavy step up the stair. He had but a moment in which to scramble back into the great stove, when the door opened and the two dealers entered, bringing candles with them to see their way.

August was scarcely conscious of danger more than he was of cold or hunger, now that he had heard Hirschvogel speak. A marvelous sense of courage, of security, of happiness, was about him, like strong and gentle arms enfolding him and lifting him upwards—upwards—upwards! Hirschvogel would defend him.

The dealers undid the shutters, and then began to wrap up the stove once more in all its straw and hay and cordage. Presently they called up their porters, and the stove, heedfully swathed and tended as though it were some prince going on a journey, was borne on the shoulders of six stout Bavarians down the stairs and out of the door. Even behind all those wrappings August felt the icy bite of the intense cold at dawn of a winter's day in Munich. The men moved the stove with exceeding gentleness and care, so that he had often been far more roughly shaken in his big brothers' arms than he was in his journey now.

The stout carriers tramped right across Munich to the railway station. Whether for a long or a short journey, whether for weal or woe, the stove with August still within it, was once more hoisted up into a great van; but this time it was not all alone, and the two dealers as well as the six porters were all with it.

Though the men grumbled about the state of the roads and the season, they were hilarious and well content, for they laughed often, and August, like a shrewd little boy as he was, thought to himself, with a terrible pang: "They have sold Hirschvogel for some great sum! They have sold him already!"

It is but an hour and a quarter that the train usually takes to pass from Munich to the Wurm-See or Lake of Starnberg; but this morning the journey was much slower, because the way was encumbered by snow. When it did reach Possenhofen and stop, and the stove was lifted out once more, August could see through the fretwork of the brass door that this Wurm-See was a calm and noble piece of water, with low wooded banks and distant mountains, a peaceful, serene place, full of rest. Before he had time to get more than a glimpse of the green gliding surface, the stove was again lifted up and placed on a large boat

BERT R. ELLIOTT

that was in waiting. The boat then moved across the lake to Leoni.

Presently they touched the pier at Leoni.

"Now, men, for a stout mile and half!" said one of the dealers to his porters, who, stout, strong men as they were, showed a disposition to grumble at their task. Encouraged by large promises, they shouldered sullenly the Nuremberg stove, grumbling again at its preposterous weight, but little dreaming that they carried within it a small, panting, trembling boy.

The way the men took was a mile and a half in length, but the road was heavy with snow, and the burden they bore was heavier still. The dealers cheered them on, swore at them and praised them in one breath. The road seemed terribly long to the anxious tradesmen, to the plodding porters, to the poor little man inside the stove, as he kept sinking and rising, sinking and rising, with each of their steps.

Where they were going he had no idea, only after a very long time he lost the sense of the fresh icy wind blowing on his face through the brass-work above, and felt by their movements

307

beneath him that they were mounting steps or stairs. Then he heard a great many different voices, but he could not understand what was being said. He felt that his bearers paused some time, then moved on and on again. Their feet went so softly he thought they must be moving on carpet, and as he felt a warm air come to him, he concluded that he was in some heated chambers. What he fancied was that he was in some museum, like that which he had seen in the city of Innsbruck.

The voices he heard were very hushed, and the steps seemed to go away, far away, leaving him alone with Hirschvogel. He dared not look out, but he peeped through the brass-work, and all he could see was a big carved lion's head in ivory, with a gold crown atop. It belonged to a velvet fauteuil, but he could not see the chair, only the ivory lion. There was a delicious fragrance in the air,—a fragrance as of flowers. "Only how can it be flowers?" thought August. "It is November!" From afar off, as it seemed, there came   dreamy, exquisite music.

He did not know it, but he was in the royal castle of Berg, and the music he heard was the music of Wagner, who was playing in a distant room.

Presently he heard a fresh step near him, and he heard a low voice say, close behind him, "So!" An exclamation no doubt, of admiration and wonder at the beauty of Hirschvogel. Then the same voice said, after a long pause, during which, as August thought, this new-comer was examining all the details of the wondrous fire-tower, "It was well bought; it is exceedingly beautiful! It is undoubtedly the work of Augustin Hirschvogel."

Then the hand of the speaker turned the round handle of the brass door, and the fainting soul of the poor little prisoner within grew sick with fear. The door was slowly drawn open, some one bent down and looked in, and the same voice called aloud, in surprise, "What is this in it? A live child!"

THE TREASURE CHEST

Then August, terrified beyond all self-control, and dominated by one master-passion, sprang out of the body of the stove and fell at the feet of the speaker.

"Oh, let me stay! Pray, meinherr, let me stay!" he sobbed. "I have come all the way with Hirschvogel!"

Some gentlemen's hands seized him, not gently by any means, and their lips angrily muttered in his ear, "Little knave, peace! be quiet! hold your tongue! It is the king!"

They were about to drag him out of the august atmosphere as if he had been some dangerous beast come there to slay, but the voice he had heard said in kind accents, "Poor child! he is very young. Let him go. Let him speak to me."

The word of a king is law to his courtiers; so, sorely against their wish, the angry and astonished chamberlains let August slide out of their grasp, and he stood there in his little rough sheepskin coat and his thick, mud-covered boots, with his curling hair all in a tangle, in the midst of the most beautiful chamber he had ever dreamed of, and in the presence of a young man with a beautiful dark face, and eyes full of dreams and fire; and the young man said to him,—

"My child, how came you here, hidden in this stove? Be not afraid, tell me the truth. I am the king."

August in an instinct of homage cast his great battered black hat with the tarnished gold tassels down on the floor of the room, and folded his little brown hands in supplication. He was too intensely in earnest to be in any way abashed; he was too lifted out of himself by his love for Hirschvogel to be conscious of any awe before any earthly majesty. He was only so glad—so glad it was the king.

"Oh, dear king!" he said, with trembling entreaty in his voice, "Hirschvogel was ours. We have loved it all our lives; and father sold it. When I saw that it did really go from us, then I said to myself I would go with it; and I have come all the way inside it. And last night it spoke and said beautiful things. And I pray you to let me live with it. I will go out every morning and cut wood for it and you, if only you will let me stay beside it. No one ever has fed it with fuel but me since I grew big enough, and it loves me;—it does indeed; it said so last night; and it said that it had been happier with us than if it were in any palace—"

And then his breath failed him, and, as he lifted his eager, pale face to the king's, great tears were falling down his cheeks.

Now, the king liked all poetic and uncommon things, and there was that in the child's face which pleased and touched him. He motioned to his gentlemen to leave the little boy alone.

"What is your name?" he asked him.

"I am August Strehla. My father is Karl Strehla. We live in Hall; and Hirschvogel has been ours so long,—so long!"

His lips quivered with a broken sob.

"And have you truly traveled in this stove all the way from Tyrol?"

"Yes," said August, "no one thought to look inside till you did."

The king laughed; then another view of the matter occurred to him. "Who bought the stove of your father?" he inquired.

"Traders of Munich," said August.

"What sum did they pay, do you know?"

"Two hundred florins," said August, with a great sigh of shame. "It was so much money, and he is so poor, and there are so many of us."

The king turned to his gentlemen-in-waiting. "Did these dealers of Munich come with the stove?"

He was answered in the affirmative. He desired them to be sought for and brought before him. As one of his chamberlains hastened on the errand, the monarch looked at August with compassion.

THE TREASURE CHEST

"You are very pale, little fellow: when did you eat last?"

"I had some bread and sausage with me; yesterday afternoon I finished it."

"You would like to eat now?"

"If I might have a little water I would be glad; my throat is very dry."

The king had water and wine brought for him, and cake also;

but August, though he drank eagerly, could not swallow anything. His mind was in too great a tumult.

"May I stay with Hirschvogel?" he said, with feverish agitation.

"Wait a little," said the king, and asked, abruptly, "What do you wish to be when you are a man?"

"A painter. I wish to be what Hirschvogel was,—I mean the master that made *my* Hirschvogel."

"I understand," said the king.

Then the two dealers were brought into their sovereign's presence. They were so terribly alarmed, not being either so innocent or so ignorant as August was, that they were trembling as though they were being led to the slaughter, and they were so utterly astonished too at a child having come all the way from Tyrol in the stove, as a gentleman of the court had just told them this child had done, that they could not tell what to say or where to look, and presented a very foolish aspect indeed.

"Did you buy this stove of this boy's father for two hundred florins?" the king asked; and his voice was no longer soft and kind as it had been when addressing the child, but very stern.

"Yes, your majesty," murmured the trembling traders.

"And how much did the gentleman who purchased it for me give to you?"

"Two thousand ducats, your majesty," muttered the dealers, frightened out of their wits, and telling the truth in their fright.

"You will give at once to this boy's father the two thousand gold ducats that you received, less the two hundred Austrian florins that you paid him," said the king. "You are great rogues. Be thankful you are not more greatly punished."

He dismissed them by a sign to his courtiers.

August heard, and felt dazzled yet miserable. Two thousand gold Bavarian ducats for his father! Why, his father would never need to go any more to the salt-baking! And yet, whether

THE TREASURE CHEST

for ducats or for florins, Hirschvogel was sold just the same, and would the king let him stay with it?—would he?

"Oh, do! please do!" he murmured, joining his little brown weather-stained hands, and kneeling before the young monarch.

He looked down on the child and smiled once more.

"Rise up, my little man," he said, in a kind voice; "kneel only to your God. Will I let you stay with your Hirschvogel? Yes, I will; you shall stay at my court, and you shall be taught to be a painter. You must grow up worthily, and win all the laurels at our Schools of Art, and if when you are twenty-one years old you have done well and bravely, then I will give you your Nuremberg stove. And now go away with this gentleman, and be not afraid, and you shall light a fire every morning in Hirschvogel, but you will not need to go out and cut the wood."

Then he smiled and stretched out his hand; the courtiers tried to make August understand that he ought to bow and touch it with his lips, but August could not understand that anyhow; he was too happy. He threw his two arms about the king's knees, and kissed his feet passionately.

August is only a scholar yet, but he is a happy scholar, and promises to be a great man. Sometimes he goes back for a few days to Hall, where the gold ducats have made his father prosperous. In the old house-room there is a large white porcelain stove of Munich, the king's gift to Dorothea and 'Gilda.

And August never goes home without going into the great church and saying his thanks to God, who blessed his strange winter's journey in the Nuremberg stove. As for his dream in the dealers' room that night, he will never admit that he did dream it; he still declares that he saw it all, and heard the voice of Hirschvogel. And who shall say that he did not, for what is the gift of the poet and the artist except to see the sights which others cannot see and hear the sounds that others cannot hear?

—*Abridged*

A CAVALIER TUNE
Boot and Saddle
Robert Browning

Boot, saddle, to horse, and away!
Rescue my castle before the hot day
Brightens to blue from its silvery gray!
    Boot, saddle, to horse, and away!

Ride past the suburbs, asleep as you'd say;
Many's the friend there, will listen and pray
"God's luck to gallants that strike up the lay—
    Boot, saddle, to horse, and away!"

Forty miles off, like a roebuck at bay,
Flouts Castle Brancepeth the Roundheads array!
Who laughs, "Good fellows ere this, by my fay,
    Boot, saddle, to horse, and away!"

Who?   My wife Gertrude; that, honest and gay,
Laughs when you talk of surrendering, "Nay!
I've better counsellors; what counsel they?
    Boot, saddle, to horse, and away!"

THE SECRET DOOR
Susan Coolidge

Knowle, in Kent, is an ancient manor-house. It stands knee-deep in rich garden and pasture lands, with hay-fields and apple-orchards stretching beyond, and solemn oak woods which whisper and shake their wise heads when the wind blows, as though possessed of secrets which must not be spoken.

Very much as it looks today, it looked two hundred and thirty years ago, when Charles the First was king of England. Blue Christmas smokes curled from the twisted chimneys in 1645, just as they will this year and the same dinnery fragrance filled the air. A few changes there may be—thicker trees, beds of gay flowers which were not known in that day; and where once the moat—a ditch-like stream of green water covered with weeds and scum—ran round the walls, is now a trimly cut border of verdant turf. But in all important respects the house keeps its old look, undisturbed by modern times and ways.

In the same nursery where modern boys and girls eat, sleep, and learn their A, B, C to-day, two children lived—little Ralph Tresham and his sister Henrietta. Quaint, old-fashioned creatures they would look to us now; but, in spite of their formal dresses and speech, they were bright and merry and happy as any children you can find among your acquaintances. Ralph's name was pronounced "Rafe," and he called his sister "Hexie."

Christmas did not come to Knowle in its usual bright shape in 1645. Gloom and sadness and anxiety overshadowed the house; and though the little ones did not understand what the cause of the anxiety was, they felt something wrong, and went about quietly whispering to each other in corners, instead of whooping and laughing, as had been their wont. They had eaten their Christmas beef, and toasted the king in a thimbleful of wine, as usual, but their mother cried when they did so; and Joyce, the old butler, had carried off the pudding with a face like a funeral. So after dinner they crept away to the nursery, and there, by the window, began a long whispered talk. Hexie had something very exciting to tell.

"Nurse thought I was asleep," she said, "but I wasn't quite; and when they began to talk I woke up. Did you know that there were such creatures as Bogies, Rafe? Dorothy thinks we have got one in our house, and that its hole is in the great gallery, because once when she was there dusting the armor, she heard a queer noise in the wall, and what else could it be? It eats a great deal, does the Bogie. That's the reason nurse is sure we have got one. It ate all the cold sheep's-head yesterday, and the day before half the big pasty. No victual is safe in the larder, the Bogie has such a big appetite, nurse says."

"I remember about the sheep's-head," said Rafe, meditatively. "Almost all of it was left, and I looked to see it come in cold; but when I asked, Joyce said there was none. Cold sheep's-head is very good. Do you remember how much Humphrey used to like it?"

"I don't remember exactly, it is so long ago," replied Hexie. "How long is it since brother Humphrey went away? Won't he ever come back?"

"I asked Winifred once, but she only said God knew, that nothing had been heard of him since the battle when the Roundheads took the king prisoner. He might be dead, or he might be escaped into foreign parts—and then she cried, oh, so hard, Hexie! But, about the Bogie, how curious it must be to meet one! Oh, I say, let us go to the gallery now, and listen if we can hear any strange noises there. Will you?"

"Oh, Rafe! I'm afraid. I don't quite like—"

"But you can't be afraid if I'm there," said Rafe, valiantly; "besides, I'll put on Humphrey's old sword which he left behind. Then if the Bogie comes—we shall see!"

Rafe spoke like a conquering hero, Hexie thought; so, though she trembled, she made no further objection, but stood by while he lifted down the sword, helped to fasten its belt over his shoulder, and followed along the passageway which led to the gallery. The heavy sword clattered and rattled as it dragged on the floor, and the sound was echoed in a ghostly way, which renewed Hexie's fears.

"Rafe! Rafe! let us go back," she cried.

"Go back yourself if you are afraid," replied Ralph, stoutly; and as going back alone through the dim passage seemed just then worse than staying where she was, Hexie stayed.

Very softly they unlatched the gallery door, and stole in. It was a long, lofty apartment, panelled with cedar-wood, to which time had given a beautiful light brown color. The ceiling, of the same wood, was carved, here and there, with shields, coats of arms, and other devices. There was little furniture; one tall cabinet, a few high-backed Dutch chairs, and some portraits hanging on the walls. The sun, not yet quite set, poured a stream of red light across the polished floor, leaving the far corners and the empty spaces formidably dusk. The children had seldom been in the gallery at this hour, and it looked to them almost like a strange place, not at all as it did at noonday when they came to jump up and down the slippery floor, and play hide-and-seek in the corners which now seemed so dark and dismal.

Even Rafe felt the difference, and shivered in spite of his bold heart and the big sword by his side. Timidly they went forward, hushing their footsteps and peering furtively into the shadows. Suddenly Hexie stopped with a little scream.

Close to them stood a huge suit of armor, larger and taller than a man. The empty eye-holes of the helmet glared out quite like real eyes, and the whole figure was terrible enough to frighten any little girl. But it was not at the armor that Hexie screamed; the iron man was an old friend of the children's. Many a game of hide-and-seek had they played around, and behind, and even inside him; for Humphrey had contrived a cunning way by which the figure could be taken to pieces and put together again; and more than once Rafe had been popped inside, and had lain shaking with laughter while Hexie vainly searched for him through all the gallery. This had not happened lately, for Rafe was hardly strong enough to manage by himself the screws and hinges which opened the armor; but he knew the iron man too well to scream at him, and so did Hexie. The object which excited her terror was something different, and so strange and surprising that it is no wonder she screamed.

Close by the armor, half hidden by a curtain of heavy tapestry, was an open door, where never door had been known to be. It stood ajar, and dimly visible inside was a narrow staircase winding upward.

"The hole of the Bogie!" gasped Hexie, clutching at Rafe's arm. He started, and felt for the sword. It rattled fearfully, and the sound completed Hexie's terror. She burst away, flew like a scared lapwing down the gallery, along the passages, and never stopped till she reached the nursery and her own bed, where, with two pillows and the quilt drawn over her head, she

THE TREASURE CHEST

lay sobbing bitterly at the thought of Ralph left behind, to be eaten perhaps by the Bogie! Poor little Hexie!

Ralph, meanwhile, stood his ground. His heart beat very fast, but he would not run away,—that was for girls. It must be owned, however, that when a moment later the sound of muffled voices became audible down the stairs, he trembled extremely, and was guilty of hiding behind the curtain.

The voices drew nearer, steps sounded, and two figures came out of the narrow doorway. Could there be two Bogies? No wonder they ate so much. But in another minute all thought of Bogies vanished from Ralph's mind, for in one of the figures he recognized his own sister Winifred.

Her companion was a man. There was something familiar in his form. It moved forward, and Ralph jumped so that the big sword rattled again. Bogie number two was his brother Humphrey, mourned as dead ever since the summer before, when so many brave gentlemen gave up their lives for King Charles at the battle of Naseby.

"What noise was that?" whispered Winifred, fearfully.

"Some sound from below," replied Humphrey, after listening a moment. "Must you go, Winnie?"

"I must, dear Humphrey. I dare not absent myself longer lest I be missed and suspected. Oh, if tomorrow were but over, and you safe on the French lugger and over the sea! I cannot breathe while this hiding goes on, and you ever in danger of being discovered and taken by the Roundheads."

"I suppose I ought to be glad also," said Humphrey, ruefully, "but to me that French lugger means exile, and loneliness for the rest of my life, perhaps. Better have laid down my life with the rest at Naseby, in striking one last blow for the king."

"Don't, don't speak so!" protested Winifred, tearfully. "You are alive, thank God; and once these wars are over we may rejoin you, and have a happy home somewhere, if not in the land of our fathers. Now, dear Humphrey, have you all you need for the night?"

"Christmas cheer," said Humphrey, in a would-be cheerful voice. "Beef and ale,—what better fare could be? You are a gallant provider, my Winnie. That sheep's-head was wondrous savory. I say though, what do the servants think of the famine I create in the larder?"

"Oh, the stupid things fancy that a Bogie has taken up his residence here. A very hungry Bogie, Joyce calls the creature!"

The brother and sister laughed; then they kissed each other.

"Good-night, Winifred."

"Good-night, brother." And Humphrey vanished up the stairs. Winifred lingered a moment; then, as if remembering something, opened the door again and ran after him. Ralph marked that she laid her hand on a particular boss in the carved wainscot, and pressed it in hard, whereon the door sprang open. He stole out, laid his hand on the same boss, and felt the spring give way under his touch. Some undefined idea of stealing in later, to make Humphrey a visit, was in his head; but he heard Winifred returning, and hurried out of the gallery. Putting back the sword in its place, he entered the nursery. No Hexie was visible, but a sobbing sound drew his attention to a tumbled heap on the bed.

"Is that you, Hexie? Why, what are you crying about?" pulling away the pillow, which she held tight.

"Oh, Rafe! Then the Bogie didn't eat you after all!" And Hexie buried her tear-stained face in his shoulder.

"Bogie! Nonsense! There are no such things as Bogies!"

"What was it, then, that lived up that dreadful stairs?"

"I can't tell you; only it was nothing at all dreadful. And, Hexie, don't say a word about that door to any one, will you? It might make great trouble if you did."

"I did tell Deborah, when she fetched the candle and asked why I cried, that I saw a strange door in the gallery," faltered Hexie, truthful, though penitent.

"Oh! Hexie, how could you? I don't like Deborah, her father is a crop-eared knave and a Roundhead. Humphrey said so one day. How could you talk to her about the door, Hexie?"

"I—don't know. I was frightened, and she asked me," sobbed Hexie. "Will it do any harm, Rafe?"

"It may," said Rafe, gloomily. "But don't cry, Hexie. You meant no harm, at all events."

"Oh, don't speak so gravely and so like Joyce," said Hexie, much troubled. She cried herself to sleep that night. Deborah, who undressed her, asked many questions about the gallery and the door.

"It was very dark, and perhaps I mistook,"—that was all Hexie could be made to say. Ralph was disturbed and wakeful, and slept later than usual next morning. He jumped up in a hurry and made what haste he could with dressing and breakfast, but it seemed as though they never took so much time before; and all the while he ate he was conscious of a stir and bustle in the house, which excited his curiosity very much. Knocking— the sound of feet—something unusual going on.

As soon as possible he slipped away from the nurse and ran to the gallery. The door was half open. He looked in, and stood still with terror. Men in brown uniforms and steel caps were there sounding the walls and tapping the floor-boards with staves—Roundheads in search of Humphrey! The gallery seemed full of them, though when Rafe counted there were but five.

"This man of iron was, in all likelihood, a Malignant also," he heard one of them say, striking the armor with his fist.

"He is somewhat old for that. Methinks that is armor of the time of that man of blood, Harry the Eighth. Move it aside Jotham, that we may search the farther panel."

So the heavy figure was thrust into a corner, and the men went on tapping with their wands. Rafe groaned within himself when he heard them declare that the wall sounded hollow, and saw them searching for a spring. Twenty times it seemed as though they must have lighted on the right place. Twenty times they just missed it.

"We were ill advised to come without tools," declared the man who seemed leader of the party. "Come thou to my shop, Peter Kettle, and thou, Bartimeus and Zerubbabel, and we will fetch such things as are needful. Jotham, stay thou here, to see that no man escapeth from the concealment behind the wall."

So four of the men went away, leaving Jotham striding up and down as on guard. Presently came a shout from beneath the window,—

"Jotham! our leader hath dropped his pouch in which are the keys of the smithy. Hasten and bring it to the outer door."

"Aye, aye!" answered Jotham, and, pouch in hand, he ran down the stairs. Now was Rafe's opportunity. Like a flash he was across the gallery, his hand on the boss. The door flew open, and he fell into the arms of Humphrey, who, sword in hand and teeth set, stood on the lower step of the staircase, prepared to sell his liberty as dearly as possible.

"Rafe! little Rafe!" he exclaimed.

"Hush! The man will come back," panted Rafe. "Come away—hide—oh, where?" Then with a sudden inspiration he dragged his brother toward the iron man. "Get inside," he cried. "They will never think of searching there! Oh, Humphrey —make haste! Get inside!"

There was no time to be lost. With the speed of desperation, Humphrey unscrewed, lifted, stepped inside the armor. Rafe slipped the fastenings together, whispering, "Shut your eyes." and flew back to his hiding-place. Just in time, for Jotham's step was on the stair, and next moment he entered the gallery, and resumed his march up and down, little dreaming that the man sought for was peeping through the helmet holes at him, not three feet away.

Presently the other soldiers came back with hammers and wrenches, and in a short time the beautiful wainscot, split into pieces, lay on the floor. Suddenly there was a shout. The secret door had flown open, and the staircase stood revealed. Four of the men, with pikes and pistols, prepared to ascend, while the fifth guarded the opening below.

At that moment Winifred entered the gallery from the farther end. She turned deadly pale when she saw the open door.

"Oh! Heaven have mercy!" she cried, and dropped half fainting into a chair.

Rafe darted across the floor and seized her hand.

"Hush," he whispered. "Don't say a word, sister. *He* is safe."

"He? Who?" cried the amazed Winifred.

But now voices sounded from above. The men were coming down. Winifred rallied her courage, rose, and went forward. She was still very white, but she spoke in a steady voice.

Her two brothers, Humphrey in his hiding-place and little Rafe by her side, both admired her greatly.

"What is the meaning of this, Jotham Green?" she demanded. "By what warrant do you enter and spoil our house?"

"By the warrant which all true men have to search for traitors," said Jotham.

"You will find none such here," responded Winifred, firmly.

"We find the lurking-place in which one such has doubtless lain," said Zerubbabel. "Where holes exist, look out for vermin."

"You are less than civil, neighbor. An old house like this has many strange nooks and corners of which the inhabitants may have neither use nor knowledge. If your search is done, I will beg you to make good the damage you have caused as best you may, and with as little noise as possible, that my mother be not alarmed. Jotham Green, you are a good workman, I know. I recollect how deftly you once repaired that cabinet for us."

All the men knew Winifred, and her calm and decided manner made its impression. Jotham slowly picked up the fragments of the pannelling and began to fit them together. The rest consulted, and at last rather sheepishly, and with a muttered half apology about "wrong information," went away, taking with them the injured woodwork, which Jotham undertook to repair. Rafe's first words after they disappeared were,—

"Winifred, you must dismiss Deborah. It is she that has betrayed us."

"How do you know that, Rafe?"

Then it all came out. Winifred listened to the tale with streaming tears.

"Oh, Rafe, my darling, how brave you were! You played the man for us today, and have saved Humphrey. The men will not return today, and tonight the lugger sails."

And Humphrey was saved. Before morning, well disguised,

he had made his way across country to a little fishing-port, embarked, and reached France without further accident.

So that strange Christmas adventure ended happily. It was all long, long ago. But still the beautiful old manor-house stands amid its gardens and pasture lands, with the silvery look of time on its gray walls. Still the armed figure keeps guard beside the secret staircase, the tapestry hangs in the old heavy folds, evening reddens the cedar walls and the polished floor, and everything occupies the same place and wears the same look that it did when little Rafe played the man in that gallery, and saved his brother Humphrey, more than two hundred years ago.

THE CAVALIER'S ESCAPE
Walter Thornbury

Trample! trample! went the roan,
  Trap! trap! went the gray;
But PAD! PAD! PAD! like a thing that was mad,
  My chestnut broke away.
It was just five miles from Salisbury town,
  And but one hour to day.

THUD! THUD! came on the heavy roan,
  Rap! rap! the mettled gray;
But my chestnut mare was of blood so rare,
  That she showed them all the way.
Spur on! spur on!—I doffed my hat,
  And wished them all good-day.

They splashed through miry rut and pool,—
  Splintered through fence and rail,
But chestnut Kate switched over the gate,—
  I saw them droop and tail.
To Salisbury town—but a mile of down,
  Once over this brook and rail.

THE TREASURE CHEST

Trap! Trap! I heard their echoing hoofs
  Past the walls of mossy stone,
The roan flew on at a staggering pace,
  But blood is better than bone.
I patted old Kate, and gave her the spur,
  For I knew it was all my own.

But trample! trample! came their steeds,
  And I saw their wolf's eyes burn,
I felt like a royal hart at bay,
  And made me ready to turn.
I looked where highest grew the May,
  And deepest arched the fern.

I flew at the first knave's sallow throat,
  One blow, and he was down.
The second rogue fired twice, and missed,
  I sliced the villain's crown,—
Clove through the rest—and flogged brave Kate,
  Fast, fast to Salisbury town!

Pad! pad! they came on the level sward,
  Thud! thud! upon the sand,—
With a gleam of swords and a burning match,
  And a shaking of flag and hand;
But one long bound, and I passed the gate,
  Safe from the canting band.

DONN P. CRANE

THE ADVENTURES OF ALEXANDER SELKIRK

Being a true Account of one Mr. Alexander Selkirk, Master of a Merchant-Man who was left ashore on a desolate Island in the South-Seas, where he lived Four Years and Four Months without seeing the Face of Man. To which is added a Description of the Island where he was cast; how he subsisted; the several Strange Things he saw; and how he used to spend his Time. Told from the Accounts of Captain Woodes Rogers, Sir Richard Steele and other Eminent Men, who had the Tale directly from the Lips of the said Alexander Selkirk in Person, he being further known to Fame by reason of his Adventures having furnished to Daniel Defoe the idea for writing of Robinson Crusoe.

IN the year 1704, there was cruising off the coast of Mexico an English galley, by name the Cinque Ports, 96 tons burden, 16 guns, and sixty odd men. The Cinque Ports had been a twelvemonth or more in those parts, at first in company with another vessel under Captain Dampier, on a voyage of exploration and adventure. In those days the greed of France and Spain to rule the world and crowd England out of the South Seas, made the relations of England with those countries none of the friendliest, and the British government commissioned private vessels to make war on the boats of the enemy wherever they might overtake them on the high seas. Of such sort was the Cinque Ports, and she had sailed along the rich gold coast of Spanish America, now and again running down some Spanish galleon, and meeting with sundry and divers adventures. Her commander was one Captain Straddling, a cross-grained, quarrelsome fellow, and he had serving under him as sailing master of the vessel, a certain hot-headed, independent young Scotchman, by name Alexander Selkirk, or Selcraig, as it is more properly written, son of a well-to-do tanner and shoemaker of Largo in Fifeshire, and a follower of the sea from his youth. Now Selkirk was an expert and able seaman, but from the start of the voyage he got on none too well with

Straddling. Straddling was an insolent bully. Right and left it was hot tongue and heavy fist wherever Straddling appeared on deck. Month after month, Selkirk held his temper in check—Straddling was his superior officer and he had a sailor's wish and training to obey. Yet was he one to brook domineering from no man, and now and again when Straddling rode his high horse, there was an outburst from Selkirk that threatened the gathering of a terrific storm.

As they sailed day after day and month after month, the Cinque Ports grew leaky and altogether unseaworthy, so Captain Straddling found himself forced at last to put in for fresh water and repairs at the island of Juan Fernandez, some four hundred miles off the coast of Chili. Juan Fernandez was lonely, wild and uninhabited. It was off the beaten track of commerce and was rarely visited by vessels of any kind, but Straddling had been forced earlier on the same voyage to put in there, and thither under stress of necessity he went again. During the three weeks or so that they lay to in the chief bay of the island, the differences between Straddling and Selkirk grew daily worse, till at last on the very day when the vessel was getting under way, an angry discussion arose. Hotter and hotter it grew. It is not improbable that fists as well as tongues came into play to settle the question, but, however that may be, the upshot of the whole matter was that Selkirk's temper took such furious fire, he burst out the door of the Captain's cabin and rushed up the companionway, shouting:

"Let me off this crazy vessel! Put me ashore, I say! I'll sail not a day longer under such an obstinate, pig-headed mule!"

The Captain followed his irate master onto the deck, bestowing upon him a string of like forceful compliments and bawling out:

"Down with the pinnace! Take him ashore! Off with the mutinous hound! He's turned out o' service!"

While the sailors swarmed to the small boat, Selkirk calmed

himself sufficiently to gather together certain of his belongings, and, having piled these into the pinnace, he was over the side of the galley and being rowed off to the shore almost before he knew it.

He saw before him a wild, luxuriant and yet savage coast, a mass of jagged, volcanic rock, hurled up in ages agone by some mighty disturbance of the earth and rudely piled into blocks and pinnacles. Mountains towered above, and over all rose the craggy peak of El Yunque (the Anvil) of which no man knew whether or no it would one day belch forth fire and overwhelm all that lay at its base with a mighty stream of lava. Yet Selkirk's spirit, at that moment, was as wild and untamed as that savage shore, and the fire within him smouldering, ready to flame, like volcanic fires of the earth. To such a state of mind the shore was inviting rather than forbidding. Anger and defiance buoyed him up. He held his head high and his eyes were glowing. Straddling himself had command of the small boat, and the moment its keel grated on the sand, Selkirk sprang lightly ashore, standing by with the utmost unconcern while the Captain gave orders concerning the unloading of his luggage.

The matter was carried through with the greatest dispatch and the sailors were soon bidding their comrade a sorrowful farewell, while Straddling sat in the boat and in surly fashion called them to make haste and be off.

All at once—Selkirk never knew how it came about so quickly,—out there, bobbing up and down on the swelling blue, half way back to the galley and going at a tremendous clip, he saw the small boat, loaded with men, and there alone on the shore he stood, Alexander Selkirk, alone, all alone!

In a trice with a sudden revulsion of feeling, it came over him what he had done. Anger and defiance were dead. The scales had fallen from his eyes. He knew what he had done. To stay alone on a savage shore—to hear no human voice—to see no

human face—for years, perhaps forever! He raised his voice in a cry that was almost a shriek, stretched out his arms toward his comrades and rushed to the very edge of the water.

"Come back! Come back! Come back!" he cried. The wind carried his voice away, and yet it seemed to him he heard from the stern of the pinnace where the Captain sat, a sound of mocking laughter. Even while it echoed in his ears, the men in the small boat boarded the larger vessel. All sail was set, and the Cinque Ports made off out of the bay and into the Pacific. He watched with straining eyes till her sails, a mere speck in the distance, dipped down behind the horizon, and the whole vast blue of ocean was left stretching empty and lone before him.

How long he stood there, almost in a stupor staring off to sea, he never knew, but suddenly he became aware that the stillness about him was so intense, it seemed of a truth to shriek in his ears. Thus brought back to himself, he looked about and observed that the sun was low in the sky. In a short time darkness would swoop down upon his solitude. Now he had no knowledge whether or no savage beasts abounded on the island, and he judged it to be most necessary that he find a shelter ere nightfall. Accordingly, though with weak and trembling knees, he searched along the shore. In a little ravine at no great distance back from the beach, he came upon a cave of moderate dimensions that offered a most excellent retreat and lay not far from a stream of fresh water.

Hither he dragged his belongings from the place on the sand where they had been dumped, and being now at liberty and of a mind to take stock of the same, he found he had with him a sea chest containing his bedding and a few extra articles of clothing, a firelock, a pound of gunpowder, a large quantity of bullets, a few pounds of tobacco, a hatchet, a knife, a kettle, a Bible, several books that concerned navigation, and his mathematical instruments. In provisions for the sustenance of life, he had but the quantity of two meals. It being then nearly dark, and no opportunity offering to search for food that night, he was obliged for the present to appease his hunger by consuming a share from his slender store. He then closed the entrance to his cave by means of his sea chest and laid himself down to sleep with his firelock close by his side. Several times during the night he fancied he heard growling and roaring as of wild beasts, but the darkness passed without incident and the sun rose with remarkable splendor.

It was early October, being spring in that latitude, and within the verdant little gorge where the cave was situated, all was bud and bloom and twitter of birds and gladsome play of sunlight and shadows. Selkirk, notwithstanding, had eyes for none of the beauties about him. He thought only of the misfortune, swift and terrible, that was come upon him. For days he sat moping and brooding by the sea shore, straining his eyes to catch sight of a sail. Not till the darkness of night made it impossible longer to watch, did he close his eyes, and then he slept but poorly. As to eating, he never ate anything at all till the extreme of hunger constrained him, and even then he took no care to make his victuals palatable. He ate only of the craw-fish and turtle to be found on the shore, for he felt spell-bound to the beach. Fortunately he had with him a kettle, and by patient trial he learned to get fire by rubbing two sticks together on his knees, after the Indian fashion. Sometimes he broiled the shell-fish and some-

times he boiled them, but he found nothing that he ate to his
taste for want of salt to season it.

The whole island was in truth rich in natural beauties, in hills
and valleys, delightful springs and leaping mountain streams, but
Selkirk saw no beauty in it anywhere. To him its loneliness, its
deadly stillness, made it all as frightful as some distorted vision of
a dream. He only left the shore to climb up to a certain high point
by the side of El Yunque, whence a gap in the trap-rock offered a
still wider view of the sea. He made no count of days, he took no
care of himself, of his clothing, or the cave in which he lived.
All his soul was absorbed in that one thought, to watch for a sail,
and he wore a beaten track from the shore to his look-out, from
his look-out to the shore.

Along in November, as he slept an uneasy sleep within his
cave, he was suddenly awakened by the increase of that growling
and roaring as of wild beasts which had disturbed his first night
on the island. It sounded somewhat between the howling of
wolves and the thunderous roar of larger beasts and was of a
nearness to make him hold all night close by his firelock. He never
closed his eyes again for uncertainty but when the sun was risen
and he stepped cautiously out of his cave towards the shore, there
before him on the beach he saw myriads of seals that had come up
out of the sea during the night. Some were in the water but
more were on the land and these were moving their heads about,
raising themselves on their flippers, roaring and bellowing. It
being Selkirk's custom at once to go to his look-out on the beach,
he approached the seals with some uncertainty as to their temper
in letting him pass through. He held his firelock ready to beat
them off with the butt in case they made at him, but he found
them so surly and determined not to give way, that he was forced
to beat a retreat before them. In a short time their numbers
had so increased as others drew up out of the sea that they lined

the shore very thick for above half a mile of ground all around the bay. It appeared this was the spot where it was their custom to come each year and raise their young, and though seals be usually peaceable creatures, as there came to be many young among them, the old ones grew still more surly. Far from moving out of the way, they would rise up on their flippers in their desire to protect the whelps and make at a man fiercely like an angry dog, if he offered to go among them. Moreover, day and night, they kept up a continuous noise of a hideous sort. So Selkirk was obliged to avoid the beach and largely to keep his look-out from the high place on the side of El Yunque, and in his present state of mind the dreadful howlings and voices of these monsters of the deep seemed almost too terrible to be borne. He had been in the past not of a nature to bear misfortune calmly, and many a time from sheer impatience and impotent inward rage against the helplessness of his wretched lot he shook his fists and cried aloud; and as no sail appeared day after day, he even meditated casting himself into the sea. "Could the thought of man," he often demanded of himself, "devise a more utterly miserable lot than life alone on a desert isle?"

And then at last one day as he was going through his sea chest in search of some trifle or other, his hand fell upon the Bible and he drew it forth with a strange tugging at his heart strings. God knows how that Bible had ever come into his chest. It was nothing that he himself cherished or would have thought of putting there. It must have been his mother who had slipped it in among the linens her hands had packed with tender care, and as he drew it forth on this particular day in the midst of that lonely island, it took his thoughts with painful vividness back home. There rose before him in a flash the rolling downs of Fifeshire, green and dotted with sheep, the great gray cliffs along the shore, and nestling beneath them in the bay, the little town of Largo. At the west end of the village there was his home, his father's cozy, homey dwelling, surrounded by its garden, and there in the lattice window sat his mother knitting, looking off to sea perhaps and longing for news of him. Unconsciously his hand caressed the Bible; he climbed the height to his look-out, sat down with the book on his lap and buried his face in his hands. He could see it all so clearly. And now there rose before him,

all overgrown with ivy, so peaceful and serene, the kirk itself. He could see the light that streamed in through its stained glass windows, the congregation there in Sabbath day attire with fresh and happy faces, and over all a Sabbath air of quiet joy and calm. He could see his mother by his side, her eyes aglow with pride in him,—so much she had expected from this, her stalwart son. And then he minded how during the very services in the kirk, his hot temper had led him to start a-brawling. His mother's eyes grew dark with shame, men thrust him out by force, and on the books of the kirk he could see the record written as with points of fire: "Alexander Selkirk having been for his indecent behavior, summoned for trial before the kirk sessions on this 27th day August, 1695, did not compear, being gone away to the seas."

Yes, that was what he had done—run away from his punishment to the seas; and, worse still, not three years agone, when he was a man grown and home once more, he had been summoned again before the kirk sessions and publicly rebuked before the whole congregation for quarreling with his brothers and raising a tumult in his father's home. Suddenly his shoulders shook with sobs and all his soul revolted against that unruly temper that had caused him so much trouble all his life. Had it not been for that same temper, he would not have been here alone and miserable on a desert island. He wept as he had not done since he was a lad at his mother's knee, and in him rose the resolution strong, henceforth to bar out that beastly fault and never let it run away with him again. The tears he shed left him greatly purified and refreshed even as the earth after a thunder storm. Slowly he opened the book on his knees and read:

"They wandered in the wilderness in a solitary way; they found no city to dwell in.

"Hungry and thirsty their soul fainted in them;

"Then they cried unto the Lord in their trouble and he delivered them out of their distresses."

And again:

"The wilderness and the solitary place shall be glad for them; and the desert shall rejoice and blossom as the rose.

"Say to them that are of a feeble heart, Be strong, fear not; behold, your God will come . . . and save you."

Suddenly those words applied to him and to his need. Misery had melted the pride of a stubborn heart, and for the first time

in his life, his thoughts drew near to the Creator of the universe.
He read on and on, and with every word he read, his loneliness
diminished; hope took the place of despair and more and more
his spirit rose within him. At length with new vigor and purpose
he closed the book and strode down from the height to his cave.

Now for him everything was changed. He realized for the
first time that life on Juan Fernandez would be what he made it.
If he lived miserably, doing nothing to better his condition, and
pinning all his hope of happiness on the chance of a stray sail
making its way toward the island at some hazy time in the future,

he might waste away a lifetime in despair. Now, now was the time to conquer every adverse circumstance, live and be happy. "Behold, *now* is the accepted time," saith St. Paul, "Behold, *now* is the day of salvation."

He set to work at once. First of all he saw that he had let his cave grow filthy. He spent some time in cleaning it out and washing of clothes and bedding. As he worked he was able sometimes to whistle. Moreover it was a remarkable fact that the howling of the seals no longer annoyed him; he could even hear their voices with pleasure as furnishing a certain sense of companionship, and the change within his own spirits made him approach them in so different a manner, with such confidence and assurance that now, when occasion demanded, he could safely make his way through them. It is true loneliness and despair returned at times to tempt him, but he had henceforth always wherewithal to resist them through reading of the scriptures and thinking on the words therein set down.

Having put things in such order about his cave as they had not been in since his arrival on the island, he began next to consider the question of food. As he had been unwilling to leave the beach and living on that food the most easily procurable there, he had been eating almost nothing but turtle, till he could scarce brook the thought of turtle again. Now he arranged at stated intervals, morning and evening, to go to his look-out on the rocks, but the rest of the time he put the matter of sails out of his mind, and went about his business of providing for his natural wants. Accordingly, he traveled inland, and on the heights back from the shore found a plenty of goats. Juan Fernandez, the Spanish sailor who had first discovered the island a century or more ago and given it his name, had resided there for some time, stocking the place with goats, and the wild creatures of this time were descendants of those domestic beasts Juan Fernandez left behind at the time of his final abandonment of the island. By means of his gun, Selkirk was thus able to provide himself with goat's flesh, and he perceived that the fruit of the pimento which is the same as the Jamaica pepper and has a most delicious smell, would season his meat instead of salt. He therefore soon learned to prepare victuals he could truly relish in place of the unpalatable stuff with which his indifference had been providing him. In particular he was able to make a most excellent broth. Being still, how- ever, greatly in want of fresh vegetables, he decided to set out and explore the island in search of the same.

He found Juan Fernandez to be about thirteen miles in length by four in width, rocky and mountainous everywhere, the moun- tains being covered with green to the sky line, except where pre- cipitous faces of rock formed a beautiful contrast to the luxuriant pale vegetation. Everywhere was a great profusion of ferns, there being two varieties of tree-ferns that raised their feathery heads to the height of a good-sized tree over many an overhanging crag or precipitous ravine. The steep paths up the hills were bordered by a thicket of flowering shrubs and herbs, one of the most remarkable of the latter throwing up leaf stalks eight and ten feet in height and forming with the leaves which frequently measured fifteen feet across, a canopy under which one could easily have ridden on horseback. In several brooks at no great distance from his cave he found water cress of an excellent flavor, and to his delight, he discovered growing in great profusion among the trees of the island, the cabbage palm which yields most edible leaf buds quite after the manner of the common cabbage.

In several places he came upon the ruins of huts or shelters that had probably been erected in times past by the few sailors preceding him who had spent periods of greater or less length on the island, though never before like him alone, being always in companies of three or four. He searched well in these places, but found nothing of any value left behind, save that from one he was able to procure a few nails. In the rank growth near these ruins however, radishes, parsnips and turnips were growing. These appeared at present to be wild, but were undoubtedly offspring of seeds originally sowed by some one of the earlier inhabitants of the island. Thus provided with a welcome addition to his food supply, Selkirk returned to his cave, a spot now quiet and serene enough since the seals had long since departed.

It was now well along in February, being the close of summer. Selkirk had long since carved on a tree the date of his arrival on the island, and by computing the number of days during which he had kept no track of the passage of time, he had from then on carried on an accurate system of markings by which he was always able to ascertain the date. With autumn coming on and winter in view, he began to think of building himself a hut. Even in that genial climate where trees were green the year around, he knew that frost was common at night in winter, snow would sometimes be found on the ground and there would be much rain, therefore he felt the need of a more habitable shelter than his cave. This he desired the more especially as he had seen from his lookout in all the time he had been on the island only one sail and that far off on the very edge of the horizon, so he felt more than ever that he was like to stay years or perhaps forever in that place.

After thinking the matter over carefully he came to this conclusion,—he must build his hut well back from the shore in a most sheltered and inaccessible spot, for by this time his powder was gone and he had no means of defence. He was now well satisfied that no savage beasts dwelt on the island, but he had this to take into consideration,—if a boat ever did land there it was as like to hold men from whom he must flee as men into whose arms he could throw himself. He knew well enough the character of the rough adventurers who sailed those seas,—buccaneers, pirates, outlaws. Moreover at this time, France and Spain being both at war with England, to fall into the hands of Frenchman or Spaniard would have been to be captured by a foe. At length he made up his mind that if a French vessel put in he would surrender, trusting the nature of the French to deal honorably by him even though he were an enemy. But if the vessel were Spanish, he would flee and hide himself and never give up, for he knew the jealousy of Spain for England was so great that it was her acknowledged policy never to let a single Englishman return to Europe who had any knowledge of the South Seas. If he were to fall into the hands of Spanish sailors they would either kill him or make him a slave to work in their rich South American mines. This much was certain then,—he must build his hut where it would be a safe retreat in case of need. Therefore he climbed the rocks by an intricate path, and finding hidden high up among them a beautiful little glade on the edge of

a spacious wood, a spot most difficult to come at, and so concealed as to be well nigh undiscoverable, he selected that spot as the site for his hut.

By the exercise of much toil and patience, he then cut down with the small axe at his disposal, a sufficient number of pimento trees for his purpose. These he was obliged to join most accurately and carefully together by means of notches, having a great scarcity of nails. On the plains and small hills of the island there abounded a species of grass which grew to the height of seven or eight feet. This he cut most laboriously with his knife, and, on being dried, it proved to produce straw resembling that of oats. With this he thatched his hut. He then constructed a framework for a bed, covered it with straw and spread thereon his bed clothes, to sleep on which was a most welcome change after months of lying on the hard ground. Being still uncertain whether or no his hut was weather-proof, he hung the walls on the inside with well tanned skins of goats.

He had now for some time, since he had used the last of his powder, been presented with a new problem in the matter of procuring his goats. Being determined however to be overcome of no adverse circumstance, he one day made after a goat on foot. The creature was too fleet for him, but a young kid crossing his path, he found himself able to overtake that and seize it with his bare hands, and as he daily exercised to increase his speed, he was soon able to overtake the grown goats as well. He made after them first as they slackened speed to climb an ascent, but with gradual practice and owing to the moderate and temperate life he led, which kept him in fine bodily trim, he was at last able to run down even the fleetest goats at full speed on the level.

With the poor tools at his command, it took him many weeks to build his hut which he made of a spacious size. But this hut being complete, he found his energy by no means flagging, and ere the rainy season began he built at no great distance from it a second and smaller hut wherein he might cook his victuals.

Thus when winter came he was well prepared to meet it. The weather was never tempestuous, but there was some frost and snow, a little hail and great quantities of rain. In the larger hut he slept and passed the long periods of downpour. It had openings for windows which rendered it exceedingly light and pleasant, and over these openings in case of need to keep out the rain or cold could be dropped the goat skin coverings. Here within, he was cozy and snug enough, and he led a most orderly and comfortable life, instituting there the simple but beautiful form of family worship to which he had been accustomed in his father's home. Soon after he left his bed and before be began the duties of the day, he sang a psalm, then read a portion of the scriptures, finishing with devout prayer. Moreover he always repeated his devotions aloud in order to hear the sound of a human voice and retain his ability to speak the English tongue. The remainder of his time he occupied himself with making various articles of furniture and carving dishes and utensils out of wood, also in studying his books on navigation.

The winter offered but one incident of any importance and that was the coming up onto the beach early in July of great quantities of sea-lions. These strange creatures differ little in shape of body from seals but they are larger (being sometimes twenty feet long and of two tons weight). They have another sort of skin, their fur being shorter and coarser than that of the seal, and their heads are much larger in proportion, with very large mouths, monstrous big eyes and exceedingly heavy whiskers, the hair of which is stiff enough to make tooth pickers. These creatures stayed from July to September and were never observed during that time to go into the water but lay covering the shore above a musket shot from the water-side. But by this time Selkirk was in such good spirits that he was quite able to make his way safely through them whenever he needed to approach the shore.

With the return of spring, he found himself in a very different state of mind from what he had been the year before. When the rains ceased and it began to bud and twitter without, his heart leaped up and was glad within him. In the woods nearby the flowers appeared and there was a sort of blackbird with a red vest that came most tamely about his dwelling. Moreover, as the season advanced, there was scarcely a plant of myrtle or of a shrub with long dark bells like the myrtle, which was not inhabited by a pair of vari-colored humming birds, no bigger than humble bees, and these little creatures whirring and buzzing over the flowers filled Selkirk with delight.

The fall before he had carefully collected seeds of the vegetables that grew in different parts of the island, and this spring he cultivated a goodly patch of ground near his hut, having no implement with which to till the ground save his knife and axe. Here he planted a garden which he kept free of weeds and in most excellent and orderly condition.

His one trouble now was that he was greatly pestered with rats, his hut being overrun with the vermin and they so bold as to gnaw his clothes and even his feet when sleeping. On considering how to rid himself of this pest, he determined to catch and tame some of the wild cats that inhabited the island. These creatures, though of a uniform yellowish gray color like the real wild-cat were not in truth that creature, as might be told from their smaller size and from their tails which were thin and tapered at the end, while the wildcat's tail is bushy and of uniform size throughout. They, like the rats, were descendants of domestic creatures that had got ashore from some boat or other that had put in in times past to wood and water at the island. Nevertheless, though they were offspring of the tamest of beasts, they were as fierce and wild as wild-cats and of an agility that made them well nigh impossible to catch, so quickly could they slip out of one's very grasp and up into the trees. They formed their nests in rocky crevices or hollow trees and when disturbed there, would rise up and give fight, snarling and spitting fiercely, every hair on their bodies bristling with rage. Selkirk, however, was able to procure some kitlings which through patient care and feeding he tamed, and these being grown, speedily delivered him from the rats and kept his hut clean of the pests ever after.

Having succeeded well in taming the cats, he began also to tame kids that he might have food within easy reach in case of need. In this wise his hut was soon surrounded with tame creatures.

Pursuing goats up the mountainsides was by no means without danger, for the soil at any great height was very light and shallow, the vegetation being mostly a scrubby undergrowth, and if a man seized hold of this to help himself up the slope, the whole was like to give way, come up by the roots and precipitate him down the steep. Once Selkirk so eagerly pursued a goat that he catched hold of it on the brink of a precipice of which he was not aware, the bushes having hid it from him. So he fell over from a great height with the goat under him and lay at the bottom of the cliffs for a matter of twenty-four hours before he came to his senses—the amount of which time he calculated by the change in the moon since last he observed it. Having then crawled a mile back to

his cottage, he there remained some ten days ere he was able to stir out again.

As time passed he began to be greatly troubled that, with so much using, his knife was wore clean to the haft. He mourned beyond measure the loss of so valuable and necessary an implement. One day, however, as he wandered on the beach, keeping a sharp lookout as he always did for aught that might be of use, what should he spy, half buried in the sand, but some iron hoops. Doubtless they had been cast away by some ship as altogether unworthy, but to him they were a treasure then more priceless than a shipload of Spanish gold. Taking them back to his hut, he there broke off a piece, beat it thin, and ground the edge upon stones. Thus by the exercise of a little ingenuity, he was able to provide himself with a knife.

The knife, as may well be believed, was not the only one of his belongings that wore out. In course of time his clothes did likewise. He then made himself a coat, cap and breeches of goatskin with the hair outside. These he stitched together with little thongs of leather which he cut from the skins and attached to a nail. Having a plenty of linen cloth by him, thanks to the care of his mother, he sewed himself shirts when his wore out, using the nail again for a needle, and for thread the worsted that he unravelled from an old pair of stockings. As his bedding gave way, he replaced that also by goatskins. Only with the wearing through of his shoes did he find here an article that he could not replace. Nevertheless, as he was forced to shift without them, he found his feet grow so hard, he could run anywhere even over the sharp jagged rocks without the slightest annoyance. Thus even the loss of his shoes remained no great inconvenience.

One day as he stood on his look-out scanning the sea for a sail (it must have been about in the second year of his solitude) he did indeed, to the joy of his soul, see a sail bearing straight for the island. Leaving all else, he stayed at the lookout, never taking his eyes off the ship, his heart beating high with hope. But as it drew well within the range of vision, he saw to his dismay that it was a high and clumsy vessel, its stem and stern built up like castles,—Spanish without a doubt. Now as he had fully made up his mind rather to stay forever on the island than fall into the hands of the Spaniards, he watched until he made sure they were going to land, and then retired at once to his inaccessible retreat, where he stayed quietly, never once moving out of it so long as they remained on the island. From among the rocks he kept a sharp lookout over their encampment below, and he found the sight of human kind and the sound of their voices so agreeable even though he knew them to be enemies of a fierce and relentless kind, that he was often almost compelled to go down and join them. More than once some of the men strayed up the rocks straight in the direction of his hut, but fortunately he had built it so far beyond the distance of any easy climb that they never penetrated so far. At last, having taken aboard wood and water, they made off and Selkirk found himself once more the solitary master of the isle.

Curiously enough, it was not many months later, that he again espied a ship coming toward the island. This time, however, she was not of so distinct a type that he could at once decide whether she was Spanish or French. Desiring a closer examination, he ran eagerly down toward the beach, and was proceeding along through the underbrush with insufficient caution, when he suddenly came straight upon several of the crew before he even so much as knew they had landed. On the instant he perceived they were Spanish and made off. The others were struck dumb with astonishment at coming suddenly on so wild appearing a man on what they had believed to be an uninhabited island. However, they recovered themselves at once, fired shots after him and followed hot on his heels. They being close upon him, he suddenly shinned up a tree and hid himself in its branches. The Spaniards pursued him to the very foot of the tree and there losing track of him lingered long on the spot just beneath him. They even looked up frequently into the branches and Selkirk's heart went pounding, for had they perceived him, he could scarcely have got out of range of their firelocks, but so dense were the leaves they did not discover him and at length they retired once more to their camp.

Henceforth, after his disappointment in this second ship, Selkirk seemed even less than ever to set his heart on leaving the island. And indeed after this no other ship again came near.

He dwelt now in a state of great cheerfulness and even joy, not only reconciled to his lot but taking much pleasure in it. For the greater part of the year the sky was cheerful and serene, the air temperate and his little hut was on the edge of a spacious wood abloom with flowers. He kept it always clean and well-ordered and had even come to ornament it with the fragrant green boughs of trees, so that it formed a delicious bower around which played soft and balmy breezes. It grew to seem to him much like home and he came back to it always after an absence with that pleasant warming of the inner man always experienced by one coming home. Moreover his cats and tame kids became exceedingly dear to his heart. Though he had at first thought of taming them only to meet his own physical needs, he soon found himself grown mightily fond of the little creatures, and as they grew to love him in return, they in some measure satisfied that natural craving for companionship and affection which dwells ever deep in the heart of man. The kids would come leaping to meet him, licking his hands almost like dogs and the cats would rub against his legs and vie with one another to curl up purring in his lap. He would amuse himself often by teaching his pets to dance and do tricks, singing rousing old songs, and himself dancing with them to the music of his own voice. It was a strange and pretty sight, that!—the great man in his rough and shaggy garments, his face softened with joy of the little creatures, dancing and springing about in their midst, as though they were friends all speaking one language, the language of love that is foreign to none of God's creatures.

Selkirk had his garden, too, and indeed by application of his wits conquered all the inconveniences of his solitude. For food he had all he could wish for of variety and profusion right at hand,—goat's flesh and milk, turtle, crawfish, fish, turnips, parsnips, radishes, cabbage, watercress, and a variety of small but delicious black plum, the only article of his diet now not easily procurable, for they grew in places hard to come at high up in the mountains, but were sufficiently delicious to repay the effort of gathering them. He perceived, too, that taste is much a matter of habit, for he had grown to relish his food seasoned with

pimento quite as well as when he had it seasoned with salt.

The wood of the pimento he used entirely for firewood and as it burned, it gave off a most delicious fragrance and served him both for warmth and candle, throwing up a splendid blaze that lit all the darkness about. He was by this time intimately familiar with all the little by-paths of his mountain kingdom and could bound from crag to crag and slip down precipices with the utmost confidence.

So as he surveyed all the beauty and comfort about him and recalled the misery of his earlier state on the island, it seemed to him that his own change of heart had indeed made the promise come true,—"The wilderness and the solitary place shall be glad for them and the desert shall rejoice and blossom as the rose."

He no longer missed the society of men. The strife and struggle of humankind seemed far away; God seemed very near. He read: "Behold the hour cometh, yea is now come that ye . . . shall leave me alone, and yet I am not alone because the Father is with me." And as he stood beneath the calm and smiling sky, with the beauty of all out-doors about, and the sea stretching endlessly before him, he felt such a sense of nearness to the great Spirit of the universe, as he had never known in all his life before, and his thoughts were full of reverence and simple childlike peace.

For four years and four months he stayed there, and then one day, the thirty-first of January, 1709, it was, he was as usual surveying the water when he descried two vessels approaching. As they drew near, he saw for a certainty they were English. It was then late in the afternoon and he kept his eyes fixed on them until dark, though he scarcely felt any elation of spirit, as he might had they come some time earlier. After nightfall he gathered plenty of pimento wood and made a great fire to signal the vessels that there was some one alive on the island. All night long he tended it, but he spent none of the time in anxious suspense. Indeed, he thought far more of dressing goat's flesh wherewith to entertain the crew on the morrow, wearied as he knew they must be through months of confinement to salt provisions, than of whether or no his exile was at last to be ended.

During the night he fancied he heard from the vessels the sound of cannon, and later it appeared that his fire had occasioned the greatest surprise and alarm on shipboard. It being believed that the island was uninhabited, the English at once concluded there must be French ships at anchor in the harbor. They had earlier sent out their pinnace to reconnoiter the island, and on seeing the blaze, at once fired the quarter deck gun and several muskets to signal her to return. Then they stood all night to their quarters with decks cleared for action in case the French made at them. As they were forced to get wood and water at any price, they did not sail away, but in the morning made into the bay where they expected to see the boats of the enemy. Finding the coast clear, however, and no sign of ships anywhere, one of the vessels let down her yawl about noon and sent it ashore. Selkirk saw the boat leave the vessel and he at once tied a piece of old linen to a pole and waved it to attract their attention. As the yawl drew near, he saw it contained eight men and heard them call to him asking where was a good place to land. He pointed out the same, and, hurrying there ahead of them, stood ready to receive them as they sprang ashore. At the moment of actually meeting with humankind again, he felt a momentary joy and embraced them each in turn. He then learned that the two vessels were the Duke and Duchess under command of Captain Woodes Rogers, and he invited the sailors hospitably to his hut, but its access was so difficult and intricate, that Captain Dover and his men soon gave over trying to make it, one, Mr. Fry, alone accompanying him there. On the beach Selkirk

entertained the sailors in the best manner he could with the goat's flesh he had prepared. As the men were long absent from their boat, the Duke sent out her pinnace to see what had become of her yawl, suspecting that if there were no French ships in the bay, there might at least be a Spanish garrison lurking somewhere about. The sailors from the pinnace discovered nothing worse than the eight men from the yawl feasting on shore with a wild man, and, perceiving on closer examination that the wild man had an expression kindly, serious, and yet cheerful, they concluded him to be none such dangerous creature as they had at first supposed and invited him to return with them on board. Accordingly, he did so, bearing roast goat's flesh for the crew. As he dined with the Captain it was a remarkable fact that he no longer relished food seasoned with salt, but found himself obliged to acquire again what he had believed to be a perfectly natural taste.

After he had recounted his adventures the renowned Captain Dampier who knew him of old and was then on board as pilot, gave him so good a character that he was at once invited to sail with the Duke as mate. In the afternoon the ships cleared and the sails were taken ashore to be mended, while all hands set to work to lay in wood and provisions. Men were sent with a bull dog to capture goats, but to the surprise of everyone, Selkirk outdistanced them all, even the dog, caught the goats with his hands and bore two of them back on his shoulders.

The Duke and Duchess remained at the island till February the twelfth refitting the ships and getting in stores, and then at last the day came when Selkirk must bid farewell to his little home in the glade, to all his beloved pets, and each spot that had grown dear to him. Whether he truly rejoiced or no, when it came to the actual point of leave-taking who knows? Who knows?

At length there he was again on shipboard and the coast of Juan Fernandez lay behind him, fading fast into mist and dreams.

He was two years still from home and on the Duke showed no more of that quarrelsome disposition that had before wrought him so much trouble. The Duke took many prizes and was most successful in its ventures against the Spanish tyrants. In several instances Selkirk was entrusted with the command of small parties sent ashore, where the property and person of the inhabitants were at his mercy, and in all such cases he showed by his mild and considerate behavior, especially towards women, that the exalted thoughts of his solitude were not of the kind to vanish.

The Duke and Duchess reached London, October 14, 1711, and Selkirk found himself when the prize was divided a rich man. He returned at once to Largo and a joyful reunion with his mother, father and brothers. But ever after he had no love for great companies of men, choosing rather solitude and the company of his own thoughts. Moreover he often longed for his pets and his peaceful island where he had felt so near to his Creator, nor did the luxuries riches could provide make him one whit happier than when his wants were confined to the simplest necessities and these supplied by his own efforts alone.

"I am now worth eight hundred pounds," he would often say "but shall never be so happy as when I was not worth a farthing."

SOLITUDE
There is a pleasure in the pathless woods,
　　There is a rapture on the lonely shore,
There is society where none intrudes
　　By the deep sea, and music in its roar.
　　　　　　　　　　—*Lord Byron.*

YOUNG MIDSHIPMAN DAVID FARRAGUT

WHEN the War of 1812 broke out, wherein the United States found herself compelled to establish by force of arms her freedom on the seas which had been over and over again violated by England, the frigate Essex, 146 feet long, 32 short-range guns, was placed under the command of Captain David Porter. He came aboard bringing with him as midshipman his little adopted son, David Farragut, who was one day to be known as America's greatest admiral. David had received his first appointment as midshipman in the United States navy at the mature age of nine, and he was now at the time of entering on his duties aboard the Essex exactly ten.

Scarcely had the Essex put to sea when adventures began. Captain Porter captured from the midst of a whole convoy of British transports a merchantman with two hundred men, and soon after a British man-of-war, the sloop Alert of twenty guns. The two ships were taken in tow, but their officers and a number of the men were ordered as prisoners aboard the Essex. Thus the Essex soon became dangerously overcrowded, her prisoners far outnumbering the members of her crew.

Among the prisoners a conspiracy was hatched to fall unexpectedly on the Americans, either kill or overpower them and so capture the frigate. On the night when the mutiny was to break out, little midshipman Farragut lay awake in his hammock. Suddenly he saw a man looming up above him and covering him with his pistol. For a moment the man gazed intently at him to make certain he was asleep, ready to shoot without mercy at a sign of the smallest movement. The boy never budged, but through half open lids he saw that the sailor was one of the British prisoners, and with remarkable keenness of wit, he guessed what was afoot on the vessel. When the Englishman, satisfied that he was asleep, stole away, David slipped noiselessly out of his hammock and made straight off to Captain Porter, dodging well out of sight of the gathering mutineers.

The Captain was asleep in his cabin when the boy broke into the room, but at first news of the mutiny, he was instantly on his feet. Perceiving in a flash the only way to save the ship, Porter rushed, half dressed as he was, onto the deck, shouting, "Fire! Fire! Fire!" The effect was wonderful. The mutineers were at once confused and alarmed, fear of fire at sea driving all thoughts of mutiny out of their heads, while the American crew remarkably well disciplined in fire drill, came tumbling up on deck and rushed each to his station with a cutlass in one hand and a blanket in the other. This sudden and unexpected appearance of the crew in perfect fighting array, finished the demoralization of the mutineers. At Captain Porter's orders, they were every one seized and secured. Thus by his coolness and keenness of wit, little midshipman Farragut's first adventure at sea was to save a ship to the American navy. The next required a still greater display of manliness and courage.

Late in the winter of 1812 the Essex was ordered on a cruise through the South Atlantic around Cape Horn and into the Pacific, there to attack the extensive fishing interests of Great Britain, to rescue any American boats and to set free captured American whalers. The proper season for rounding Cape Horn had long since passed and the course of the Essex would lie through a region exceedingly tempestuous in winter. Moreover the ports along the coast were all friendly to England, and the Essex could not hope to refit or revictual in any of their harbors. She would have to depend solely on her own resources. Undaunted by the perils that lay before them, Captain Porter and his crew, little David Farragut among them, set out upon this distant cruise in the last days of January, 1813.

As the Essex neared the Horn, the most violent storms broke over her, lifting the waves into raging mountains of water and hurling them against the frail little boat with gigantic force. But in spite of all dangers and hardships she kept resolutely on. At length she sighted the rocky, barren shore line of the Ga-la'pa-go Islands off the coast of Ecuador, which Porter had learned were the favorite rendezvous for the British whalers. Here they cruised about in a leisurely fashion, little David and other members of the crew frequently going ashore to fish, hunt the huge tortoises for which the place was famous, or to pick the luscious Galapagos pears. But as the British whalers appeared in these waters, they captured them all successively till at last every single one had fallen a victim to the Essex and numerous American prisoners had been freed from the hands of the enemy. Captain Porter then found himself with nine vessels under him and such a number of prisoners that he was obliged to put back to the mainland of Ecuador and make preparations to send the prize ships he had taken back for safe keeping to the harbor of Valparaiso, Chile, one of the few South American ports that was friendly to the United States. One of these prizes which had been turned into a United States cruiser and christened The Essex Junior, he detailed as escort to the convoy on the return. He then ordered each of his officers as prizemaster to command one of the captured vessels, but not having officers enough to go around, he found himself forced to select some one among the crew to command the American ship Barclay which he had recaptured from the enemy. His choice for this responsible task fell on Midshipman Farragut. With a party of seamen under him, the boy was sent aboard, having orders to manage the Barclay on her long voyage to Chile. Imagine it! At the age of twelve in command of a vessel. It was a tremendously important event, and the boy was rightfully proud of the confidence reposed in him.

The Captain of the Barclay who had been in command when the vessel was captured by the enemy, was a huge Yankee from New Bedford, a violent tempered old fellow, and he was furious at being superseded by a "nutshell of a boy"as he contemptuously called young David. For such an old sea-dog to be placed under the orders of a twelve-year old boy seemed galling enough to his pride and he secretly determined to put the young whippersnapper in his proper place the very moment the other ships had departed. Accordingly, when the Essex Junior and the convoy made off to southward, and Captain Porter had disappeared to the northward, the Captain of the Barclay still kept his vessel contemptuously at anchor, making no preparations to follow, and flaunting his intention of remaining where he was exactly so long as it pleased him.

Little Midshipman Farragut saw that his hour of trial had come. He must play the man now and assume the command entrusted to him, order the ship under way and see her off on her journey, or else acknowledge himself too little to fulfill the responsibility Captain Porter had laid upon him, yield up his

command and let the Captain have his own way ever after. Though he secretly shook in his boots like every one else in the presence of the grizzly old fellow, he nevertheless went straight to him and ordered quietly: "Have the maintopsail filled away, and close up at once with the convoy."

At this the Captain burst forth in a fury. He would go where he pleased and when he pleased. He would steer for New Zealand or the moon if he liked! And he cried out to the sailors standing about:

"Let no man dare touch a rope without my orders. I'll shoot if you do. I've no mind to trust myself with a damned little nutshell! I'll go my own course and shoot the dog who takes orders from any but me."

Unfortunately, however, he did not have his pistols with him to carry out this magnificent threat, so he plunged down the companionway after them. The men stood about irresolute. It was a moment for great decision. Little Farragut turned to his right hand man of the crew.

"Have the maintopsail filled away!" he repeated with still more positive emphasis. His pluck turned the tide with the men.

THE TREASURE CHEST

"Ay, ay, sir," came the sailor's cheerful response, and from that time on, young David was undisputed master of the vessel. He at once set vigorously about giving all necessary orders to make sail, and calmly notified the Captain below not to come on deck with his pistols unless he wished to go overboard! The Captain, perceiving that the crew remained faithful to the little officer detailed them, and that David would in truth have no difficulty whatever in having him pitched over into the sea, decided in the interests of his own continued health and well-being to draw in his horns and obey. Thus on the long voyage back to Chile, David was in command and he carried out that great responsibility with a skill, good judgment and self-reliance, and yet with a freedom from all conceit or unnecessary self-assertion which was remarkable in a lad of twelve.

The little "nutshell" was assuredly given plenty of opportunity to prove his mettle aboard the Essex, for when after faithfully performing his mission he once more returned on the Essex Junior to join that vessel at the Galapago Islands, it was with news that the British government had been so aroused by tales of the destruction the Essex had wrought to her commerce and fisheries in the Pacific, that she was sending out the frigate Phoebe and two sloops to capture her.

On hearing this, Captain Porter at once sailed westward to the Mar-que'sas Islands where he could overhaul the Essex without danger from British men-of-war and make ready for the coming struggle with a greatly superior force. Here the Essex and Essex Junior lay for six months. The crews were daily drilled in the use of the guns, cutlasses and muskets and trained with that perfect discipline for which Captain Porter was famous.

During this time, David and the other midshipmen, when not at their studies or drill, were allowed ashore, where they gathered bananas, yams, bread-fruit and cocoanuts, and made friends with the sturdy brown native boys, who taught them to throw the spear, walk on stilts and especially to perform many wonderful feats in swimming.

At last, all preparations being made, the Essex and Essex Junior returned to Valparaiso Harbor, arriving on the twenty-third of February, 1814. Five days later the frigate Phoebe and the sloop Cherub appeared in the bay. Half the crew of the Essex were ashore at the time on leave, and Captain Hillyar of the Phoebe, being informed of this, at once determined to seize her while she must fall an easy prey, in spite of the fact that Valparaiso Harbor was neutral water where no hostile engagements could lawfully occur. But Captain Porter had been on the look-out. A signal gun brought every one of his men in fifteen minutes back to his station. When the Phoebe came dashing up within fifteen feet of the Essex, Captain Hillyar, instead of finding a vessel at his mercy, to his intense surprise, found every American at his gun, with matches burning and cutlasses drawn, in such a formidable state of defence that he speedily backed away, and tried to pass off his hostile approach with some clumsy compliments to Captain Porter. Captain Porter replied to his compliments with a politeness so grim that the Phoebe was more than ever anxious to get out of his reach and in her haste to accomplish this, she placed herself in such a position that Captain Porter could easily have raked her fore and aft with his guns and done for her once for all. But his principles of honor forbade him to violate the neutrality of the harbor, so he let the Phoebe go free, though he later discovered to his immense cost that Captain Hillyar was not a man to return such an act of courtesy.

The English ships, after provisioning, went outside the harbor and maintained a blockade of the two American vessels.

THE TREASURE CHEST

Week after week they cruised up and down just outside the bay, so that the Americans could not possibly slip through.

On March twenty-eighth, a heavy gale swept into the harbor and Porter decided to take advantage of the weather to run the blockade. At first it looked as though he would succeed, but on her way the Essex was struck by a violent squall that carried away her maintopsail. Escape in such a disabled state was impossible, so Porter tried to regain his safe position in the harbor, but the Essex was only able to struggle as far back as a small bay about a quarter of a mile off shore. She was, however, still within neutral waters and had every reason to expect that Hillyar would respect that neutrality, remembering how Porter had refused to fire on him when he had the Phoebe so entirely at his mercy. But Porter soon saw his mistake. As soon as the British discerned the plight of the Essex, the two vessels both bore down together on the crippled frigate, now separated from her companion, and opened their broadsides on her. Then began one of the most nobly contested defences in history, the odds being from the beginning three to one against the Essex.

Through the frightful scenes that followed, Midshipman Farragut bore himself like a man, now carrying messages for Captain Porter, now helping with a gun, now fetching powder, now supporting a wounded man down below. Once he was knocked down a hatch by the explosion of a cannon ball. Again a shot tore away one of his coat-tails, but still the little midshipman remained at his post in the midst of the fray. At length fire broke out on the ship, and was nearing the powder magazine. Men came running up from below with their clothing on fire. Captain Porter ordered them to jump overboard and swim for their lives. Then, finding that the ship was in a sinking condition, he surrendered in order to save the wounded.

On the following day, David Farragut went aboard the

Phoebe, a prisoner, and was sent into the steerage with the British middies. He was almost in tears over the capture of the Essex, but was roused from his grief by the sight of an English midshipman calmly appropriating his—David's—beloved pet pig Murphy.

"That's my pig!" shrieked David, seizing Murphy by the ear.

"Fight for it then!" jeered the others.

Without more ado David stripped off his jacket and pitched into the young Englishman in short order, with such excellent results that in a few moments he had most soundly and satisfactorily trounced him. Thereafter he took Master Murphy under his arm and walked off, feeling that he had thus in some degree wiped out the disgrace of the American defeat!

Soon after this, David was sent back to America with the other officers on parole, and thus ended his connection with the famous frigate Essex, whereon he got the training that years later in the war for the preservation of the American Union, made possible the splendid victories of New Orleans and Mobile Bay,—victories won against almost impossible odds by the man that grew out of that self-same boy who was midshipman David Farragut.

THE TREASURE CHEST

PRINCESS NELLY AND THE SENECA CHIEF*
A True Story

IN the days of the American Revolution, the whole of western Pennsylvania was inhabited by different tribes of Indians. Of these, the Delawares were friends of the whites and took part with the United States; the Iroquois, on the contrary, were friends and allies of England. Very few white settlers had ventured into those parts at that time, for the life of frontiersmen amid such roving bands of hostile red men was one of constant peril and alarm. Even those who felt themselves in some measure protected by their friendly neighbors, the Delawares, never lost sight of the caution required by their exposed position.

Only in the vicinity of the military garrison at Pittsburg, or Fort Pitt as it was then called, was there any sense of security among the settlers. Here on the banks of the Plum River, a tributary of the Alleghany, there settled one Mr. Lytle, from Baltimore, with his wife and children. For some time they lived in uneventful comfort, experiencing no hostile visits from the Indians. The neighbors, it is true, having had more experience of frontier life, and being therefore more awake to the cunning and unexpected nature of the savages, had more than once annoyed Mr. Lytle by false alarms, till he had come to believe the stories of danger entirely exaggerated, visions called up by weak and foolish fear; and he quite relaxed his own vigilance, sinking into an easy going sense of security.

One day in the autumn of 1779, he set out early in the morning with all his serving men to help a neighbor at some distance raise a new building on his farm, thereby leaving his wife and children without a single man to protect them. After the noonday meal, Maggie and Tom, the two younger children, aged four and six respectively, went out to romp in the garden. Eleanor,

*This is a story of the little girl who later became Mrs. John Kinzie, one of the earliest settlers of Chicago.

363

or Nelly, the oldest, a pretty child of nine, and her brother, two years younger, were at play in a little wooded hollow in the rear of their father's house. Around them lay great trees of the forest, which Mr. Lytle had recently felled, with branches still untrimmed, and over these they climbed with merry laughter.

It was an afternoon of glowing splendor; the meadows swam in golden haze, the hillsides loomed aloft in gold with fleeting purple shadows, the river swept its shining path through banks of flaming autumn color, and over all there seemed to lie a wondrous golden peace. Behind the children in the cabin, could be heard the voice of their mother as she sang at her work. No scene could have appeared more homelike and serene. But suddenly Nelly stopped short in the midst of her play and clutched her brother wildly by the shoulder.

"Look," she whispered, "behind that log."

The boy peered off in the direction which his sister had indicated. Behind the green and untrimmed boughs of one of those fallen forest giants, what was it moving?—a squirrel, a fawn, or was it a red face?—a gaily colored bird or a clump of colored feathers on the head of a savage Indian?

The boy answered not a word. Seizing his sister by the hand, he dragged her off toward the house. The children were accustomed to seeing friendly Delawares about the place. These good Indians now and again made them visits, and some among them the Lytle family held in the warmest affection. But then, these came honestly straight to the house; they never came lurking, sneaking, hiding. The sight Nelly and the boy had seen, indistinct though it was, had roused in their minds the memory of all those stories of Indian cruelties, with which the neighbors had delighted to regale them. Breathless, the two burst into the cabin.

"Mother," they cried and the voice of each was more shrill

than the other, "Mother, there is a strange Indian down in the hollow hiding behind the trees."

The mother looked quietly up from her knitting, half smiling, half annoyed.

"What! only one?" she said. "Usually you fancy a score at least! My dear children, when will you stop alarming us all for nothing? The neighbors' children have frightened you out of your wits with their ridiculous stories. You know quite well our farm is too near Fort Pitt for the Indians to dare give us trouble. If there be any Indians there at all, it is one of our good friends, the Delawares. When will you stop mistaking every whisk of a squirrel's tail among the leaves, for a band of Indians? Go back to your play and put aside childish fears. Even your little brother and sister, out there in the garden, have not such childish fancies. You must learn to have greater courage."

Nelly and her brother hung their heads, humbled by the rebuke. It was true they had more than once before come running with false alarms, yet now they turned away with lagging feet to obey their mother. This time they felt so sure of what they had seen! The play was all gone out of them. Out past the garden they went where Maggie and Tom were at play. The two little ones giggled and hid as the older ones passed by, making strange and marvelous noises intended to frighten their elders. But Nelly and her brother paid no heed. They went slowly back to the little hollow.

A different place it seemed now from what it had been a few moments before. The golden peace had fled; a lurid loneliness brooded about, the shadows had grown fantastic. So far, so very far away it seemed from the shelter of the house. Nelly and her brother had no wish to play. They seated themselves on a fallen log and held close to each other.

"Hark!" whispered Nelly. "There's a rustling among the bushes."

Just at that moment, "Bob-white!" a quail whistled somewhere near them. Almost immediately, "Bob-white!" a second note answered the first.

"It is never birds that are calling like that!" said the boy.

The children were gazing so intently before them, in the direction of the fallen log where they thought they had seen the red man, that everything else about sank out of their vision entirely. Suddenly big red hands were clapped over their mouths from behind and they felt themselves seized in an iron grasp. Then two great Indians lifted them from their feet and carried them into the forest. Behind them still faintly sounded, as if from another world, the voice of their mother singing and the ringing silvery laughter of little Maggie and Tom.

At some distance from the house, the Indians set the children down to walk by themselves, making grimly threatening gestures to force them to keep silence. Then they hurried them off through the forest and soon joined a band of their fellows. So tall and fierce and splendidly dressed were the captors of the children, that the little ones guessed at once they must be enemies. They could not possibly be the Delawares of the neighborhood.

For some little distance, they dragged and drove the children along in silence. The little boy whimpered once—it was a dreadful plight to be in—but then he squared his shoulders, sniffed back his tears, flung back his head, and marched sturdily on his way. As to Nelly, now that the worst had come to pass, her spirit rose undaunted to meet it. There was no more timorousness about her; she took her brother's hand firmly in hers with a motherly air of protection and walked staunchly along by his side, her eyes flashing lightnings if one of the Indians but showed signs of molesting the boy.

Neither child had the slightest idea what was about to happen to them, but the overcolored pictures drawn for them by their

THE TREASURE CHEST

neighbors, made them expect the worst. Through the leafy
aisles of the forest, on and on they marched. Toward nightfall
as they drew far away from all white settlements, the Indians
somewhat relaxed the vigilant guard they had been keeping over
the children. When it began to grow dusk, they halted, made

their camp for the night, lit their camp fire, and set their watches to guard against surprise. Then the children were left to their own devices. The two sat down together on the grass at a little distance from their captors, and believing themselves no longer noticed, gave way for the first time to tears. Nelly took her little brother in her arms and the two wept together at thought of the uncertainty of their fate, of their peaceful home, and the loving mother from whom they had been torn.

Suddenly, as they gave vent to their grief, there stood before them a tall and majestic Indian of a strong and forceful countenance, yet strangely mild and gentle. Immovable though his features were, like those of all Indians, he still seemed to feel compassion for the little ones. In his strange Indian tongue with gutturals and low grunts, he even tried to soothe them. He pulled up great armfuls of the long grass that grew near their camping place and made them a bed. Then he shared with them his own stock of dried meat and parched corn and gave them to understand by signs that no further evil was intended them.

Scarcely had he settled them, somewhat calmed and comforted, on the bed he had prepared, than in the glare of the camp fire there appeared a second party of Indians belonging to the same band. As they loomed up out of the darkness, the light picked out the gaudy colors in their feathers and beads, casting the rest into deep shadow, and shone on their paint-streaked faces and chests with a gleam as of burnished copper. With them they brought a white prisoner. Her pale face shining almost like marble in contrast to their own, stood out distinctly in the blaze against the black background of the forest. Then the children saw that the prisoner was none other than their mother.

With little shrieks of relief they ran and clung to her skirts and she covered them with kisses. The Indians did not attempt to separate them, but allowed the mother to go off with the children to the couch that had been prepared for them. Then the mother told the little ones how the Indians had fallen upon her while she was at work, all unsuspecting of danger, and had borne her off a prisoner.

"And Maggie and Tom in the garden, where are they? What have the Indians done to them?" sobbed Nelly.

The mother bowed her head, her features working in anguish.

"I do not know," she whispered, barely commanding her trembling voice. "I do not know where my little ones are, but I hope they escaped with Lizzie." (Lizzie was the servant-maid.) "Lizzie disappeared the moment the Indians came."

Then from the depths of her heart, in her hour of terrible doubt and need, the mother called upon Him who is able to save, and felt herself strengthened and comforted.

Mrs. Lytle guessed from their peculiar manner of painting that their captors were Senecas, one of the six nations that then formed the tribe of the Iroquois. Doubtless they had left their village with the intention of falling on some band of their enemies, the Delawares, but, failing this, had satisfied themselves by capturing a few white settlers. She devoutly hoped their purpose was to hold the prisoners for ransom, and this seemed most reasonable to suppose, since no violence had been offered them.

Early the next morning the savages started once more on their march. It then appeared that the mild and compassionate Indian who had shared his supper with the children the night

before, was none other than the chief, Corn-Planter himself. Day after day they marched, but the prisoners were not ill-treated, and Corn-Planter seemed to have taken a wonderful fancy to Nelly. Again and again he took her up to ride on his horse before him, offered her some little trinket, or shared with her his food, and at nightfall he never failed to see that a couch of soft grass was prepared for her. On his marked partiality for Nelly, Mrs. Lytle built bright hopes that he would keep them all in safety and yield them up soon for ransom.

At length the party reached the picturesque little village of the Senecas, nestling mid fragrant, dusky pines, tall white oaks and spreading chestnuts, near the head waters of the Alleghany, at a place now called Olean Point in southwestern New York.

Corn-Planter at once took his prisoners to the principal lodge of the village. Herein dwelt his mother, widow of the former chief, a dignified, stately old woman, who was called by the rest the Old Queen. To her Corn-Planter said:

"Take the white woman and her children and treat them kindly. Many horses and guns will be given to buy them back."

But when Mrs. Lytle and her children had left the lodge, he added: "My mother, I bring to you the little white girl to take the place of the brother who was killed by the Lenape six moons ago. She shall be to you a daughter, to me a sister, and she shall dwell in our lodge forever. The boy and his mother may be bought for a ransom, but little sister shall be ours. Her they shall never have again."

So the Old Queen took Nelly to her heart in place of the little boy she had lost, and showed her every sign of affection that an Indian can display. Moreover, as her son had commanded, she provided for the prisoners every comfort made possible by the simple manner of life in the village. Thus hope rose still higher in the bosom of Mrs. Lytle and her children. Alas! they knew not that the very fondness on which they founded their brightest hopes for freedom meant the most serious barrier to any chance of liberation for Nelly.

Meantime, late in the evening of the day when Mrs. Lytle and the children had been captured, the father came whistling home. No lights in the windows of the house! Within, no fire on the hearth, no kettle simmering above with grateful aroma of the evening meal, not a single human being anywhere about! Only the mother's knitting hastily dropped in a chair, and a dilapidated rag doll deserted in a corner!

Alarmed beyond measure, the unhappy father hastened off to his nearest neighbor, who lived at a considerable distance. His calls, as he pounded on their door and frantically begged for news, aroused them from their sleep. They had no tidings to give him, but one and all, they joined in the search for the missing ones.

At length, in the house of another neighbor, they found the servant-maid. Between many tears, she managed to tell Mr. Lytle how the Indians had descended upon the house. At the first alarm, she said, she had run to an outer kitchen and hidden under a large brewing tub. There she had remained until the departure of the Indians, when she fled at once to a place of safety. All she knew concerning the family was that her mistress had been carried off and doubtless the children too, but that, so far as she had observed, no violence had been offered them.

The father and his neighbors then continued the whole night long to scour the neighborhood, searching everywhere about. Towards morning Mr. Lytle remembered an old settler who lived all alone far up the valley. To his cabin he and his friends immediately went, and from him they learned that, as he was at work in his field just before sunset, he had observed a party of strange Indians passing at some distance from him. As they wound along the brow of the hill, their forms clearly silhouetted against

371

the sky, he could see that they had with them a prisoner who was a white woman. Here, the miserable father felt sure was news of his wife at last, and he determined to go at once with his friends to Fort Pitt, to ask advice and assistance of the Commandant and Indian agent there.

Accordingly they proceeded down the valley just as the sun was rising. On their way they came suddenly upon a hut which they had searched the night before and found apparently deserted. To their surprise they now saw standing on the high bank before it a little boy and girl holding fast to each others' hands. Mr. Lytle at once recognized his two youngest children, Maggie and Tom, and in another moment they were fast in his arms and pouring out their tale in his ears.

"We were in the garden, father," cried the boy, "when the Indians came, so many Indians, into the yard right by the house!"

"An' 'en," sobbed the little girl, "Tommy he pulled me over the fence, an' we hided ourselves in the bushes and runned an' runned so far! An' where's my mother? I want my mother!"

It appeared that the boy, who was only six years of age, had indeed shown the most remarkable courage, devotion and intelligence in saving himself and his sister from the red men. He had on the very first alarm half pulled and half pushed the little girl over the fence into a neighboring field overrun with blackberry bushes and wild raspberry. Here they hid themselves, having the sense and self-command to make no outcry at all until all was quiet and no Indians in sight, when they attempted to force a way through the field in a direction opposite to the house. Unfortunately, the little girl in her play in the garden had pulled off her shoes and stockings, and the ground being very rough, uneven, and covered with briers, she soon found her feet so cut and bruised, that she sank to the ground and declared she could not go a single step further. Then the boy took off his own

stockings, put them on her feet, and gave her also his shoes, himself going barefoot over the torturing ground.

The little creature obediently tried to scuffle along in the shoes so many sizes too large, but they kept slipping off altogether so she could not possibly wear them. Then the boy took back the shoes, but he stuck faithfully by his sister, patiently coaxing and encouraging her on, lifting her over the roughest spots and part of the time half carrying her.

Thus they made their way at length out of the field and into an unenclosed pasture ground. Here, to their great delight, they saw some cows, securely and peacefully feeding. These cows as they knew, belonged to an old woman named Granny Myers who lived some little distance away. But in what direction from the pasture her cottage lay, they had not the slightest idea. With a wisdom that might have done credit to a grown man, the boy said: "Let's hide ourselves until sunset. Then the cows will go home and we can follow them."

Accordingly, this was what the children did, but when they reached Granny Myers' hut, in the wake of the lowing cattle, what was their dismay to find the house close-locked and deserted. The old woman had been called by some business down the valley and did not return that night. Tired and hungry, Maggie and Tom could go no further. With much effort they managed to get a few drops of milk from the cows, then laid themselves down to sleep under an old bedstead that stood behind the house. When their father and his searching party approached the place during the night, they had occasioned fresh terror to the children, who mistook the shouts and calls by means of which the searchers sought to arouse the inmates of the house, for the whoop of Indians, and, far from revealing themselves, they had crept closer together and kept as far out of sight as possible. When found in the morning they were debating what step to take next in order to reach safety.

Mr. Lytle, having then placed his two youngest children in security at Fort Pitt, told his tale to the Commandant there, who was readily interested in the matter and furnished the father with a detachment of soldiers to aid in the search. Circumstances soon pointed to the Senecas as the probable marauders, and the relief party at once directed their search among the villages of that tribe. It was necessary, however, to make their inquiries with the greatest caution, for all the tribes of the Iroquois being allies of Great Britain, were decidedly hostile to the Americans. Thus a long time passed before the father reached the village of Corn-Planter on the head waters of the Alleghany.

What was his unspeakable joy to find here his wife and the two older children. At once he began to enter into negotiations with Corn-Planter for ransoming his family. Mrs. Lytle and the boy?—Yes, Corn-Planter readily agreed on a price for them and set them free at once, but Nelly!—No, never! She was the adopted child of the tribe, she was his sister! He had taken her to supply to his mother the place of the little brother who was gone; she was dear to him and he would not part with her. To every entreaty of the father and mother, even of Nelly herself, to every increase of the price offered for the child, Corn-Planter only grunted, "Ugh! Ugh!" and shook his head with decision.

At length, finding every effort useless, the father was compelled to take his sorrowful departure, and set out once more for home with such of his loved ones as he had been fortunate enough to recover. Little Nelly threw herself into the arms of her father and mother almost in despair as they bade each other a last farewell, and the hearts of all were heavy with grief. But there was nothing else to be done, and the mother could only commend the child with a simple faith which was all that could possibly give her comfort in such an hour of trial, to the tender mercy and care of the Father of all. Then Mr. and Mrs. Lytle and their son set out on their melancholy journey homeward, trusting that some future attempt would be more effectual in recovering their daughter.

Never for a moment did Mr. Lytle relax his efforts in Nelly's behalf. He left his family in Pittsburg, and then, hoping that a British officer, as representative of a country that was the friend and ally of the Iroquois, might have more influence with Corn-Planter than those who were regarded as enemies, he undertook an expedition to the Canadian frontier, a long and dangerous enough journey in those days, hoping to gain the assistance of the British Indian Agent, Colonel Johnson. His story of what had occurred warmly interested the feelings of that benevolent officer. In spite of the fact that the United States and Great Britain were at war, Colonel Johnson saw in the grief-stricken father no enemy, but a fellow man commanding his sympathy on the grounds of their common humanity. He, therefore, promised to spare no exertions in attempting to recover little Nelly. This promise he faithfully fulfilled. As soon as the opening of the Spring made such a journey possible, he went in person to the village of Corn-Planter and made him a most splendid offer of guns and horses if he would release the child. But Corn-Planter was inexorable. He answered the British Agent as he had answered the Americans with nothing more than two grunts and a most decisive shake of his head.

So, slowly the months lengthened out into years, and still Princess Nelly dwelt in the lodge of the Old Queen, the beloved of Chief Corn-Planter, and his mother, and all the tribe. Nothing could exceed the consideration and affection with which she was treated by all. The principal seat in the lodge was reserved for her, the most delicate food was invariably saved for her, all the handsomest silver brooches and strings of wampum were used to make fine her garments; no efforts were spared to make her happy and cause her to forget her former home and dear ones.

For a long time Nelly resisted any attempts at consolation, crying out continually for her mother, but at length, as the kindness of the Indians remained unfailing, she grew somewhat more reconciled to her lot, and even happy in the great affection which Corn-Planter showered upon her. More and more, love for his little sister wound itself around the big chief's heart; more and more his tenderness for her became a part of his very being. As he followed the game in the woods, as he led his band of warriors through the pathless depths of the forest, thoughts of the little sister awaiting him by the hearth in his mother's lodge, shed a greater warmth into his life than the very warmth of the sun itself. Nelly, being by nature affectionate, the unbounded tenderness of those among whom she dwelt called forth a certain response in her heart. Though she could never cease longing for her own dear mother, she grew to regard Corn-Planter and the Old Queen with remarkable love and reverence. She learned to speak their language and even found much joy in sharing the bustling life of the village. Wherever she went about, whether gathering wild rice from the river in her little birch bark canoe, hoeing the corn in the cornfield, or playing at ball or bowl, she always displayed such ceaseless activity and unbounded energy, that the Indians gave her the name of The Ship Under Full Sail, and by that poetic title they always called her.

Thus four years passed by; four times the months rolled their slow round from the Moon of Leaves to the Moon of Snow-shoes, from the Moon of Snow-shoes to the Moon of Leaves, while Nelly dwelt in the little village on the banks of the Alleghany. Then in 1783 came the peace between the United States and Great Britain which ended the War of the Revolution. In consequence a general pacification of the Indian tribes took place and fresh hopes of recovering their daughter arose in the hearts of Mr. and Mrs. Lytle. They removed with their family to Fort Niagara, near which was the Great Council Fire of the Senecas, whither, once every year, came the sachems and chiefs from the various Seneca villages to decide the weighty affairs of the nation. The kindly Colonel Johnson readily undertook fresh negotiations with Corn-Planter and in order to make sure of success, he again proceeded in person to the village at Olean Point.

His visit occurred at the most propitious of seasons, for the Indians were celebrating the Festival of the Corn when he arrived

among them.   It was the one season of all the year most remarkable for general joy and happiness.   Gaily was the village decked
with golden ears of corn and glowing autumn leaves while here
and there rose arbors of fresh green boughs.   Men, women and
children, in gala dress, were living out-of-doors.   Young men
and dusky maidens stripped the husks from off the ears with
merry laughter; here some played games of ball, tossing little
balls of deer-skin, there gaily painted warriors in the brightest
gala garments, gathered in a dance to the tom! tom! of the drum
and the shrieking of the rattle, while the squaws kept time with
awkward movements on the edges of the circle.   Beneath the
fragrant pine trees old men squatted looking on, smoking their
pipes in solemn silence, and now and then grunting approval.

In the merry village, Colonel Johnson was received with all
consideration as was due to his position and long friendship with
the tribe.   When he spoke of little Nelly she was summoned in
to meet him and it appeared at once that nothing had been spared
to make her garments splendid.   A petticoat of blue broadcloth
she wore, bordered with gay colored ribbons, a sack of black silk
ornamented with three rows of silver brooches.   Around her neck
were strings and strings of purple wampum.   Her hair was clubbed
behind and loaded with beads, her leggins were of scarlet cloth,
her moccasins of deer-skin embroidered with porcupine quills.

All the love that had been showered upon the child was evi-
denced in her garments.   Nevertheless, when she had withdrawn,
Colonel Johnson, observing that the joyous festival had warmed
and opened the hearts of all, ventured to tell Corn-Planter how
the mother and father of his little sister had given up their home
and friends and come hundreds of miles to settle in a strange
land on the bare hope of sometimes looking on their loved one
or even perhaps of embracing her.   Then at last the heart of
the chief was softened.   There was soon to be held at Fort Nia-

gara, on the British side of the river, the Grand Council of the Senecas, and thither Corn-Planter promised to come, bringing his sister with him, that her parents might just have a glimpse of her. But he exacted a most solemn promise from Colonel Johnson that no effort should be made to reclaim the child and even that no proposal should be made to him to part with her.

Accordingly, in due time, Chief Corn-Planter set out, with Princess Nelly on horseback beside him, her heart beating with joy at thought of seeing her mother. Nelly had promised the Chief that she would never leave him without his permission, and he had perfect faith in her word.

Meantime, as the chiefs and warriors arrived in successive bands at the fort, the anxious parents watched longingly for a first sight of their daughter. At length the party was discerned emerging from the forest on the American side of the river, and Mr. and Mrs. Lytle could see at a glance that the little captive was with them. Surrounded by all the officers and ladies of the fort, they stood on the grassy bank, scarce able to contain themselves for longing impatience.

Boats were sent across by the commanding officer to fetch Corn-Planter and his party, but when they arrived the Chief alone entered one of them with his little sister. To his young men he said: "Stand here with the horses and wait until I return."

He held his darling close by the hand until the river was passed, until the boat touched the bank, then the child, no longer to be restrained, rushed forward into her mother's arms, and the two began hugging and kissing each other as though they had been fairly famished with longing.

When he beheld that sight, the great chief could withstand no longer. He spoke no word, but made an eloquent gesture of surrender. Then he turned and ordered the oarsmen to row him back alone to the further bank. All the way over the river,

he stood in the stern of the boat, looking back with folded arms for a farewell glimpse of his loved one,—majestic, almost heroic, a noble statue in bronze, savage though he was, of sublime renunciation. No arguments nor entreaties could induce him to remain at the Council. Having gained the opposite side of the river, he called his braves about him and made off into the forest.

Mr. Lytle could scarcely believe that Corn-Planter's relinquishment of Nelly was really permanent. Dreading lest he should change his mind after a few weeks and again take steps to recover her, the father determined to change his place of abode once more. In compliance with this decision, he crossed Lake Erie with his family and settled in the neighborhood of Detroit where he continued to live thereafter.

And so it came about that little Nelly saw her good friend, the Chief, no more, but she never forgot him. Throughout all her life there remained in her heart a tender memory of the strong and forceful warrior, who had been to her as gentle as a woman.

THE TREASURE CHEST

HIAWATHA'S FASTING*
A Legend of the First Indian Corn
Henry Wadsworth Longfellow

You shall hear how Hi-a-wa'tha
Prayed and fasted in the forest,
Not for greater skill in hunting,
Not for greater craft in fishing,
Not for triumphs in the battle,
And renown among the warriors,
But for profit of the people,
For advantage of the nations.

First he built a lodge for fasting,
Built a wigwam in the forest,
By the shining Big-Sea-Water.
In the blithe and pleasant Spring-time,
In the Moon of Leaves he built it,
And, with dreams and visions many,
Seven whole days and nights he fasted.

On the first day of his fasting
Through the leafy woods he wandered;
Saw the deer start from the thicket,
Saw the rabbit in his burrow,
Heard the pheasant, Be'na, drumming,
Heard the squirrel, Ad-ji-dau'mo,
Rattling in his hoard of acorns,
Saw the pigeon, the O-me'me,
Building nests among the pine-trees,
And in flocks the wild goose, Wa'wa,
Flying to the fen-lands northward,
Whirring, wailing far above him.
"Master of Life!" he cried, desponding,
"Must our lives depend on these things?"

*Used by permission of, and by special arrangement with, Houghton Mifflin Company, the publishers.

On the next day of his fasting
By the river's brink he wandered,
Through the Musk'o-day, the meadow,
Saw the wild rice, Mah-no-mo'nee,
Saw the blueberry, Mee-nah'ga,
And the strawberry, O-dah'min,
And the grape-vine, the Be-mah'gut,
Trailing o'er the alder-branches,
Filling all the air with fragrance!
"Master of Life!" he cried, desponding,
"Must our lives depend on these things?"

On the third day of his fasting
By the lake he sat and pondered,
By the still, transparent water;
Saw the sturgeon, Nah'ma, leaping,
Scattering drops like beads of wampum,
Saw the yellow perch, the Sah'wa,
Like a sunbeam in the water,
Saw the pike, the Mask-e-no'zha,
And the Shaw'-ga-shee', the craw-fish!
"Master of Life!" he cried, desponding,
"Must our lives depend on these things?"

On the fourth day of his fasting
In his lodge he lay exhausted;
From his couch of leaves and branches
Gazing with half-open eyelids,
Full of shadowy dreams and visions,
On the dizzy, swimming landscape,
On the gleaming of the water,
On the splendor of the sunset.

And he saw a youth approaching,
Dressed in garments green and yellow,

Coming through the purple twilight,
Through the splendor of the sunset;
Plumes of green bent o'er his forehead,
And his hair was soft and golden.
 Standing at the open doorway,
Long he looked at Hiawatha,
Looked with pity and compassion
On his wasted form and features,
And, in accents like the sighing
Of the South-Wind in the tree-tops,
Said he, "O my Hiawatha!
All your prayers are heard in heaven,
For you pray not like the others;
Not for greater skill in hunting,
Not for greater craft in fishing,
Not for triumph in the battle,
Nor renown among the warriors,
But for profit of the people,
For advantage of the nations.
 "From the Master of Life descending,
I, the friend of man, Mon-da'min,
Come to warn you and instruct you,
How by struggle and by labor
You shall gain what you have prayed for.
Rise up from your bed of branches,
Rise, O youth, and wrestle with me!"
 Faint with famine, Hiawatha
Started from his bed of branches,
From the twilight of his wigwam
Forth into the flush of sunset
Came, and wrestled with Mon-da'min;
At his touch he felt new courage,

Felt new life and hope and vigor
Run through every nerve and fibre.
So they wrestled there together
In the glory of the sunset,
And the more they strove and struggled,
Stronger still grew Hiawatha;
Till the darkness fell around them,
And the heron, the Shuh-shuh'gah,
From her nest among the pine-trees,
Gave a cry of lamentation,
Gave a scream of pain and famine.
"'Tis enough!" then said Monda'min.
Smiling upon Hiawatha,
"But to-morrow, when the sun sets,
I will come again to try you."
And he vanished, and was seen not;
Whether sinking as the rain sinks,
Whether rising as the mists rise,
Hiawatha saw not, knew not,
Only saw that he had vanished,
Leaving him alone and fainting,
With the misty lake below him,
And the reeling stars above him.
On the morrow and the next day,
When the sun through heaven descending,
Like a red and burning cinder
From the heart of the Great Spirit,
Fell into the western waters,
Came Monda'min for the trial,
For the strife with Hiawatha;
Came as silent as the dew comes,
From the empty air appearing,

THE TREASURE CHEST

Into empty air returning,
Taking shape when earth it touches,
But invisible to all men
In its coming and its going.

 Thrice they wrestled there together
In the glory of the sunset,
Till the darkness fell around them,
Till the heron, the Shuh-shuh′ gah,
From her nest among the pine-trees,
Uttered her loud cry of famine,
And Monda′min paused to listen.

 Tall and beautiful he stood there,
In his garments green and yellow;
To and fro his **plumes** above him
Waved and nodded with his breathing,
And the sweat of the encounter
Stood like drops of dew upon him.

And he cried, "O Hiawatha!
Bravely have you wrestled with me,
Thrice have wrestled stoutly with me,
And the Master of Life, who sees us,
He will give to you the triumph!"
Then he smiled, and said: "To-morrow
Is the last day of your conflict,
Is the last day of your fasting.
You will conquer and o′ercome me;
Make a bed for me to lie in,
Where the rain may fall upon me,
Where the sun may come and warm me;
Strip these garments, green and yellow,
Strip this nodding plumage from me,
Lay me in the earth, and make it

Soft and loose and light above me.
  "Let no hand disturb my slumber,
Let no weed nor worm molest me,
Let not Kah-gah-gee′, the raven,
Come to haunt me and molest me,
Only come yourself to watch me,
Till I wake, and start, and quicken,
Till I leap into the sunshine."
  And thus saying, he departed;
Peacefully slept Hiawatha,
But he heard the Wa-wo-nais′sa,
Heard the whip-poor-will complaining,
Perched upon his lonely wigwam;
Heard the rushing Se-bo-wish′a,
Heard the rivulet rippling near him,
Talking to the darksome forest;
Heard the sighing of the branches,
As they lifted and subsided
At the passing of the night-wind,
Heard them, as one hears in slumber
Far-off murmurs, dreamy whispers;
Peacefully slept Hiawatha.
  On the morrow came No-ko′mis,
On the seventh day of his fasting,
Came with food for Hiawatha,
Came imploring and bewailing,
Lest his hunger should o'ercome him,
Lest his fasting should be fatal.
  But he tasted not, and touched not.
Only said to her, "No-ko′mis,
Wait until the sun is setting,
Till the darkness falls around us,

Till the heron, the Shuh-shuh'gah,
Crying from the desolate marshes,
Tells us that the day is ended."
  Homeward weeping went No-ko'mis,
Sorrowing for her Hiawatha,
Fearing lest his strength should fail him,
Lest his fasting should be fatal.
He meanwhile sat weary waiting
For the coming of Monda'min,
Till the shadows, pointing eastward,
Lengthened over field and forest,
Till the sun dropped from the heaven,
As a red leaf in the Autumn
Falls and floats upon the water,
Falls and sinks into its bosom.
  And behold! the young Monda'min,
With his soft and shining tresses,
With his garments green and yellow,
With his long and glossy plumage,
Stood and beckoned at the doorway.
And as one in slumber walking,
Pale and haggard, but undaunted,
From the wigwam Hiawatha
Came and wrestled with Monda'min.
  Round about him spun the landscape,
Sky and forest reeled together,
And his strong heart leaped within him,
As the sturgeon leaps and struggles
In a net to break its meshes.
Like a ring of fire around him
Blazed and flared the red horizon,
And a hundred suns seemed looking

At the combat of the wrestlers.
　　Suddenly upon the greensward
All alone stood Hiawatha,
Panting with his wild exertion,
Palpitating with the struggle;
And before him, breathless, lifeless,
Lay the youth, with hair dishevelled,
Plumage torn, and garments tattered;
Dead he lay there in the sunset.
　　And victorious Hiawatha
Made the grave as he commanded,
Stripped the garments from Monda'min,
Stripped his tattered plumage from him,
Laid him in the earth, and made it
Soft and loose and light above him;
And the heron, the Shuh-shuh'gah,
From the melancholy moorlands,
Gave a cry of lamentation,
Gave a cry of pain and anguish.
　　Homeward then went Hiawatha
To the lodge of old Noko'mis
And the seven days of fasting
Were accomplished and completed.
But the place was not forgotten
Where he wrestled with Monda'min;
Nor forgotten nor neglected
Was the grave where lay Monda'min,
Sleeping in the rain and sunshine;
Where his scattered plumes and garments
Faded in the rain and sunshine.
　　Day by day did Hiawatha
Go to wait and watch beside it;

THE TREASURE CHEST

Kept the dark mould soft above it,
Kept it clean from weeds and insects,
Drove away, with scoffs and shoutings,
Kah-gah-gee', the king of ravens.

Till at length a small green feather
From the earth shot slowly upward,
Then another and another,
And before the Summer ended
Stood the maize in all its beauty,
With its shining robes about it,
And its long, soft, yellow tresses;
And in rapture Hiawatha
Cried aloud, "It is Monda'min!
Yes, the friend of man, Monda'min!"

Then he called to old Noko'mis
And I-a'goo, the great boaster,
Showed them where the maize was growing,
Told them of his wondrous vision,
Of his wrestling and his triumph,
Of this new gift to the nations,
Which should be their food forever.

And still later, when the Autumn
Changed the long, green leaves to yellow,
And the soft and juicy kernels
Grew like wampum hard and yellow,
Then the ripened ears he gathered,
Stripped the withered husks from off them,
As he once had stripped the wrestler,
Gave the first Feast of Monda'min,
And made known unto the people
This new gift of the Great Spirit.

GEORGE ROGERS CLARK AND THE CONQUEST
OF THE NORTHWEST*
Theodore Roosevelt

IN 1776, when independence was declared, the United States included only the thirteen original States on the sea-board. With the exception of a few hunters there were no white men west of the Allegheny Mountains, and there was not even an American hunter in the great country out of which we have since made the States of Illinois, Indiana, Ohio, Michigan, and Wisconsin. All this region north of the Ohio River then formed a part of the Province of Quebec. It was a wilderness of forests and prairies, teeming with game, and inhabited by many warlike tribes of Indians.

Here and there through it were dotted quaint little towns of French Creoles, the most important being Detroit, Vincennes on the Wabash, and Kaskaskia and Kahokia on the Illinois. These French villages were ruled by British officers commanding small bodies of regular soldiers or Tory rangers and Creole partizans. The towns were completely in the power of the British government, none of the American States had actual possession of a foot of property in the Northwestern Territory.

The Northwest was acquired in the midst of the Revolution only by armed conquest, and if it had not been so acquired, it would have remained a part of the British Dominion of Canada.

The man to whom this conquest was due was a famous backwoods leader, a mighty hunter, a noted Indian-fighter, George Rogers Clark. He was a very strong man, with light hair and blue eyes. He was of good Virginian family. Early in his youth, he embarked on the adventurous career of a backwoods surveyor, exactly as Washington and so many other young Virginians of spirit did at that period. He traveled out to Kentucky soon after

*Taken from *Hero Tales from American History* by the permission of the publishers, The Century Co.

it was founded by Boone, and lived there for a year, either at the stations or camping by himself in the woods, surveying, hunting, and making war against the Indians like any other settler, but all the time his mind was bent on vaster schemes than were dreamed of by the men around him. He had his spies out in the Northwestern Territory, and became convinced that with a small force of resolute backwoodsmen he could conquer it for the United States. When he went back to Virginia, Governor Patrick Henry entered heartily into Clark's schemes and gave him authority to fit out a force for his purpose.

In 1778, after encountering endless difficulties and delays, he finally raised a hundred and fifty backwoods riflemen. In May they started down the Ohio in flatboats to undertake the allotted task. They drifted and rowed downstream to the Falls of the Ohio, where Clark founded a log-hamlet, which has since become the great city of Louisville. Here he halted for some days and was joined by fifty or sixty volunteers, but a number of the men deserted, and when, after an eclipse of the sun, Clark again pushed off to go down with the current, his force was but about one hundred and sixty riflemen. All, however, were men on whom he could depend—men well used to frontier warfare. They were tall, stalwart backwoodsmen, clad in the hunting-shirt and leggings that formed the national dress of their kind, and armed with the distinctive weapon of the backwoods, the long-barreled, small-bore rifle.

Before reaching the Mississippi the little flotilla landed, and Clark led his men northward against the Illinois towns. In one of them, Kaskaskia, dwelt the British commander of the entire district up to Detroit. The small garrison and the Creole militia taken together outnumbered Clark's force, and they were in close alliance with the Indians roundabout. Clark was anxious to take the town by surprise and avoid bloodshed, as he believed he could win over the Creoles to the American side. Marching

cautiously by night and generally hiding by day, he came to the outskirts of the little village on the evening of July 4, and lay in the woods near by until after nightfall. Fortune favored him. That evening the officers of the garrison had given a great ball to the mirth-loving Creoles, and almost the entire population of the village had gathered in the fort, where the dance was held. While the revelry was at its height, Clark and his backwoodsmen, treading silently through the darkness, came into the town, surprised the sentries, and surrounded the fort without causing any alarm.

All the British and French capable of bearing arms were gathered in the fort to take part in or look on at the merrymaking. When his men were posted Clark walked boldly forward through the open door, and, leaning against the wall, looked at the dancers as they whirled around in the light of the flaring torches. For some moments no one noticed him. Then an Indian who had been lying with his chin on his hand, looking carefully over the gaunt figure of the stranger, sprang to his feet, and uttered the wild war-whoop. Immediately the dancing ceased and the men ran to and fro in confusion, but Clark, stepping forward, bade them be at their ease, but to remember that henceforth they danced under the flag of the United States, and not under that of Great Britain.

The surprise was complete, and no resistance was attempted. For twenty-four hours the Creoles were in abject terror. Then Clark summoned their chief men together and explained that he came as their ally, and not as their foe, and that if they would join with him they should be citizens of the American Republic, and treated in all respects on an equality with their comrades. The Creoles, caring little for the British, and rather fickle of nature, accepted the proposition with joy, and with the most enthusiastic loyalty toward Clark. Not only that, but sending messengers to their kinsmen on the Wabash, they persuaded the people of Vincennes likewise to cast off their allegiance to the British king, and to hoist the American flag.

So far, Clark had conquered with greater ease than he had dared to hope. But when the news reached the British governor, Hamilton, at Detroit, he at once prepared to reconquer the land. He had much greater forces at his command than Clark had, and in the fall of that year he came down to Vincennes by stream and portage, in a great fleet of canoes bearing five hundred fighting men—British regulars, French partisans, and Indians. The Vincennes Creoles refused to fight against the British, and the American officer who had been sent thither by Clark had no alternative but to surrender. If Hamilton had then pushed on and struck Clark in Illinois, having more than treble Clark's force, he could hardly have failed to win the victory, but the season was late and the journey so difficult that he did not believe it could be taken. Accordingly he disbanded the Indians and sent some of his troops back to Detroit, announcing that when spring came he would march against Clark in Illinois.

If Clark in turn had awaited the blow he would have surely met defeat, but he was a greater man than his antagonist, and he did what the other deemed impossible.

Finding that Hamilton had sent home some of his troops and dispersed all his Indians, Clark realized that his chance was to strike before Hamilton's soldiers assembled again in the spring. Accordingly he gathered together the pick of his men, together with a few Creoles, one hundred and seventy all told, and set out for Vincennes. At first the journey was easy enough, for they passed across the snowy Illinois prairies, broken by great reaches of lofty woods. They killed elk, buffalo, and deer for food, there being no difficulty in getting all they wanted to eat, and at night they built huge fires by which to sleep, and feasted "like Indian war-dancers," as Clark said in his report.

But when, in the middle of February, they reached the drowned lands of the Wabash, where the ice had just broken up and everything was flooded, the difficulties seemed almost insuperable, and the march became painful and laborious to a degree. All day long the troops waded in the icy water, and at night they could with difficulty find some little hillock on which to sleep. Only Clark's indomitable courage and cheerfulness kept the party in heart and enabled them to persevere. However, persevere they did, and at last, on February 23, they came in sight of the town of Vincennes. They captured a Creole who was out shooting ducks, and from him learned that their approach was utterly unsuspected, and that there were many Indians in town.

Clark was now in some doubt as to how to make his fight. The British regulars dwelt in a small fort at one end of the town, where they had two light guns, but Clark feared lest, if he made a sudden night attack, the townspeople and Indians would, from sheer fright, turn against him. He accordingly arranged, just before he himself marched in, to send in the captured duck-hunter, conveying a warning to the Indians and the Creoles that he was about to attack the town, but that his only quarrel was with the British, and that if the other inhabitants would stay in their own homes they would not be molested.

Sending the duck-hunter ahead, Clark took up his march and entered the town just after night-fall. The news conveyed by the released hunter astounded the townspeople, and they talked it over eagerly, and were in doubt what to do. The Indians, not knowing how great might be the force that would assail the town, at once took refuge in the neighboring woods, while the Creoles retired to their own houses. The British knew nothing of what had happened until the Americans had actually entered the streets of the little village. Rushing forward, Clark's men soon penned the regulars within their fort, where they kept them surrounded all night. The next day a party of Indian warriors, who in the British interest had been ravaging the settlements of Kentucky, arrived and entered the town, ignorant that the Americans had captured it. Marching boldly forward to the fort, they suddenly found it beleaguered, and before they could flee they were seized by the backwoodsmen. In their belts they carried the scalps of the slain settlers. The savages were taken red-handed, and the American frontiersmen were in no mood to show mercy. All the Indians were tomahawked in sight of the fort.

For some time the British defended themselves well, but at length their guns were disabled, all of the gunners being picked off by the backwoods marksmen, and finally the garrison dared not so much as appear at a port-hole, so deadly was the fire from the long rifles. Under such circumstances Hamilton was forced to surrender. No attempt was afterward made to molest the Americans in the land they had won, and upon the conclusion of peace the Northwest, which had been conquered by Clark, became part of the United States.

THE BOYHOOD OF ROBERT FULTON

A dillar, a dollar, a ten o' clock scholar—that was what Robert Fulton was on the day that he stood, self-conscious and apologetic, before the austere old Quaker schoolmaster, Caleb Johnson, in the little town of Lancaster, Pennsylvania. An important personage was the schoolmaster of those days—the early days of the American Revolution,—and Caleb grasped his birch rod sternly as he peered over his huge rimmed spectacles at the little truant before him.

"Robert Fulton!" he cried. "Why does thee come so late? Wasting thy time on the streets, I suppose, in idle dilly-dallying! Thee will grow up a lazy, empty-headed good-for-naught!" And he held his birch rod in a state of unpleasant preparation for immediate and summary vengeance. The boy's cheeks glowed.

"Nay!" he cried eagerly. "I am late I know and I am sorry but I have not been lazy nor idle. I have spent the time at Nicholas Miller's shop making somewhat of which I had need!" And he held up to the astonished schoolmaster a perfectly turned lead pencil in a day when lead pencils were not the easily procured article that they have been in later years. "I pounded out the lead, made the wooden case and fitted the lead into it all myself," went on the boy, "and when I'm at tasks like that I forget how time is passing."

The children looked up from their books open-mouthed with wonder and old Caleb himself could not repress a sudden gleam of interest. It was indeed a remarkably well made pencil. Beneath his crusty exterior the schoolmaster had a heart by no means lacking in warmth, and he secretly felt more than a little interest in this strange pupil of his. It was true Robert's thoughts all too frequently wandered from his studies, yet on such occasions it almost invariably proved that, far from being idle, he had been solving some knotty problem, originating some wonderful idea how he could make this or that marvelous contrivance to meet some need of his own, his mother's or his friends'. So, though Caleb's dignity still demanded that he mutter something beneath his breath, shake his head and finger his birch-rod threateningly as he motioned the culprit to take his seat, he said to himself in secret that the world would yet hear from that original little urchin who had just escaped a trouncing.

Robert Fulton was indeed the most original boy of his time in the little town of Lancaster. He seemed invariably able to supply his own wants, no matter how strange they were, by most remarkable articles of his own design and construction. As he grew somewhat older, two absorbing interests claimed his life,— the study of machinery and the study of art. For with that lead pencil which he had so carefully turned in Nicholas Miller's shop he soon began to draw. He drew sign-boards for the inns of the town to earn money for his support; but what interested him still more, he sketched parts of machinery in the various shops of the village and made himself so useful to the mechanics that they always welcomed his visits. Indeed he used to draw plans and designs for all sorts of things which he himself wished to construct, and while he was not always prepared to recite in

Master Caleb Johnson's school on the particular lesson for the day, he read and studied greedily both in school and out all the books he could find on matters that interested him, — mathematics, chemistry, mechanics and all related subjects.

On the approach of the Fourth of July, 1778, when Robert

was thirteen years old, the boys of Lancaster planned a wonderful celebration in honor of the second anniversary of the Declaration of Independence. The war was still in hot progress and their bubbling boyish devotion to the cause of liberty was in direst need of a safety valve in order to let off steam. So they had planned to illuminate the city splendidly with candles. On the first day of July, however, the city council, gravely discussing the necessity for pressing economy in such trying times, and most particularly taking into consideration the great scarcity of tallow, issued solemn orders that no lighting of candles should be permitted to celebrate the Fourth.

A sad blow indeed to the boys! They stood before the signboard announcing this sorry injunction, with their hands in their pockets and their faces long and sober. Robert Fulton alone wasted no time in regrets. He stood for a few moments lost in thought. Then home he went and buried himself for a time in a book. Afterward he hurried away to the brush maker's and exchanged the candles he had been saving for gun powder. At a second shop near by, he bought some sheets of cardboard, and the clerk in this latter shop felt a flash of curiosity as he handed the boy his purchase.

"What are you going to do with that cardboard?" he asked.

The boy answered eagerly: "We are forbidden to light the streets with candles, so I'm going to light the sky with rockets!"

The man laughed heartily as though the words were a joke. Fire works were then practically unknown in Europe and America, though they had long been used in China.

"Light the sky!" he chuckled. "Why, that's impossible."

The boy flung back his head with an air of positive certainty.

"Impossible!" he cried. "No sir! There is nothing impossible!"

And sure enough! When the great night came, and the sun sank down into the tops of the trees beyond the Conestoga

River, the boys gathered in the center of the city square and built a gigantic bon-fire. When the leaping of the flames and the shouts of the lads had drawn to the place all the people of Lancaster, the youngsters turned to a row of cardboard cylinders attached to sticks that were lying on the grass at a safe distance from the blaze. Under Robert's direction they had made these cylinders, and it had required the greatest care and mathematical accuracy to have them of exactly the proper length and thickness, and the stick exactly the proper length in proportion to the size of the cylinders. The head of the rocket was filled with powder and a number of little balls, most carefully compounded by Robert himself and consisting of various ingredients to make colored fire. All this—the compounding of materials, the proper dimensions and proportions—Robert had carefully studied out from the general description which he had read in his book.

When the boys set off the rockets, "Oh and Ah!" cried the astonished crowd. A big report, then a streak of fire shooting up like a hissing dragon into the air and finally high above their heads a burst of glorious colored stars.

The citizens of Lancaster had no words but of praise that night for the intelligent little lad who had worked out for them such a celebration and the boys themselves felt that rockets far outdid candles as a means of venting youthful spirits.

After this Robert continued more constantly than ever to haunt the factories where arms were being made for the Continental army, and he proved so good a draughtsman, such a student of mechanics and of such an inventive turn of mind, that he was often able to give the workmen valuable suggestions. Always and eternally he was experimenting, experimenting, experimenting. Sometimes he worked quite mysteriously on problems he would not discuss with his fellows. Once he continued day after day to go to the druggist's for quicksilver. Great was the curiosity to know what he could be doing with that strange elusive metal that acts as if bewitched. No one ever discovered; he kept it a deep, dark secret, but his comrades thenceforth nicknamed him "Quicksilver Bob."

In 1779 when he was fourteen years old, Quicksilver Bob met among the factory youths an intelligent lad four years older than he who rejoiced in the name of Christopher Gumpf. Now the father of Christopher was an enthusiastic fisherman and he kept an old flat boat padlocked to a tree on the banks of the Conestoga. Often he would invite the boys to go with him on fishing trips up the river. On holidays they would all three set out with bait and lunch for a glorious day up stream. The flat boat was propelled by a pole, and the boys took turns at poling. But it was a hard and tedious task pushing the clumsy, heavy old scow for a long distance up stream, so then and there Robert's active mind began to work on the problem of saving labor in locomotion by water. During a visit of a week with an aunt in New Britain, he planned and made a small model of a boat to be propelled by side paddles. The model was too large to be carried home, so Robert on his departure left it in his aunt's attic. Little did she guess that day that in after years it should be her most cherished treasure.

THE TREASURE CHEST

On returning to Lancaster, Fulton confided his plan for moving a boat by paddle wheels to Christopher. After much secret hammering, sawing and planing in the woods by the river, the two lads together made a set of side paddles to move their old friend, the scow. The paddle wheels were joined by a bar and worked by a crank, so that one boy, standing in the center of the boat could turn the crank, which would turn the bar, which would turn the paddle wheels, which would propel the boat!

When the contrivance was finished Christopher himself could hardly believe it would work, but Robert, with no doubts whatever, stepped into the boat, confidently laid hold of the crank and turned it with a vim. Off went the scow, gliding along upstream, and the boys spent a day of delighted triumph, enjoying their success and the astonished faces of the spectators who stopped, open mouthed, to watch them from the banks of the Conestoga. Very little effort now sent the boat a long way. It was much easier and faster than the old fashioned method of poling.

So it was in the little town of Lancaster on the Conestoga Creek, with only a few witnesses who little dreamed what the contrivance would lead to, that the boy, Robert Fulton, began to plan his solution to the problem of navigation. Years later, in place of a few astonished rustics lining a creek to see a paddle wheeled scow, crowds of people were to line the banks of the Hudson to see the Clermont, the first successful steamboat ever launched, steam its way up the river, puffing out its message to all the world that it brought an end to the days of sail-boats and ushered in the dawn of the era of steam navigation. And the inventor of the Clermont, the boat that revolutionized the method of travel by water, was this same Robert Fulton, who had proclaimed as a boy with all simple but fervent sincerity, that to him who has courage and purpose, patience and faith, "nothing is impossible."

DONN P. CRANE

GIDEON, THE WARRIOR
Judges VI:1-16, 33-40, VII, VIII:22, 23, 28

And the children of Israel did evil in the sight of the Lord; and the Lord delivered them into the hand of Mid'i-an seven years. And the hand of Mid'i-an prevailed against Israel; and because of the Mid'i-an-ites, the children of Israel made them the dens which are in the mountains, and caves, and strongholds.

And so it was that the Mid'i-an-ites came up, and the Am a-lek-ites, and the children of the East, and they encamped against the children of Israel, and destroyed the increase of the earth, and left no sustenance for Israel, neither sheep, nor ox, nor ass. For they came up with their cattle and their tents, and they came as grasshoppers for multitude; for they and their camels were without number, and they entered into the land to destroy it.

And Israel was greatly impoverished because of the Mid′i-an-ites; and the children of Israel cried unto the Lord. And it came to pass when the children of Israel cried unto the Lord, that the Lord sent a prophet unto the children of Israel, which said unto them:

"Thus saith the Lord God of Israel, 'I brought you up from Egypt, and brought you forth out of the land of bondage; and I delivered you out of the hand of the Egyptians, and out of the hand of all that oppressed you, and drave them out from before you and gave you their land.' And I said unto you, 'I am the Lord your God; fear not the gods of the Am′or-ites, in whose land you dwell. But ye have not obeyed my voice.'"

And there came an angel of the Lord, and sat under an oak which was in Oph′rah, that pertained unto Jo′ash, the A′bi-ez′rite. And his son Gid′e-on threshed wheat by the winepress, to hide it from the Midianites. And the angel of the Lord appeared unto him, and said unto him, "The Lord is with thee, thou mighty man of valor."

And Gideon said unto him, "Oh, my Lord, if the Lord be with us, why then is all this befallen us? And where be all his miracles, which our fathers told us of, saying, 'Did not the Lord bring us up from Egypt?' But now the Lord hath forsaken us, and delivered us into the hands of the Midianites."

And the Lord looked upon him and said, "Go in this thy might, and thou shalt save Israel from the hands of the Midianites. Have not I sent thee?"

And Gideon said unto him: "Oh, my Lord, wherewith shall I save Israel? Behold my family is poor in Ma-nas'seh, and I am the least in my father's house."

And the Lord said unto him: "Surely I will be with thee, and thou shalt smite the Midianites as one man."

Then all the Midianites and the Amalekites and the children of the East were gathered together and pitched in the valley of Jez're-el. But the Spirit of the Lord came upon Gideon, and he blew a trumpet; and A'bi-e'zer was gathered after him; and he sent messengers throughout all Ma-nas'seh; who also were gathered after him, and he sent messengers unto Ash'er, and unto Zeb'u-lun, and unto Naph'ta-li; and they came up to meet them.

And Gideon said unto God: "If thou wilt save Israel by mine hand, as thou has said, behold! I will put a fleece of wool on the floor, and if the dew be on the fleece only, and it be dry upon all the earth beside, then shall I know that thou wilt save Israel by mine hand, as thou hast said."

And it was so, for he rose up early on the morrow, and wringed the dew out of the fleece, a bowl full of water.

And Gideon said unto God: "Let not thine anger be hot against me, and I will speak but this once: let me prove, I pray thee, but this once with the fleece. Let it now be dry upon the fleece, and upon all the ground let there be dew."

And God did so that night; for it was dry upon the fleece only, and there was dew on all the ground.

Then Gideon and all the people that were with him, rose up early, and pitched beside the well of Ha'rod; so that the host of the Midianites were on the north side of them, by the hill of Mo'reh, in the valley.

And the Lord said unto Gideon: "The people that are with thee are too many for me to give the Midianites into their hands, lest Israel vaunt themselves against me, saying, 'Mine *own* hand hath saved me.' Now therefore, go to; proclaim in the ears of the people saying, 'Whosoever is fearful and afraid, let him return and depart early from Mount Gil'e-ad.' "

And there returned of the people twenty and two thousand, and there remained ten thousand.

And the Lord said unto Gideon: "The people are yet too many. Bring them down unto the water and I will try them for thee there. And it shall be that of whom I say unto thee, 'This shall go with thee,' the same shall go with thee; and of whomsoever I say unto thee, 'The same shall not go with thee,' the same shall not go."

So he brought down the people unto the water, and the Lord said unto Gideon: "Every one that lappeth of the water with his tongue, as a dog lappeth, him shalt thou set by himself; likewise everyone that boweth down upon his knees to drink."

And the number of them that lapped, putting their hand to their mouth, were three hundred men. But all the rest of the people bowed down upon their knees to drink water.

And the Lord said unto Gideon: "By the three hundred men that lapped will I save you, and deliver the Midianites into thine hand. Let all the other people go, every man unto his place."

So the people took victuals in their hand, and their trumpets, and he sent all the rest of Israel every man unto his tent, and retained but those three hundred men only. And the host of Midian was beneath him in the valley.

And it came to pass the same night, that the Lord said unto him: "Arise, get thee down unto the host; for I have delivered it into thine hand. But if thou fear to go down, go thou with Phu'rah thy servant down to the host. And thou shalt hear what they say, and afterward shall thine hand be strengthened to go down against the host."

Then went he down with Phurah his servant unto the outside

of the armed men that were in the host. And the Midianites, and the Amalekites and all the children of the East lay along in the valley like grasshoppers for multitude; and their camels were without number, as the sand by the seaside for multitude.

And when Gideon was come, behold! there was a man that told a dream unto his fellow, and said: "Behold! I dreamed a dream, and lo! a cake of barley bread tumbled into the host of Midian, and came unto a tent and smote it that it fell, and over-turned it that the tent lay along."

And his fellow answered and said: "This is nothing else save the sword of Gideon, the son of Joash, a man of Israel; for into his hand hath God delivered Midian and all the host."

And it was so when Gideon heard the telling of the dream, and the interpretation thereof, that he worshipped and returned into the host of Israel and said: "Arise, for the Lord hath de-livered into your hand the host of Midian."

And he divided the three hundred men into three companies, and he put a trumpet in every man's hand, with empty pitchers, and torches within the pitchers. And he said unto them: "Look on me and do likewise. And behold! when I come to the out-side of the camp, it shall be that, as I do, so shall ye do. When I blow a trumpet, I and all that are with me, then blow ye the trumpets also on every side of all the camp, and say, '*The Sword of the Lord and of Gideon!*'"

So Gideon and the hundred men that were with him, came unto the outside of the camp in the beginning of the middle watch, and they had but newly set the watch. And they blew the trumpets and brake the pitchers that were in their hands. And the three companies blew the trumpets, and brake the pitchers that were in their hands, and held the torches in their left hands, and the trumpets in their right hands to blow withal. And they cried, "*The sword of the Lord and of Gideon!*"

And they stood every man in his place round about the camp, and the Midianites thought an host was come upon them and they ran and the children of Israel shouted and put them to flight. And the three hundred blew the trumpets and the Lord set every man's sword against his fellow, even throughout all the host of Midian, and the Midianites fled. And the men of Israel gathered themselves together and pursued after the Midianites.

Then the men of Israel said unto Gideon: "Rule thou over us, both thou and thy son, and thy son's son also, for thou hast delivered us from the hand of Midian."

And Gideon said unto them: "I will not rule over you, neither shall my son rule over you; the Lord shall rule over you."

Thus was Midian subdued before the children of Israel, so that they lifted up their heads no more. And the country was in quietness forty years in the days of Gideon.

DANIEL IN THE LIONS' DEN
Daniel, 6.

It pleased King Da-ri′us to set over the kingdom of Bab′y-lon an hundred and twenty princes which should be over the whole kingdom; and over these three presidents, of whom that Daniel who was of the captives of Judah, was first, that the princes might give accounts unto the presidents, and the king should have no damage. Then this Daniel was preferred above the presidents and princes because an excellent spirit was in him, and the king thought to set him over the whole realm.

Then the presidents and princes sought to find occasion against Daniel concerning the kingdom. But they could find none occasion nor fault, forasmuch as he was faithful, neither was there any error or fault found in him.

Then said these men, "We shall not find any occasion against this Daniel, except we find it against him concerning the law of his God."

Then these presidents and princes assembled together to the King and said thus unto him:

"King Darius, live forever! All the presidents of the king-dom, the governors and the princes, the counsellors and the captains, have consulted together to establish a royal statute and to make a firm decree, that whosoever shall ask a petition of any God or man for thirty days, save of thee, O King, he shall be cast into the den of lions. Now, O King, establish the decree, and sign the writing, that it be not changed, according to the law of the Medes and Persians, which altereth not."

Wherefore King Darius signed the writing and the decree.

Now when Daniel knew that the writing was signed, he went into his house; and his windows being opened in his chamber toward Jerusalem, he kneeled upon his knees three times a day, and prayed and gave thanks before his God as he did aforetime.

Then these men assembled, and found Daniel praying and making supplication before his God. Then they came near, and spake before the King concerning the King's decree:

"Hast thou not signed a decree that every man that shall ask a petition of any God or man within thirty days, save of thee, O King, shall be cast into the den of lions?"

The King answered and said:

"The thing is true according to the law of the Medes and Persians which altereth not."

Then answered they and said before the King:

"That Daniel which is of the children of the captivity of Judah regardeth not thee, O King, nor the decree that thou hast signed, but maketh his petition three times a day."

Then the King, when he heard these words, was sore displeased with himself, and set his heart on Daniel to deliver him. And he labored till the going down of the sun to deliver him.

Then these men assembled unto the King and said unto the King:

"Know, O King, that the law of the Medes and Persians is that no decree or statute which the King establisheth may be changed."

Then the King commanded and they brought Daniel and cast him into the den of lions. Now the King spake and said unto Daniel:

"Thy God whom thou servest continually, he will deliver thee."

And a stone was brought and laid upon the mouth of the den, and the King sealed it with his own signet, and with the signet of his lords; that the purpose might not be changed concerning Daniel.

Then the King went to his palace, and passed the night fasting; neither were instruments of music brought before him, and his sleep went from him.

Then the King arose very early in the morning, and went in haste unto the den of lions. And when he came to the den, he cried with a lamentable voice unto Daniel. And the King spake and said to Daniel.

"O Daniel, servant of the living God, is thy God whom thou servest continually, able to deliver thee from the lions?"

Then said Daniel unto the King:

"O King, live forever! My God hath sent his angel, and hath shut the lions' mouths, that they have not hurt me; foras-

much as before him innocency was found in me; and also before thee, O King, have I done no hurt."

Then was the King exceeding glad for him, and commanded that they should take Daniel up out of the den. So Daniel was taken up out of the den, and no manner of hurt was found upon him, because he believed in his God.

And the King commanded and they brought those men which had

accused Daniel, and they cast *them* into the den of lions; and the lions had the mastery of them.

Then King Darius wrote unto all peoples, nations and languages, that dwell in all the earth:

"Peace be multiplied unto you! I make a decree, that in every dominion of my kingdom, men tremble and fear before the God of Daniel; for he is the living God, and steadfast forever, and his kingdom that which shall not be destroyed, and his dominion shall be even unto the end. He delivereth and rescueth, and he worketh signs and wonders in heaven and in earth, who hath delivered Daniel from the power of the lions."

So this Daniel prospered in the reign of Darius, and in the reign of Cyrus, the Persian.

411

THE ADVENTURES OF PERSEUS
A Greek Myth

THERE dwelt once in Argos, a King's daughter named Dan′a-e and her infant son, Per′seus. Now Ac-ris′i-us, the father of Danae, had one day been terrified half out of his wits by the words of an oracle which solemnly declared that the child of his daughter, Danae, should be the cause of his death. Thereafter, blindly accepting the words of the oracle as true, and heeding naught but his own foolish fears, Acrisius caused Danae and her son to be seized out of the strong tower wherein he had confined them, shut fast in an iron bound chest, and cast into the sea.

Up and down on the boundless deep rocked the chest, now borne high aloft on the crest of a giant wave, and now plunged headlong down into the foaming trough of the sea. Within, Danae held close her babe, and prayed to be delivered. Out and out they drifted, far and far and far. At last the waters heaved them up onto the shore of an island, and the chest was entangled fast in a fisherman's net.

Now the fisherman was amazed when he drew up out of the sea an iron-bound box, and found it to contain a young mother and child of marvelous beauty. Straightway he led them to his own cottage and commended them to the care of his wife. It then appeared that the name of the island whereon they had been cast, was Ser′i-phus, and the fisherman was Dic′tys, no less a personage than brother to King Pol-y-dec′tes himself. In the cottage of Dictys and his good wife, Danae and her son were sheltered till Perseus grew to manhood.

Then it chanced one day that Polydectes cast his eyes on Danae and determined to have her for his queen. But Danae would have none of Polydectes, for he was a tyrant both wicked and cruel. By this time Perseus was grown a youth of such strength and promise that he was well able to defend his mother, and Polydectes perceived that if he would worry the lovely Danae into becoming his bride, he must rid himself of her stalwart son. Therefore he called to him the young Perseus and said:

"Youth, you have found in my kingdom an asylum and a home from the days of your infancy. Now that you are grown to manhood, it is but meet that you should repay the courtesy thus extended to you. You have reached the age when men of valor go venturing, to rid the world of monsters. Go you, therefore, in quest of the gorgon, Med-u'-sa, who lays waste all the surrounding countryside, and show your face no more within my kingdom until you bring to me her head."

Now Perseus withdrew from the presence of King Polydectes almost in despair. He would have shrunk from no ordinary adventure possible to a hero, but the gorgons, as he knew full well, were the most hideous monsters in the world. Three terrible sisters they were, hateful, venomous, cruel. They had faces like women, but their bodies were those of beasts, all covered with scales of brass and iron so hard that no sword could pierce them; enormous were their wings and they gleamed with sinister flash of golden feathers; they had tusks instead of teeth, and sharp, cruel, brazen claws. Their hair was writhing serpents, that would curl and twist and hiss, and dart out long, forked tongues to sting. Worst of all, so hard and cold and hateful was their stare, that he who looked full in their faces froze immediately into stone.

"Now how," mused Perseus, "is a man to give battle to such horrid creatures when he may not even look on them?"

Nevertheless, he bade a sad farewell to his mother, and wandered along the shore lost in sorrowful thoughts and longing for some wise counsel. Suddenly there glowed about him a light seven times brighter than the sun. He looked up in amazement

and lo! there before him, resting lightly on the sand, stood a beautiful woman in long white robes with a shining helmet on her head, a staff in her hand, and a shield on her arm,—Min-er'va, the goddess of Wisdom herself.

"Perseus," said she, "take this shield. So brightly is it polished that if you keep your eyes fixed upon it, you will see the gorgons reflected therein, and can give them battle without ever needing to look in their faces."

With a mighty leaping of his heart, Perseus gave thanks, yet he said: "Though I look in the shield, where shall I find among mortals a sword that can pierce through their heavy scales?"

Even as he spoke, there came a slight rustling through the air, and hovering there on his other side appeared a youth with winged sandals and cap, in one hand a winged staff, about which two serpents were twined, and in the other a crooked sword that shone like a flame.

"You shall use my sword," said the youth, for he was Mer'-cu-ry, messenger from O-lymp'us whence came the help of the gods to men who had deserved it.

THE TREASURE CHEST

Then Minerva bade the young Perseus seek out the Three Gray Sisters, cousins of the gorgons, and force from them the secret of where the Gorgon's Isle lay. Guided by Mercury, Perseus made off.

Far, far to westward he journeyed, till he came to a barren, desolate shore, where was everlasting twilight. Gray was the sky, and gray were the giant rocks; gray were the straggling trunks of the leafless trees, and gray was the misty sea. As the two approached the place, there loomed up before them three old hags in flowing gray robes with unkempt white locks hanging over their shoulders, scarce to be told from the great gray waves with crests of white that came dashing up on the shore. Perseus perceived that these three old hags possessed but one tooth and one eye among them. These they passed about from one to another and each in turn clapped the tooth into her toothless gums, and the eye into a socket in her forehead. As Perseus and Mercury groped their way cautiously towards them, it became apparent

that the old hags were just at that moment quarreling over whose turn it was to have the eye. One held the brilliant orb gleaming in her hand, and all were scolding, gesticulating, screeching. Thus, the while they wrangled, not one of the three could see at all.

"Quick," whispered Mercury to Perseus. "Now is your chance. Seize the eye and do not return it till they tell you the secret. They will never tell you otherwise."

In a flash Perseus stepped forward, nimbly seized the eye, and withdrew again to a little distance. Then there burst forth a perfect storm from the three old hags, for each thought the other had snatched the eye, but Perseus cried out boldly:

"I have your eye,—I, a youth from beyond the seas, nor will I return it until you tell me where lies the Island of the Gorgons."

The old hags begged and whined and scolded; they tried to grope their way stealthily to him to snatch back the eye unawares, but Perseus kept well out of reach and held firm. So at last they told him that he must go still farther westward, and there seek out certain nymphs who kept a pair of winged sandals, a magic pouch and a wonderful helmet that could render its wearer invisible. These nymphs would direct him just how to reach the Island of the Gorgons.

At that Perseus gave the Gray Women back their eye, and with Mercury journeyed once more forward. In good time, they reached a beautiful glade in the forest, where the sunlight filtered in blotches of gold through the leaves, and a group of graceful nymphs with wreaths and garlands of flowers, disported themselves about the banks of a clear, blue pool. To them Perseus presented himself and told his tale. At once they hushed their mirth and musical laughter.

"We will gladly aid the hero who goes forth to conquer the gorgon, Medusa," they cried, and they tripped lightly away, brought back the winged sandals and bound them on Perseus' feet. About his neck they hung the magic pouch, and placed on his head the helmet of darkness. When they had thus provided him, they pointed out the Island of the Gorgons lying low, like a bank of dun gray clouds, on the dim horizon.

Now in his winged sandals Perseus could mount up into the air as safely as Mercury. Far, far up he soared, cleaving the air like a bird, now skimming over the chequered green earth that lay spread out far below, and now over the shining blue sea. It was midnight when Perseus at length heard a calm voice speak by his side, grave, yet melodious and mild.

"There below," it said, "lies the Island of the Gorgons." And now it was not Mercury who spoke, but Minerva, come once more in the hour of need to give Perseus counsel. Wrapped from sight in the helmet of darkness, Perseus sank downward. The moon was flooding the earth with silver, and he saw below him a rocky coast, stone, stone, everywhere stone, shining white and cold in the cold, white light. Suddenly from among the black shadows at the base of a barren cliff, there flashed a baleful gleam, and he knew it must be a moonbeam cast back from the horrid scales on the backs of the gorgons. Boldly he descended thither.

"Be cautious," said Minerva, "look into your shield."

Then in the full-glowing light of the moon, he looked into his shield and behold! a hideous sight,—the three hateful sisters fast

asleep, their scales and golden wings glistening, their brazen claws outspread as though ready to clutch, the snakes on their heads writhing even in sleep, and hissing now and again. Even as he looked, one of the dreadful creatures moved as though to awake.

"That is Medusa," said Minerva, "strike on the instant and do not miss your first stroke."

In a flash Perseus obeyed. The gorgon opened her freezing eyes, but Perseus, looking ever into the shield, cleaved off the head with a single stroke of his

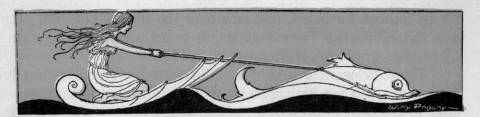

sword, seized it, snakes and all, and dropped it into the magic
pouch.

"Well done," cried Mercury.

"Now fly," said Minerva, "for the others are awakening."

On his winged sandals, Perseus sped swiftly upward, but not
a moment too soon. Medusa's sisters, awakened by the noise
of his stroke, perceived what had been done, and flew in a frenzy
of rage to the shore, every snake on their heads a-bristle with
fury. He could hear the rushing of their wings, the rattle of their
brazen claws, the hissing of the serpents, as they mounted up
into the air in pursuit. But, thanks to the helmet of darkness,
he was hidden from their sight, and made off from them in safety.

Perseus then bade farewell to Mercury and Minerva, and set out
alone to return to Seriphus. But it chanced on the way that he
passed through the country of E-thi-o'pi-a, which was ruled over by
King Ceph'eus. Now there was come up at this time out of the
deep a terrible sea monster, that ravaged the coast of Ethiopia, a
huge, scaly creature with wings like a dragon and a tail like a fish.
It came up and carried off oxen and people, and even destroyed
whole villages. The men of Ethiopia had done all in their power
to rid themselves of the monster, but in vain,—there was not
one among them able to stand before him. Then came forward
a wise old man of the people and said:

"Lo! our queen, Cass-i-o-pe'i-a, swelled with pride of her own
beauty, did boast herself lovelier than the sea-nymphs, that drive
their chariots with swift-skimming dolphins through the waves.

THE TREASURE CHEST

This frightful monster is come up out of the sea as a punishment to her vanity, and never will he retire till the guilty queen offer to him her dearest treasure, even An-drom'e-da, her daughter."

Throughout all the kingdom, then, was weeping and wailing, and most of all in the palace. Nevertheless, the people must at all costs be rid of the monster, so they seized the lovely Andromeda, bound her fast with chains to a mighty rock on the shore and left her a prey to the beast. Andromeda wrung her hands; the people stood afar off and watched, but they dared not let her free. Even Phin'eus, whose promised bride she was, stood by and made no effort to save her. Pale and motionless as a marble statue, save for her hair that waved in the breeze, she stood.

Then lo! up out of the sea like a mountain he rose,—the great sea-monster! Andromeda shrieked; the wretched mother and father wrung their hands; Phineus shrank back, slunk away, and hid himself in fear. But there in that moment of despair, borne

Willy Pogány

up in the air by his winged sandals, appeared the hero, Perseus.

"O virgin," he cried, "undeserving those chains. I am come to deliver you."

With a sudden swoop the youth darted down on the back of the monster, lighting just at the base of the neck where the creature could not strike at him with his fangs. Into his shoulder Perseus plunged his sword. Now here, now there, he worried him, piercing first this side, then that, and darting ever out of his reach by means of his wings. With a furious splashing the monster churned all the water about into foam. At length Perseus' wings were drenched. He dared no longer trust them. Alighting now on a rock and holding fast to a projecting fragment, as the monster floated near, he gave him his death blow. The serpent turned over on his back and floated with belly upward.

The people, gathered on the shore, raised a shout till all the hills reechoed. The parents, transported with joy, called Perseus their deliverer, and the hero himself released Andromeda from the rocks. Then was the lovely Andromeda promised to Perseus in marriage. Every house in the city was wreathed and hung with garlands. In the palace itself a banquet was spread and all was joy and festivity.

But suddenly a noise was heard of warlike clamor. With a numerous party of swaggering, brawling followers, there burst into the festal hall, Phineus, demanding the maiden as his own. It was in vain that Cepheus cried: "You should have claimed her when she lay bound to the rock, the monster's victim. He who neglects his claim at such a time, forfeits it altogether."

Phineus made no reply, but hurled his javelin at Perseus. It missed its mark and fell harmless. Then the cowardly assailant ran and took shelter behind the altar. His act was the signal for a general onset by his band upon the guests of Cepheus. Perseus and his friends defended themselves and maintained for some time the unequal conflict, but the numbers of the assailants were far too great. Destruction seemed inevitable. Then with a loud voice Perseus cried: "If I have any friend here, let him turn away his eyes." And he suddenly held aloft the head of the gorgon, Medusa.

"Seek not to frighten us with your jugglery," cried one of the brawlers and raised his javelin to throw, but lo! he was turned to stone in the very act. A second was about to plunge his sword into a prostrate foe, but his arm stiffened and he could thrust not a hairsbreadth forward. A third, in the midst of a taunting boast, froze with mouth wide open. Phineus, beholding the dreadful result of his unjust aggression, felt confounded. He called aloud to his friends and got no answer. He touched them and found them stone. Then he fell on his knees before Perseus, to sue for his own wretched life, but in the very attitude he, too, was turned to stone.

Then was the marriage of Perseus and Andromeda fulfilled. King Cepheus gave Perseus a ship with stalwart rowers; he and his queen bade a fond farewell to their daughter, Andromeda, and Perseus and his bride set out for Seriphus.

Now it had happened that while Perseus had been away on his adventures, Polydectes had never once left off worrying Danae to force her to be his queen. His followers were as wicked as he, and in all the island was none to protect the lovely young matron, save Dictys, the good fisherman. At last, in his anger, the King cast Danae and Dictys both into dungeons, and there the two lay languishing when the ship of Perseus dropped anchor in the harbor.

Perseus made straight for the palace. The King was at meat surrounded by his wicked retainers. When he saw come into the hall the youth whom he had thought out of his way forever, he was sunk at first in confusion. In a moment more he cried out:

"How dare you come here without the head of Medusa?"

"O King," Perseus answered, "I have the head in my pouch."

"Ho, ho!" mocked the King, "if you have in truth performed this unheard-of act, then show us the head."

"Nay," answered Perseus. "I am loath to hold it up. I tell you I have it here in my pouch."

"Ho! ho!" jeered all the King's followers. "He has it in his pouch, yet he will not produce it! Base deceiver, he but pretends to have done the deed. It is no Medusa head he has in his pouch. He dares not show us what lies there."

"Come, come," called the King, "if you have there the head, out with it on the instant! Else with your own head you shall pay for the cheat."

Threatening, taunting, gibing, the King's men pressed about Perseus. "As you will, then," shouted the hero, and he held it aloft,—the snaky head of Medusa. In a flash, about him were a white marble hall, a white marble table with white marble food and marble statues of men.

Having thus freed the island from the base tyranny of Polydectes, Perseus went to embrace his mother, set her free, and lead her to his Andromeda. Dictys likewise he freed and made King of Seriphus in place of his worthless brother. To Minerva Perseus returned her shield along with the gift of the head of Medusa. To Mercury he gave back the sword. Then Perseus and Andromeda, with Danae, their mother, once more sailed away and after many adventures Perseus found a kingdom for himself. Long and wisely he reigned, and lived happily thenceforward.

Willy Pogany

THE LABORS OF HERCULES
A Greek Myth

Among all the Greek heroes about whom the old Greek harpers sung, who was more dearly loved than Her'cu-les—Hercules, the patient, Hercules the strong?

When Hercules was but a babe a few months old, his mother, Alc-me'ne, left him once asleep in a brazen warrior's shield that served him for a cradle. There came creeping upon him while he slept, two venemous serpents. Just as the snakes were about to strike, Hercules awoke. With a crow of delight, as though he had found a new plaything, and without a sign of fear, the little one seized the serpents, one in each hand. Straight by the neck he grasped them and held on tight. When his mother came in and found him thus, she was struck almost dumb at the sight, but the snakes were already strangled, and the infant Hercules safe. So began the strong man's conquests over evil.

Hercules grew to manhood possessed of marvelous courage and strength and carefully trained in all that befitted a hero. One day when he was still a youth, dwelling for a time among herdsmen on the mountains, he lay down in a lonely valley to sleep through the noonday heat. In his sleep he had a strange dream. He seemed to be following a path that suddenly split into two, branching off in opposite directions, and he knew not which road to take in order to pursue his journey. One road looked broad and easy and led down to a pleasant city whence he saw the gleam of marble palaces mid green and tempting gardens. The other was steep and rocky. It was hard to climb and led endlessly upward, growing rockier and rougher at every step, till it disappeared in the clouds. As Hercules stood hesitating which road to choose, there came dancing down the smooth and easy highway a gay and laughing maiden. She beckoned to him and called:

"Come with me, Hercules, down into the pleasant city. There you need not labor all day long in the heat of the sun. You may sit continually in fragrant gardens, hearken to the plash of fountains and the songs of birds, and slaves will serve you with all you need."

As Hercules looked toward the city, the piping of merry music faintly reached his ears to invite and tempt him still further. But lo! just then in the second path appeared a second young maiden, quite different from the first. She wore plain white garments and her eyes were grave, yet quiet, sweet and calm.

"My sister deceives you, Hercules," said she. "The pleasant things offered you down below are not worth the having. They are toys of which you will tire in a day and must be bought with a price of which you little dream. Do not descend thither, but climb the mountain path with me. You will find it rough and difficult, 'tis true. Yet, breasting its heights, you will there find real delights of which you can never tire. Moreover, if you have the courage to climb, this road will lead you to Mt. Olympus itself and there you shall live forever with the gods who cannot die."

And then in his dream Hercules turned his back on the gay and laughing maiden and took the mountain road. Thus did he choose the labors by means of which he turned his strength to good account for men.

Now Hercules had a cousin named Eu-rys'theus, King of My-ce'nae, who was a few days older than he. It had therefore been decreed that Hercules should be the slave of Eurystheus and in all things serve and obey him. Only on condition that he successfully performed twelve tasks that Eurystheus should set him, could he ever again be free. When Hercules presented himself at the court of King Eurystheus, he was already remarkable for his broad shoulders and the enormous muscles of his arms, while Eurystheus was miserably puny, timid, frail and weak. When Eurystheus for the first time beheld his powerful cousin, he was terrified at his strength, and he resolved to set him the hardest and most dangerous tasks that wit of man could possibly devise.

At this time in a beautiful grove that surrounded the temple of Ju'pi-ter in Ne-me'a, a fierce lion had its den. This lion was laying waste the whole countryside, so the people lived in constant terror of its ravages. The first task which Eurystheus set Hercules was to kill the Nemean lion. The young man set out with only his bow and arrows for weapons, but as he journeyed along, he found a sturdy olive tree by the roadside. With a single wrench, he pulled up the whole stout tree by its roots and made himself a club.

As he drew nearer the lion's haunts, nowhere did he meet with man, woman or child, for all had been so terrified, that they kept within doors, leaving their flocks to its mercy. At length Hercules came to the beautiful grove by the Temple of Jupiter and there he watched all day long. Towards night the lion came creeping home to its lair. It was a tremendous creature, fierce and terrible. Hercules twanged his bow and sent an arrow flying. The arrow struck the beast, but so tough was its hide that the sharp point glanced aside and fell harmless. The lion snarled, showed its fierce teeth, and looked about for its foe. A second arrow Hercules shot, but it glanced aside like the first. Ere he could shoot a third, the lion had espied him. It crouched and sprang straight at his throat. Hercules knocked it aside with a powerful blow from his club, then as it rose ramping and clawing the air, he seized its neck with both hands and hung on fast till he slew it.

His first task thus accomplished, Hercules went back to Eurystheus, wearing the skin of the lion over his shoulder while the head of the beast rested on his own like a kind of helmet. Henceforth Hercules was always to be distinguished by the lion's skin which he wore and the enormous club which he carried. When he came in such fashion into Eurystheus' presence, the coward was as frightened as though he had suddenly seen the Nemean lion itself before him. Yet when he was somewhat calmed he said:

"Hercules has slain the Nemean lion, 'tis true, still, the lion was but a beast after all. I will send him now to dispose of a hideous monster."

So he sent for Hercules and bade him kill the powerful Ler'ne-an hydra. This hydra was a tremendous serpent with nine heads, one of which was immortal and could not possibly be slain. It had its den near a fountain that supplied all the region about with water and it drove the unfortunate peasants away, so they had no means whatever whereby to slake their thirst.

Hercules took with him his young nephew I'o-laus, and off they started. In an oozy, evil-smelling marsh, they found the hydra, twisting its nine ugly heads in the air and breathing forth poison. Hercules made at it at once, but whenever he cut off a head, two grew in its place, so at every stroke it only became more formidable.

"Ho, Iolaus, set fire to yon grove of young trees," cried Hercules, "and keep me supplied with the burning brands."

Then he applied a brand to the neck wherever he cut off a head, and so prevented the new heads from growing. At length the immortal head alone was left. This Hercules had cleaved from the body, but it still spit its venomous poison as fiercely as before. So Hercules rolled a huge rock over it, and left it buried deep where it could never do further harm.

Now when Eurystheus found that his cousin had slain the hydra as well as the lion, he began to think there was no evil creature that Hercules could not kill.

"But," he mused, "his third task shall be harder still. After all it is no great task to kill. I shall bid him bring me *alive* the fierce Er-y-man'thi-an boar."

Accordingly he gave orders, and off went Hercules as before. Straight to Mt. Erymanthus he went and struggled long with the famous wild boar, but he caught him at length with his naked hands and brought him back on his shoulders. When King Eurystheus saw Hercules coming home with the boar alive on his shoulders, he was so badly frightened that he ran and jumped into a great bronze

pot in one corner of his palace, pulling down the cover in haste to keep himself well out of sight. He did not run so quickly however, but that Hercules caught just a glimpse of him as the cover went banging down.

"Ho, ho!" he cried out gravely, but with a twinkling eye, "this pot is just the place in which to keep a boar that is like to tear men to pieces." And he quickly lifted the lid and popped in the boar on top of the King. Loud was the outcry, you may be sure, till Hercules dragged out the two, the King in one hand, the boar in the other, both kicking, struggling, roaring!

"His strength seems equal to any deed," said Eurystheus to

himself, "yet will I get the best of him this time by setting a task that demands not strength, but fleetness of foot, and superhuman endurance." Then he summoned Hercules to him and bade him bring him alive the stag of Di-an'a. This stag had often befooled the hunters of that region. It was most marvelously fleet of foot and few had ever seen it. But report had said it had horns of gold, and hoofs of brass. It could make the most wonderful leaps and was never wearied, no matter how long the dogs might have chased it. It had been seen browsing oftener than else-where close to the steps of Diana's temple, and many people be-lieved it was under the protection of that goddess.

So Hercules set out for the Temple of Diana, and watched and waited patiently. At last it appeared,—the golden antlered creature, a sight of wondrous beauty. Every muscle a-quiver it stood, cautious and alert, ready to dart away at the slightest whisper of danger.

Hercules sprang towards it at once. It gave a mighty leap and made off, swift as the flying wind. But Hercules made after it, hot on its heels. Over hill, over dale it flew, through forest and meadow, over shallow stream and broad deep river, on and on and on. A whole year long it ran, over nearly the whole of Europe, and a whole year long Hercules followed, till at last he wearied it out, and it fled back, exhausted and panting, to seek shelter in Diana's Temple. Even there Hercules would have seized it, but just then a flood of silver light shone gently round about, and there before him appeared a lovely lady in short white garments, with a bow and quiver at her back and a half moon on her crown. It was Diana herself, goddess of the moon and of the chase, and to her the stag ran trembling.

"You must not lay hands on this stag," she said. "It belongs to me. But return to King Eurystheus, and tell him how your endurance has wearied it out and how but for me you would have had it. I promise you he shall consider that your fourth labor is accomplished."

Now Eurystheus was almost at a loss how further to test such a Hercules, but he thought: "I have tried his strength, his endurance and agility. I will now try his wits, and send him on an adventure that only the devising of some skillful plan can ever accomplish."

In the valley of Stym-pha'lus there had come an enormous flock of strange birds that did great damage to crops and herds, and even carried off children. These birds had claws of iron, and feathers of metal, sharp at the end, which they had the power of throwing down on their enemies. No fleetness of foot, endurance, or bodily strength could dispose of such foes as these, that could not be prevented from darting up into the air out of reach. So Eurystheus bade Hercules save the valley of Stymphalus from these ugly birds. Hercules wisely decided at once not to fight with such creatures. Instead, he went quietly into the deep dark wood where they had their nests by the side of a noisome pool. Holding his bronze shield above his head to protect himself from their feathers, he rang a great bell and at the same time beat on his shield with his lance. Frightened at this hideous noise the birds flew up in such numbers that they darkened all the sky. As they flew over Hercules' head, their feathers fell fast like hail on his shield, but he continued to ring the bell and beat the shield till every one of the birds had disappeared from the place, so frightened by the noise that none ever dared return.

Thereafter, Eurystheus set Hercules five well-nigh impossible labors more. First, he must clean out in one day the filthy stables of King Au-ge'us wherein the King had kept three thousand oxen for thirty years without ever cleansing their stalls. The refuse was piled mountain high, but Hercules dug a trench, turned the waters of two great rivers through the stables and cleaned them

thoroughly in one day. Then he must fetch to Mycenae alive the raging white bull of Crete, but he seized it by its horns and held it so firmly in spite of its terrible struggles that the bull saw it had met its master and followed him like a lamb. For his eighth labor he captured the savage man-eating horses of King Di-o-me'des; for the ninth he brought back the girdle of Hip-pol'y-ta, Queen of the Am'a-zons, a fierce tribe of warlike women who were never defeated in battle; for the tenth he overcame the giant Ger'y-on with his three great bodies, his three great heads, and six arms that waved like a windmill.

When Hercules always succeeded, his cousin was in despair. For his eleventh labor, Eurystheus set him what he deemed the most impossible task of all. He bade him never again show his face in Mycenae unless he brought back three golden apples from the Garden of the Hes-per'i-des, for he knew full well that no man on earth knew where to find that garden. But Hercules would not be daunted. He set out to westward where the sky glows golden at sunset. There, thought he, behind that golden gate should lie such a garden of golden fruit. He journeyed long and he journeyed far, but at last he came to a beautiful spot on the banks of a river, where a band of graceful river nymphs played hide and seek mid the rocks. As soon as they perceived the hero, they ran laughing, with ropes of flowers, to seize him and make him their prisoner. Then they led him into a shady beech grove, where they bade him sit on a grassy knoll and offered him refreshment of luscious purple grapes. But Hercules would not linger.

He begged the nymphs to tell him where lay the Garden of the Hesperides of which he was in search.

"You must seek out Pro'teus, the Old Man of the Sea," they told him. "He knows every land whereon the ocean laps, but he will never tell you this secret unless you compel him. You must catch him and hold him fast no matter what may happen until he tells you the truth."

Thanking the nymphs for their kindness, Hercules again set out. He followed the river on and on till he heard the mighty boom of the sea. Then he advanced cautiously to the shore and there he saw fast asleep, lulled by the roar of the waters, a little old man whose hair and beard flowed down like a tangle of seaweed. Here, for certain, was the Old Man of the Sea himself and no doubt at all about it. So Hercules stepped forward, quickly

seized him by an arm and a leg, and held him fast.

"Tell me," he cried, "where lies the Garden of the Hesperides."

Proteus awoke in a fright, and the next instant Hercules found he was holding in his hands no little old man, but a struggling stag. The change was astounding enough but still Hercules held on tight. Then the stag became a sea bird screaming to be free, the sea bird changed to a fierce three-headed dog, the three-headed dog to a savage giant, the giant to a monstrous snake. But the more terrifying were the forms which the old man assumed, the tighter Hercules held him. At last perceiving that Hercules could not be frightened into letting him go, Proteus appeared in his own rightful form once more and told him the truth.

"Go down into Africa," he said, "where the giant At'las holds up the sky and Atlas will get the apples for you."

So Hercules set out for Africa, but he had scarcely touched the African shore, when he was attacked by the terrible giant, An-tae'us, who let no man pass him alive. This giant was son of the earth, and the most difficult of all giants to conquer, for whenever he was knocked down, he gained fresh strength from the dust and sprang up stronger than ever. But Hercules, knowing it was from the earth his strength had come, lifted him high above his head and held him there, struggling and kicking, separated from the source of his power, till the life was crushed out of him. Then he went again on his way.

Being wearied somewhat by the struggle, he soon lay down for a little rest and fell asleep. Suddenly he awoke, feeling as if he had been stung by a thousand insects. As he sat up and rubbed his eyes, what should he see about but a multitude of Pygmies,—

man could
cules down
nd gloomy
he hideous
us. Who
gates had
would of
for here,

hasm be-
gleamed
gs as of
e to the
the deep
the way,
d his tail
ld be when
e at him.
ry shad-
himself
ycenae.

h, and
ke my

stood
g his
st no
grip,

saw
that

ble bees, who had climbed up over
ith their tiny bows and arrows.
n angered by their little teasing
ed with a loud resounding guffaw,
way, save a very few that Hercules
up in a corner of his lion's skin to
s.

ered on and on till he saw looming
it looked to be, yet it was only a
hung about his face like a beard and
s. He was holding up his hands and
ore the blue dome of the sky. At last,
cules, nothing daunted by the fearful
er which even Atlas groaned, offered to
ing the burden himself, if Atlas would
ples from the Garden of the Hesperides.
lling, for the nymphs who guarded the
to him the adventure was nothing more
rcules climbed a mountain nearby to be
ook the sky on his
tremendous weight
r the apples.

ame the giant, but so
his holiday, that he
give Hercules the slip
er with the sky on his
saw through the trick,
the clumsy fellow, and
the apples.
rcules had accomplished
elve labors, Eurystheus
. He could think of only

433

 one task more that it seemed no
ever achieve. He would send Her
into the under-world, the dark a
abode of Plu'to, to bring thence t
three-headed watch-dog Cer'ber
that had entered those gloomy
ever been known to return? This
a certain be the end of Hercules
men said, was the abode of death.

Hercules journeyed away till he came to a deep c
tween two black and frowning rocks. Far, far below
waters black as ink and now and again strange rumblir
thunder shook the earth. Here was the only entranc
under-world. Still Hercules knew no fear. Down into
black hole he climbed. There before him guarding
he saw Cerberus with his three savage heads an r him
like a snake. The dog let him enter readily. It wou s was
he sought again to go out that the creature would makees wer

Straight to Pluto's throne through the dark and dr a l
ows went Hercules without once turning aside. Of Pluto
he demanded permission to carry his watch-dog back to M
Pluto was struck with his daring.

"Hercules," said he, "you have done and suffered muc
proved yourself a true hero. Go, therefore. You shall ta
watch-dog back if you can conquer him barehanded."

So Hercules returned once more to the gate. There
Cerberus, no more quiet, but bristling with rage, showir
savage teeth, and crouching ready to spring. Hercules lo
time. He seized the dog on the spot with his vice-like
and dragged him straight off to Eurystheus.

When Eurystheus saw this remarkable sight, when he
that Hercules had conquered even death and come back from

under-world whence men said none could ever return, he at once set his cousin free. At length the terms of his bondage had all been fulfilled. Nevertheless, Eurystheus strictly forbade Hercules ever again to enter the gates of Mycenae.

Thereafter, Hercules, now at last his own master, wandered over the earth ridding the world of many a monstrous evil and doing mighty deeds for the good of all mankind. When the end of his earth journey came, he laid himself down on a funeral pyre and bade men set it aflame. Bright purifying flames sprang leaping up about him. All that could ever die they burned away. Then the real Hercules, the immortal Hercules came out from the fire all shining and glorious. A rainbow appeared in the sky. Lo! it was Iris's bridge that led from earth to heaven. A moment after the clouds broke away; Iris in all her shimmering colors appeared and Mercury with his winged shoes. Over the rainbow bridge they led the immortal Hercules, as the maid of his dream had promised, to Mt. Olympus itself, there to live forever among the gods with all who are truly heroes.

THOR'S JOURNEY TO JO'TUN-HEIM
A Norse Myth

WHEN the lightning leaps from cliff to cliff across the sky, and the thunder roars and rumbles, reverberating, rolling, crashing, then is the brazen chariot of Thor, the Thunderer, rolling and rattling over the heavens;—thus said the Norsemen, sons of the Northland. From the hoofs of the goats that draw his chariot fly blazing sparks, about his head gleams a crown of burning flame. In his strong right hand he grips his red hot hammer, Mjol'ner, from whence spring thunderbolts. It is against the great frost giants who dwell in Jo'tun-heim that Thor makes war—the giants who send forth ice and snow and bitter winds to nip the tender buds and kill the flowers; who wrap the earth in wintry mists and ruin harvests by their tempests.

It happened once that the storm giants held the earth too long in bondage. Frozen lay the rivers, and frozen the earth till long past the time for the coming of swallows, and no man could till the ground or plant the tender seed. Then from far off Asgard where dwell the gods, came Thor, Thor, the friend of farmers, Thor, the Deliverer, to do battle with the giants.

At the close of day Thor and Lo'ki, his companion, came to a cottage on the edge of a wood. Then rapped Thor on the door with his iron gauntlet, and called those within to give them food and shelter. Shelter the poor people gladly gave but food they had not to offer. So Thor raised his hammer and slew his own goats to serve for their supper. Amazed stood the poor peasants before him, but thus spake Thor:

"Eat, eat what ye will! Only heed this command,—break no single one of the bones, but cast them all when ye have finished into the skins on the floor."

Then Thor ate his fill, and Loki likewise, and the peasant, and his wife, and Thi-al'fi, their son, and Rosk'va, their daughter.

THE TREASURE CHEST

But Thi-al'fi, the greedy one, secretly broke a bone, to come at the sweet, juicy marrow; then he cast the pieces onto the skin with the rest of the bones. Early on the morrow up rose Thor from his couch and over the goats' skins and bones flourished good Mjol'ner, his hammer. Lithe and light, lively and brisk, up sprang the goats, handsome and whole as before. Only one, alas! limped as he ran. Then Thor knew that some one had disobeyed him. Dark grew his brow as the storm cloud; he raised his powerful hammer and all stood about in terror.

"Some one has disobeyed me!"

On his knees fell Thi-al'fi before him confessing his fault, and such was his sorrow and terror that Thor relented and let his hammer fall harmless.

"Rise," he said, "but for thy fault thou and thy sister Rosk'va shall follow me henceforth and be my servants forever."

Then did Thor leave his chariot and his goats in the charge of the peasant, bidding him give them good care against his return, and he set off once more with Lo'ki, Thi-al'fi and Rosk'va on foot for the realm of the giants. All day through a bleak and desolate land they journeyed into a land of mist and fog and gloom. At nightfall they sought for a shelter. Before them out of the mist loomed dim outlines of a house. They entered a spacious doorway, broad and high. Within was no one, neither fire, nor light, nor food. Flinging themselves wearily on the floor, Thor and his companions fell asleep.

Not long had they slept when a strange trembling shook the earth and awoke them,—a roar and long drawn rumbling.

"It is an earthquake!" cried Thi-al'fi. Thereat Thor sent Loki and the others for safety into an inner room that seemed to be one of five branching off from the outer hall, while he himself stood guard at the door. When day began to dawn, lo! he saw through the mist a tremendous giant lying near and he perceived that the

437

upheaval which they had thought an earthquake the night before was but the noise of his snoring! Boldly he approached the giant.

"Awake!" he cried, "and tell me who thou art."

"Who be I?" cried the giant, stretching and looking about. "Skry'mir, my little fellow,—Skry'mir, the giant,—that's who I be. But where hast thou taken my mitten?"

At that Thor perceived that the house wherein they had slept was naught but the giant's glove! He called his comrades to come forth and out they stepped from the thumb! Loudly guffawed the giant.

"Ho, ho! little ones!" laughed he. "Where do ye journey? Whither away so bold?"

When he heard they were travelling to Jo'tun-heim he offered to be their guide. All day long they journeyed and all day long did Skry'mir belittle them and make them believe themselves good-for-naught. At nightfall, ere he dropped off to sleep, he offered them whatever food they might wish to take from the great provision bag that hung on his shoulder. But when they tried to open the bag, not all four together, as Skry'mir had known full well, could unfasten the knots by which the giant had tied it. Then was Thor sorely wroth that Skry'mir should make them appear such weaklings, and he raised his hammer and dealt him a fearful blow on the forehead. The giant opened one sleepy eye.

"Was that a leaf fell on me?" said he.

A second time Thor lifted his hammer and hurled it with all his force at the head of the giant. But Skry'mir only murmured: "Methought an acorn dropped on my head."

Now Thor put forth such strength as never he knew he had, and smote the giant on the temple. "There must be birds overhead," said Skry'mir. "A feather just now tickled me."

Then did Thor go back to his comrades. Early on the morrow, Skry'mir pointed out the shortest road to Jo'tun-heim, and then took leave of his fellows. But first he said: "O Thor, I would give thee advice. Think not to stand up against the mighty ones

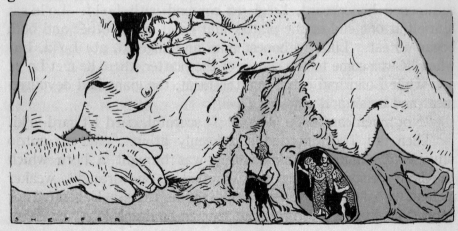

whom thou wilt find in Jo'tun-heim. Prepare to bow thyself
rather before them, for I be the smallest among them!"

In spite of his words, on went Thor, and soon there before
him and his comrades loomed up a glittering city of ice, with
spires and pinnacles of icicles. So high it was that they had to
bend back their heads to see its top. Slipping between the
enormous bars of the gate, the travellers presented themselves
in the great hall before Ut'gard-lo'ki, the King of the Giants
about whom, on benches, sat his tremendous followers.

"Oho!" cried the King of the Giants, squinting contemptuously
down as if at some little fly on the floor, which he could scarcely
discover. "Whom have we here? Little Thor, as I live, out of
Asgard. I have heard thou art small, but in truth I had never
thought so small! 'Tis said thou hast strength, though, and can
perform many great exploits! I scarce can believe it! Yet
come, let us see what thou and thy comrades can do against my
giants. Choose your own feat. At what will ye first contend?"

Then cried Lo'ki who had fasted long enough to feel great
hunger: "In eating will I contend with any man among ye."

A great platter of meat the King ordered into the hall, and
summoned his servant, Lo'gi, to contend with Lo'ki. Lo'ki sat
himself at one end of the platter and Lo'gi at the other and both
began to eat. Like an honest man an-hungered, ate Lo'ki, but
when he was come to the center of the platter, there he met Lo'gi,
and while Lo'ki had eaten but the meat, the giant had devoured
meat and bones and platter as well!

"Not much can ye do at eating!" scornful, cried Ut'gard-lo'ki.

Then did Thor, nettled and keenly athirst, offer to outdo
anyone at drinking. Immediately was brought a horn which
the King declared strong men emptied at one draught, weaker
men at two and the veriest weaklings at three. Eagerly Thor
applied his lips to the rim. But though he drank long and deep,

the water seemed not to grow less by so much as a hair's breadth. Again he tried and again. The horn remained ever full.

"Not much can ye do at drinking," scornful, cried Ut'gard-lo'ki.

Then cried Thi-al'fi that he would run a race with any among the giants. Came one named Hu'gi, and, though Thi-al'fi kept hot on his heels in three different races, Hu'gi ever outstripped him.

"Not much can ye do at running," scornful, cried Ut'gard-lo'ki.

Next shouted Thor that he would contend in lifting.

"Lift me then my house cat," cried the King. " 'Tis a triflng game at which we only exercise children. I should never propose it to Thor save that I have found him so puny a little stripling."

Angrily, Thor seized the cat. At first he could not budge her. Then he arched her back from the ground, then he lifted one mighty paw. The faces of the giants turned pale, still Ut'gard-lo'ki called, "Not much can ye do at lifting!"

Last of all, cried Thor in a fury: "Let me contend at wrestling."

"My poor old nurse, El'li, belike is a fit match for thee," jibed the King and into the hall came a feeble old hag, weak-seeming and bent nearly double. Yet she seized Thor in a grip like a vise. Valiantly he struggled, but the more he tightened his hold, the firmer stood El'li, till at last she had him on his knees. Then cried Ut'gard-lo'ki: "No more will we contend. In truth ye are good for naught!"

On the morrow at daybreak, Thor and his comrades, sad and heavy hearted, set out once more for home. Ut'gard-lo'ki accompanied them outside the gates of the city. Once there, he cried: "How now, Thor, hast thou met mightier men than thou? Is it so easy as thou didst think to conquer the giants?"

"Nay," Thor made honest answer, "I have come off badly. My heart sinks with shame that I have proved such a weakling!"

Then was the King struck with the blunt and open truth of him who never yet uttered untruth, and he cried:

"Oh Thor, of Asgard, thou goest hence from my kingdom,—
forever and aye I trust, and now will I too speak the truth. Not
by superior force, as ye think have ye been defeated. It has all
been done by magic. All things have been made to seem to you
other than they were. Even have we made you think yourselves
weak and puny, when our very bones rattled for trembling and
fear of your strength. I myself am Skry'mir and any one of thy
mighty blows would have done for me, had I not in the mist,
which distorts all things out of their natural shape, made thee
believe a mountain my head. Not me didst thou strike but the
mountain. Lo'gi against whom Lo'ki contended in eating is
wild-fire, the devourer; Hu'gi against whom Thi-al'fi ran is thought,
and who can run faster than thought? The horn from which
thou, Thor, didst drink is connected with the ocean so thou

442

couldst never have drained it unless thou couldst drink dry the ocean. El'li the wrestler, is old age, who throws so many strong men, and the cat thou couldst not lift is the Mid'gard serpent that encircles the world. Yet didst thou nearly outdo Lo'gi, Hu'gi and El'li and lift the Mid'gard serpent, and thou didst drink so much of the sea that on earth men thought the tide had gone out. By trickery only have we kept you from your triumph, but in trickery are we clever. If ye be wise come no more against us. With deception and illusion will we meet you always."

Then in his righteous wrath Thor lifted up his hammer. The might that was his, the power that was his, once more he knew. But as he swung good Mjol'ner, the giant vanished—vanished, too, the whole city of freezing ice and snow. Retreated had the giants before the power of Thor, perceived by them when to Thor himself his prowess had seemed so little. Fled had the giants before him. Then once more smiled the earth, free from the fetters of frost, ready for seed and bloom, and back to Asgard went Thor with Lo'ki, Thi-al'fi and Rosk'va.

THOR
Henry Wadsworth Longfellow

I am the God Thor,
I am the War God,
I am the Thunderer!
Here in my Northland,
My fastness and fortress,
Reign I forever!

Here amid icebergs,
Rule I the nations;
This is my hammer,
Mjolner, the mighty;
Giants and sorcerers
Cannot withstand it!

—*from The Saga of King Olaf.*

THE STEALING OF I-DU'NA
A Norse Myth

IT happened once that O'din, the All-father, King of the gods, with Hoe'nir, his brother, and Lo'ki, the mischief-maker, started out of As'gard, the home of the gods, down across the Bridge of the Rainbow, to journey around the world. At eventide they came to a densely wooded mountain, and being anhungered, yet finding no dwelling in sight, they caught an ox from a herd that stood grazing near and dressed the meat for their supper. Then did Lo'ki, god of fire, kindle a flame to cook the food, but the time being come for the meat to be done, lo! it was raw as in the beginning. Another fire made Lo'ki, but all in vain. As raw was the meat as before. Then Lo'ki, O'din and Hoe'nir heard a noise in the branches above them. Looking up they perceived an eagle fanning the meat with his wings and sending a cold wind upon it that prevented it from roasting.

"Done to a turn will your meat be," croaked the eagle, "if you will promise me as much as I can eat."

"Nay, then!" cried the three out of Asgard. "Join us and eat what thou wilt."

So the eagle left off fanning the meat; it was soon cooked and they all went to help themselves. But the eagle, first of all, seized three-quarters of the whole ox. Then was Lo'ki angered. Seizing a stick lying near, he began to belabor the greedy bird. No sooner had he done so, than one end of the pole stuck fast in the eagle's feathers, and the other stuck fast to Loki's hands. Up flew the bird and off trailed Loki after him. Scraped through briery thickets and straggling branches of trees, jammed against rocks and stones, his arms nearly torn from their sockets, so was Loki dragged. Then he knew that the eagle was in truth no eagle, but Thi-as'si, the fierce frost giant. In vain he begged for mercy. The bird flew on the faster. Again and again he begged.

"On one condition only will I let thee go," croaked Thi-as'si, "that thou lure out of Asgard the lovely I-d'una, and give her into my power with a dish of her magic apples, partaking of which keeps the dwellers in Asgard forever young."

At length Thi-as'si wrung from Loki the sorry promise to do as he bade him, and Loki was set free. Bedraggled and torn, back went Loki to Asgard.

Now I-du'na, Spirit of the Spring and of immortal youth, was loveliest of all the goddesses in Asgard. Tender green were her garments, on her head a wreath of flowers. Lightly she glided over the earth. At her approach the trees burst into bloom; myriads of flowers sprang up; tinkling brooks awoke and laughed and leapt for joy. Everywhere was stir, activity and life. Never was age where Iduna was, but always youth— eternal youth. And Iduna kept carefully guarded in her charge a tree that bore wonderful apples, which made him who ate them forever young. It was to partake of that eternal youth that the cruel frost giant wished to get possession of Iduna and her apples.

The husband of Iduna was Bra'gi, the god of poesy, who sings the wondrous song of life that scales the highest heavens and searches the depths of hell. Whenever he sings and plays on his golden harp, the flowers that spring up at Iduna's approach reveal their inmost charm and grace, the blending colors of earth and sky reveal their inmost harmony, the laughter of brooks, the songs of birds reveal their inmost joy; all nature finds a tongue and speaks and yields up the very secret of her being. To separate Iduna from Bragi was no easy task, but Loki waited until he saw the minstrel go forth on a journey from Asgard to earth, leaving Iduna unguarded. Then the mischief-maker went whither Iduna wandered alone in the midst of her flowery gardens.

"Iduna," said he, "just without the gates of Asgard I have found a tree that bears finer apples than thine. Sweeter to the taste are they and lovelier, and indeed I doubt not they restore youth and strength as well as thine."

"Nay, now," cried Iduna, "in all the world are none such apples as mine."

"Come then with me and see," said Loki. "And bring with thee a dish of thine own apples that we may compare the two."

Into a crystal dish did Iduna then put her precious apples and off with the wily Lo'ki went she. Scarcely were the two without the safe protected gates of Asgard than Thiassi in his eagle plumage swooped down upon Iduna. As the storm swoops, as the storm rushes, when down from the mountain tops the wild north wind comes roaring, so came Thiassi. From his frosty wings fell snow, from his breath exhaled the cold that blasted all about. In his talons seized he Iduna and bore her off to his wintry home in the storm-bound land of Thrym'heim. There he shut her up in a chamber in the rocks, against which all day long resounded the boom and crash of the sea.

Each day he came and asked her to give him a bite of her apples, for not unless Iduna herself gave out the precious fruit would he who partook thereof find his youth and strength renewed. And every day Iduna stoutly refused. He whined and begged and threatened—in vain! For no such creature of evil was the gift of eternal youth. And when Thiassi himself thrust his great fist in the dish to seize an apple, the fruit only dwindled and shrunk till it disappeared altogether.

Long were the days, long were the months while Iduna stayed in Thrymheim. In Asgard, the heavens, and Midgard, the earth, spring and summer were gone. Cold winter held sway; leaves turned brown and fell; bird songs were hushed; flowers withered and drooped on their stalks; brooklets froze up into motionless silence, and all things seemed old and dying. In Asgard old age came stealing even upon the gods. Where, O, where was Iduna? Bragi mourned for her, Odin mourned for her, mourned all the dwellers in Asgard, mourned all the people of earth.

Then did Odin, the All-father, summon a council to consider what should be done. Thither all Asgard gathered—save Loki. Loki dared not appear. When Odin perceived that Loki alone was absent, he ordered Bragi to fetch him the maker-of-mischief. In the presence of Odin, before the might of his majesty, Loki was forced to pour out the tale of what he had done. Sternly Odin bade him go and bring back Iduna or never more dare show his face in Asgard.

So Loki borrowed of the goddess Frey'a her cloak of falcon feathers, and with this he was able to fly over land and sea to the rockbound coast of Thrymheim. Here in her gloomy cell he found the lovely Iduna. Thiassi, it chanced, was from home, so Loki forced his way through a narrow opening into her prison. Much she rejoiced to see him. He turned her at once into a swallow and flew off with her in his talons.

Not far had he gone, when he heard a rushing behind him. There in rapid pursuit was Thiassi. On and on flew Loki! On and on flew Thiassi, gaining little by little. On the walls of Asgard stood the gods wrinkled, and bent, and gray, watching far to southward over the sea, watching, longing for the coming of Iduna. At length they made out the falcon, Loki, and Thiassi hot on his heels. Long and anxiously watched they. Now Thiassi seemed pouncing on Loki's back, but always Loki escaped and flew with his precious burden on and on and on.

As he neared the city of refuge Loki's strength seemed almost failing. Then up rose the dwellers in Asgard and lit great fires on the walls that leapt and flamed to the heavens. Safe through the blaze and smoke dashed Loki,—Loki the god of fire, but when Thiassi, creature of cold and storm, plunged blundering through, down he fell, suffocating, to his end beneath the mighty hammer of Thor. Then Loki let loose the swallow and up sprang the lovely Iduna herself, to be tenderly welcomed by Bragi, Odin and all the rest. And with Iduna and her apples, back to Asgard came youth and the joyous life of the Spring.

HOW THE GODDESS OF SPRING CAME TO SCORING
Charles Kingsley

White were the moorlands,
And frozen before her;
Green were the moorlands,
And blooming behind her.
Out of her gold locks
Shaking the spring flowers,
Out of her garments
Shaking the south wind,
Around in the birches,
Awaking the throstles,
And making chaste housewives all,
Long for their heroes home;
Loving and love-giving,
Came she to Scoring.
—*from The Longbeard's Saga.*